SCIENCE:
A MAINSPRING OF CIVILIZATION

In these fascinating essays which appeared originally in the *Journal of World History,* world-famous scholars discuss the evolution of science from the pre-history of man to the present day.

V. Gordon Childe traces the origins of science from the epoch when man unconsciously applied scientific principles to shape the rude tools that were fundamental to his survival. R. C. Majumdar, J. Filliozat, K. Yabuuti, J. M. Millas-Vallicrosa, and others discuss the advance of science through the centuries. The science of antiquity, particularly mathematics, is shown in the great civilization of the Near and Far East. Its progress in remote centers of theological study in the Catholic-orientated Middle Ages, its brilliant advance during the humanistic Renaissance, is described by B. Gille, M. D. Chenu, Nicola Abbagnano.

The final section of the book is devoted to science in the twentieth century, with the rise of technology and the development of the new sciences of man. A Russian scholar, A. A. Zvorikine, examines the relationship between technology and society; two Americans, H. Margenau and J. E. Smith, survey the field of physics, suggesting a re-evaluation of scientific and philosophical positions. And another American, Clyde Kluckhohn, writes about "Anthropology in the Twentieth Century."

In all, some sixteen authorities provide an open-minded, exciting, new view of science and the role it plays in the progress of mankind.

MENTOR and SIGNET Books
of Related Interest

THE NINETEENTH CENTURY WORLD; Readings in the
History of Mankind
Guy Métraux and François Crouzet, eds.
The Nineteenth Century in terms of politics, social
forces, science, technology, religion, philosophy, the
arts; discussed in fifteen essays by R. R. Palmer,
Werner Conze, Henri Gouhier and others.
(#MQ506—95¢)

AFTER THE SEVENTH DAY *by Ritchie Calder*
A lively history of civilization in terms of man's genius
for mastering his environment, and his terrible power
for destruction. (#MT453—75¢)

SCIENCE IN OUR LIVES *by Ritchie Calder*
An exciting factual story of the beginning and development of modern science, the relationship between its
special fields, and its impact upon our daily lives.
(#P2124—60¢)

ONE TWO THREE . . . INFINITY *by George Gamow*
Current facts and speculations of science presented by
a leading physicist. (#MD97—50¢)

THE EVOLUTION OF SCIENCE

READINGS FROM THE HISTORY OF MANKIND

EDITED FOR THE INTERNATIONAL COMMISSION
FOR A HISTORY OF THE SCIENTIFIC AND
CULTURAL DEVELOPMENT OF MANKIND

by Guy S. Métraux and François Crouzet

*A MENTOR BOOK PUBLISHED BY
THE NEW AMERICAN LIBRARY*

Reprinted from the *Journal of World History*, which is published by Editions de la Baconnière, Neuchâtel, Switzerland,
for the International Commission for a History of the
Scientific and Cultural Development of Mankind, with
the financial support of Unesco.

FIRST PRINTING, JUNE, 1963

Library of Congress Catalog Card Number 63-18009

All materials in this book express the opinion
of the respective authors and do not
necessarily represent the opinions of the International Commission for a History of the Scientific
and Cultural Development of Mankind.

MENTOR TRADEMARK REG. U.S. PAT. OFF. AND FOREIGN COUNTRIES
REGISTERED TRADEMARK—MARCA REGISTRADA
HECHO EN CHICAGO, U.S.A.

*MENTOR BOOKS are published in the United States by
The New American Library of World Literature, Inc.,
501 Madison Avenue, New York 22, New York,
in Canada by The New American Library of Canada Limited,
156 Front Street West, Toronto 1, Ontario,
in the United Kingdom by The New English Library Limited,
Barnard's Inn, Holborn, London, E.C. 1, England*

PRINTED IN THE UNITED STATES OF AMERICA

CONTENTS

EDITORS' PREFACE   *xi*

SCIENCE AND MAN: AN INTRODUCTORY ESSAY
   Ritchie Calder   *xvii*

Part One: The Origins of Science: Prehistory and Antiquity

THE PREHISTORY OF SCIENCE: ARCHAEOLOGICAL
   DOCUMENTS   V. Gordon Childe   34
SCIENTIFIC SPIRIT IN ANCIENT INDIA   R. C. Majumdar 77
INDIA AND SCIENTIFIC EXCHANGES IN ANTIQUITY
   J. Filliozat   88

Part Two: The Development of Science: The Middle Ages

SCIENCES IN CHINA FROM THE FOURTH TO THE END
   OF THE TWELFTH CENTURY   Kiyosi Yabuuti   108
TRANSLATIONS OF ORIENTAL SCIENTIFIC WORKS (TO
   THE END OF THE THIRTEENTH CENTURY)   J. M.
   Millas-Vallicrosa   128
TECHNOLOGICAL DEVELOPMENTS IN EUROPE: 1100
   TO 1400   Bertrand Gille   168
NATURE AND MAN AT THE SCHOOL OF CHARTRES
   IN THE TWELFTH CENTURY   M. D. Chenu   220

Part Three: Science, Religion, Humanism

ITALIAN RENAISSANCE HUMANISM   Nicola
    Abbagnano   238
SCIENCE AND REFORMATION   R. Hooykaas   258
CATHOLICISM, PROTESTANTISM, AND THE DEVELOP-
    MENT OF SCIENCE IN THE SIXTEENTH AND
    SEVENTEENTH CENTURIES   François Russo   291

Part Four: Modern Science

TECHNICAL PROGRESS AND SOCIETY   A. A. Zvorikine 322
STRUCTURE AND COMPLEXITY OF THE UNIVERSE
    Pierre Auger   340
PHILOSOPHY OF PHYSICAL SCIENCE IN THE TWENTIETH
    CENTURY   H. Margenau and J. E. Smith   362
ANTHROPOLOGY IN THE TWENTIETH CENTURY
    Clyde Kluckhohn   396
INDEX   423

CONTRIBUTORS

GUY S. MÉTRAUX, Secretary-General, International Commission for a History of the Scientific and Cultural Development of Mankind

FRANÇOIS CROUZET, Editorial Secretary, *Journal of World History;* Professor at the University of Lille

RITCHIE CALDER, University of Edinburgh

The late V. GORDON CHILDE, University of London

R. C. MAJUMDAR, Vice-President, International Commission for a History of the Scientific and Cultural Development of Mankind; sometime Professor of Ancient Indian History

J. FILLIOZAT, Collège de France, Paris

KIYOSI YABUUTI, Research Institute of Humanistic Science, Kyoto University

J. M. MILLAS-VALLICROSA, Faculty of Philosophy and Letters, University of Barcelona

BERTRAND GILLE, National Archives, Paris

M. D. CHENU, O.P., President of the Thomist Society

NICOLA ABBAGNANO, History of Philosophy Seminar, University of Turin

R. HOOYKAAS, Free University, Amsterdam

FRANÇOIS RUSSO, S.J., Consultant, International Catholic Coordinating Centre for Unesco; International Secretariat for Scientific Questions, Pax Romana

A. A. ZVORIKINE, Vice-President, International Commission for a History of the Scientific and Cultural Development of Mankind; Institute of History, USSR Academy of Sciences, Moscow

PIERRE AUGER, Director-General, European Organization for Space Research; Professor at the University of Paris

H. MARGENAU, Professor of Physics and Natural Philosophy, Yale University

J. E. SMITH, Professor of Philosophy, Yale University

The late CLYDE KLUCKHOHN, Harvard University

THE EVOLUTION
OF SCIENCE

EDITORS' PREFACE

The articles published here appeared originally in the *Journal of World History,* issued under the auspices of the International Commission for a History of the Scientific and Cultural Development of Mankind.[1] As now presented, these articles constitute a companion to the *History of Mankind: Cultural and Scientific Development*[2] for the preparation of which they were especially written. They are also a valuable addition to the critical apparatus of modern historical scholarship.

When making a selection among the many articles on science and technique published in the *Journal of World History,* the editors gave priority to materials reflecting contemporary thinking on general questions rather than adding to the historical literature of various branches of science. We do not pretend that the whole field has been covered, or even that the questions examined herein have been definitely settled. The history of science is a new discipline; the impact of science on society still remains largely a matter of conjecture

[1] *Journal of World History—Cahiers d'Histoire Mondiale—Cuadernos de Historia Mundial,* Vols. I–II (Paris: Librairie des Méridiens, 1953-1955); Vols. III ff (Boudry, Neuchâtel: Editions de la Baconnière, 1956-   ). Quarterly publication with articles in French, English, and Spanish.

[2] Prepared under the auspices of the International Commission for a History of the Scientific and Cultural Development of Mankind, issued under the title *History of Mankind: Cultural and Scientific Development* (London: Allen & Unwin; New York: Harper & Row, 1963-   ), 6 vols. Vol. I; *Prehistory and the Beginnings of Civilization,* Jacquetta Hawkes and Sir Leonard Woolley; Vol. II, *Classical Civilizations and the Orient, 1200 B.C.–400 A.D.,* Luigi Pareti, Paolo Brezzi, and Luciano Petech; Vol. III, *The World: 400 A.D.–1300 A.D.,* Gaston Wiet, Vadime Elisséeff, and Philippe Wolff; Vol. IV, *The World, A.D. 1300 to the End of the Eighteenth Century,* Louis Gottschalk; Vol. V, *The Nineteenth Century,* by Charles Morazé et al.; Vol. VI, *The Twentieth Century,* by Caroline F. Ware, K. M. Panikkar, and Jan M. Romein.

and requires much original research. The materials selected for this book constitute a panorama of some of the problems that the historian of science, as well as the historian of society, encounters at key periods in the history of mankind.

The editors hope to provide the reader with ideas and suggestions on the development of science in its worldwide and more general context, i.e., outside the cultural and mental limits that tradition and habit have imposed. In addition, we hope that this book will show to what extent, at every turn in the evolution of mankind, science was a force, although often an unacknowledged one.

We decided to concentrate our attention on questions that, in the course of analysis of original sources, can but retain the attention of the reader because of their social, philosophical, or cultural impact, and their far-reaching implication for the history of mankind.

In trying to situate science in its proper historical context, we often have the tendency to follow the broad canvas applied generally to Western history in which certain areas, cultures, or events have been defined to constitute logical milestones. This is a useful device because it offers a pattern that can be easily grasped. In reality, the coincidence between general history and scientific development is perhaps artificial, since all the factors that affect the evolution of science have not yet been fully established. The cultural circumstances, the climate of opinion that make one age more "scientific" than another, have yet to be fully analyzed and understood. The only certainties that exist are that, on the one hand, science and scientific process are universal, and that, on the other hand, social, cultural, and economic factors directly affect scientific development. The impact of science on the twentieth century is as much a reflection of the progress made by science as it is a reflection of the degree of receptivity of our age to science. It would seem that science was ever present in the history of human society—but in a latent state, in the mind of thinkers, in the shape of certain artifacts, in the application of a few abstract principles for limited results. It was never, however, at the very center of thought and was strongly related to practical effects, whether of a religious nature (astronomical computations), or for economic purposes (the use of numbers), or for industrial production (the use of metals).

The first article, by the late V. Gordon Childe, describes what can be termed "the prehistory of science," which coincided with the prehistory of man, an epoch when, to survive in a hostile environment, man unconsciously applied primary scientific thinking in shaping efficient tools. Many of the Paleolithic and Neolithic implements, which required in their manufacture so much accumulated experience and controlled skill, embody scientific principles and methods empirically construed. The use of these tools empowered man to control to some extent natural resources, facilitated his daily life, and gradually enabled him to shape a milieu that permitted urbanization, which, in turn, was the mainspring of civilization.

The essay of V. Gordon Childe on the most remote origins of science is followed by an article by R. C. Majumdar on scientific thought in ancient India. It briefly outlines the significant place of science in an ancient and great civilization that is better known for its literary and philosophical contributions. Yet science reached a high stage of development, especially in mathematics, to which it brought the decimal system of notation and the use of the zero. Professor Filliozat, a French student of Indian culture, describes the complex scientific relationships that existed at an early date between India and the Eastern Mediterranean basin. Scientific exchanges resulted in a process of cross-fertilization that, then as now, is fundamental for the development of science.

These three articles make up the first section of this book and, since it deals with the origins of science, the reader might ask why the achievements of the Egyptians and of the Sumerians, of the Greeks and of the Chinese, do not appear. The omission is deliberate: no general article can encompass their importance to the future development of science. Moreover, original materials, detailed studies, histories of individual scientific thinkers, analyses of single scientific facts, are by now available throughout the world in publications ranging from the most technical monographs to the broadest essays in vulgarization.

In the second section, which we have entitled "The Development of Science: The Middle Ages," we present several articles covering the centuries that bridge the Fall of Rome to the Renaissance: one thousand years that have still to be assessed in terms of scientific progress. Recent studies, especially those not limited to Europe, disclose an intellectual ferment and technological developments that were at the basis of social and economic change that, in turn and at a later date, enabled science to thrive and mankind to go ahead in the conquest of the world and the understanding of the universe. Scientific and technological progress is noted in China, as explained by Professor Yabuuti; is apparent in the momentous work of scientific translations by Jewish scholars working in Spain; is conclusively proved by the many applications of science and the creation of technology that ranged from the harnessing of natural energy to the rational use of animal traction. The article by B. Gille shows by what intricate process, and in which circumstances, so many basic inventions were made or applied in Europe before the twelfth century.

It is in a climate of change, to a large extent parallel to technical development, that the first great centers of learning were created. There, as the Reverend Father Chenu points out, scientific theory began to appear in the speculations of theologians and philosophers: the place of the École de Chartres is quite unique at this point. By establishing an order of the universe that could be verified, by showing that nature was "penetrable and predictable," the foundations of a science of man were laid within the framework of medieval thinking. From there on man himself was always to find a place in relation to the natural universe, both animate and inanimate.

Much debate has taken place about the twelfth-century Renaissance, which has been analyzed by Father Chenu. Between this period and the "Rinascimento," there is a continuum of thought, a relationship of cause and effect, that is now well known to historians. That is why the third section of this book begins with an article on man and nature in the Italian Renaissance. It carries over—from a different angle—some of the questions explored by medieval thinkers.

In this third section two articles are published together on the controversial question of the relationship between science and various forms of religious expression. A prominent Dutch historian, Professor Hooykaas, of the Free University of Amsterdam, summarizes the argumentation of Protestant scholars. The Reverend Father F. Russo, S.J., a distinguished Catholic writer, analyzes each argument and offers another interpretation. This scholarly controversy is by no means finished: much additional research is needed before it can be settled. Professor Hooykaas and Father Russo have devoted many studies to the exploration of this question. They will undoubtedly publish further materials in defense of their respective positions. The editors of this book believe that every student of science, as well as every student of history, should be aware of the deep significance of this problem, which, perhaps, prefigures the conflict between science and culture in the twentieth century. These two articles present an excellent exposition of a vital, intellectual debate.

The reader will certainly be surprised that our table of contents does not contain any specific articles on the scientific revolution of the seventeenth century, or on the formidable strides made in every branch of science and technology in the eighteenth and nineteenth centuries. As we did for science in antiquity, we must refer him to primary and secondary sources available on these periods. Several articles dealing with nineteenth-century developments appear in the companion volume to this book.

Our intention in selecting for the final section four articles devoted to science in the twentieth century was to highlight some of the problems that were already apparent at earlier times but which have now acquired an importance that bears on every aspect of life. Social, economic activity is nowadays affected more or less directly by science; philosophical thinking is marked by science; even some of the most basic scientific laws are affected by new theories, new research, new applications. To give an idea of the magnitude of this development we have chosen two articles dealing with theoretical aspects and two with human aspects. A Russian scholar, Professor Zvorikine, examines the relationship of technical progress and the evolution of society—a key problem in this age of discovery and technical applications. Professor Pierre Auger, of France, takes up first in its historical perspective and then within its modern context the difficult question of the structure and the complexity of the universe. In his essay he traces the eternally present duality between the continuous and the discontinuous, between law and structure, size and complexity, quantity and quality. Two American scholars, surveying the field of modern physics, suggest that now the state of knowledge calls for a reconsideration of many scientific principles and even of our philosophical positions.

Lastly, in this section devoted to science in the twentieth century, we have included a survey of modern anthropology by the late Clyde Kluckhohn. It is fitting that this collection should contain an essay on the new "science of man." Indeed, science is universal, and its methods, approach, assumptions even, permeate all phases of thinking. As in the twelfth century or in the Renaissance, the scientific thinker today will sooner or later consider the place and function of man in relation to the universe and in relation to his fellow men.

Both man and nature are one: he who studies nature studies man.

To introduce this book the editors requested Professor Ritchie Calder to write a survey of the impact of science on society in mid-twentieth century. In his essay, especially written for this collection, Professor Calder analyzes some of the major implications of science in a world that more and more is becoming dependent upon its scientists.

The contributions of scholars from nine countries have been assembled. Some are markedly Marxists, others are avowedly Catholics or Protestants, some come from the Orient, others are connected with European or American institutions of higher learning. Between them there is a common bond: science, its significance, its evolution, its application. The International Commission for a History of the Scientific and Cultural Development of Mankind hopes that this book will encourage additional studies within the line it suggests and in keeping with the spirit in which it was written: an open-minded examination of questions that are of import to the understanding of mankind's evolution through history.

Guy S. Métraux
François Crouzet

Unesco House, Paris, France
July, 1962

SCIENCE AND MAN:

AN INTRODUCTORY ESSAY

Ritchie Calder

Most of the world's great scientists are still alive. That is another way of saying that in the past twenty, or at most thirty years greater scientific advances have been made than in all previous history since man, the tool-making animal, began to use the brain that distinguished him from other creatures and started to experiment with his environment. Contemporary man can make this boast, but it involves a heavy responsibility because the experiments in which he is now engaged, using what we call science or technology, are no longer limited to the inquisitive individual or to a laboratory but can involve all mankind, all living species, the biosphere on which life depends, the planet earth itself and the forces beyond it.

In the past twenty years man has penetrated the secrets of matter and by the energy released from the nucleus of the atom has acquired the power to veto the evolution of his own species. Man has broken the bounds of his own planet, has voyaged into space, and, by the electronic extension of his own senses has reached out for the planets of the solar system. With his radiotelescopes, which did not exist twenty years ago, he has gone even farther—beyond his own galaxy, the Milky Way, to the bounds of the universe. From this Edge of Beyond he can pick up signals that have been traveling for 10,000 million years and can get radio accounts of cosmic catastrophes of 400 million years ago. Man, having probed the nature of matter, is now probing the nature of life itself.

In the chemistry of DNA (deoxyribonucleic acid) the physicists, the chemists, and the geneticists are deciphering the code by which cells reproduce themselves and by which the hereditary traits of one generation are passed on to the next. Presently, they will know how to recode those "instructions" and to alter or control the nature of the species, in a man-made evolutionary process.

Man has mechanically, or electronically, reproduced his senses, evolved instruments more sensitive than the human eye, the human ear, or the human touch. He has reproduced, in what are inadequately called "computers," many of the faculties of the human brain. As calculating machines they can do, in thousandths of a second, reckonings that with pencil and pad would take months. These machines can also control the machines that make machines; they can put rockets into orbit; they are equipped with "memories" of such capacity that it is theoretically possible to store all the information in all the libraries of all the world in an electronic storage system no bigger than a cigar box. There are machines that can "learn" and correct mistakes from acquired "experience." It has been claimed that it is possible for a machine to make a "value-judgment," at least in the limited sense, that it can take a set of facts and arrive at logical conclusions the programmers never anticipated.

Man, as the result of a medical breakthrough less than thirty years ago, has acquired death control. With the advent of new chemical drugs that could, instead of treating symptoms as in the past, directly attack the micro-organic causes of disease, he began to gain mastery over infections. This was reinforced by the discovery of the antibiotics, beginning with penicillin, which extended the range of the attack. The development of the insecticides, like DDT, has given man means to control the insect-borne diseases, such as malaria. And the work on "interferon" is further extending this control to the virus diseases. As a result the human population of the world, which took 200,000 years to reach the present figure of three billion, has gathered a momentum that will double that figure, to six billion in less than forty years.

Man, the scientist and technologist, has outstripped man, the moral or natural philosopher. Discoveries aggregate, with speed and portentousness, without much evidence that the moral philosophers and theologians can evaluate them as part of the meaning and purpose of man, or that the natural philosophers can integrate them in the unity of Nature.

The safecrackers found the combination of the nucleus before the locksmith knew how it worked, in the sense that atomic energy was released with cataclysmic force, while nuclear physicists are still trying to find out what is the structure of the nucleus. The products of this science are stockpiled as nuclear bombs with a destructive capacity expressed as "X times overkill" and the by-products are spread throughout the total environment as radioactive elements that never existed in nature but that can combine with the living processes. With a limitation of biological knowledge, which lacks the precision and arrogant confidence that the physicists and chemists have in their measurements, there may be debate as to the qualitative and quantitative effects on present and future generations; however, there can be no doubt that, by what we do today, we are mortgaging the genetic capital of future generations. Yet those who are supposed to make the moral judgments are perplexed and inarticulate.

A high-level H-bomb test in the Van Allen Belt that could conceivably interfere with the magnetic forces of the earth drew protests from leading scientists. The Prime Minister of Great Britain went on parliamentary record with the remark, "Until only a short time ago, nobody knew the Van Allen Belt existed. If it should be temporarily disturbed I do not think any great harm will come to the world."

This was in reply to a sober statement by Sir Bernard Lovell, head of the Jodrell Bank Radio Astronomy Station: "These proposals to make nuclear explosions in space arise from a small group of military scientists, unknown and unidentified to the world at large, who have persuaded their masters to make a series of huge gambles . . . . On the scale of the cosmos, they are dealing with fireworks. Nevertheless, the earth is so minute on the cosmic scale and its environment is controlled by the delicate balance of such great natural forces that one must view with dismay a potential interference with these processes before they are investigated by the delicate tools of the true scientist."

This raises profound philosophical questions: Science is not wisdom; it is knowledge. Wisdom is knowledge tempered by judgment. With the rapid advance of science, with the hourly multiplication of inventions, and the apocalyptic portents of megaton experiments, where are the people who can exercise judgment about science? The expert himself is not qualified to do so and is very often the faceless man at the elbow of the uninformed. In the anonymity of an adviser, he is not exposed to the scrutiny and debate of his peers, which is the historic function of the learned societies of science, where nothing is taken for granted.

The scientist who is a statesman is rare; the statesman who knows anything about science is even more rare. Men of affairs may have their publicly known advisers who are scientists of distinction, but these in turn are also subject to the pressures of "faceless men," of their own colleagues, promoting new ideas. The sanction of public opinion does not operate effectively because people at large are not only ill-informed about science but are intimidated by it. Science exists to remove superstition, to find natural explanations for phenomena, but it is now itself regarded with a superstitious awe, and the scientist has acquired the dangerous position of the demigod.

Here then is the dilemma: The judgments about science are often made by men of affairs who know little about science but who are impressed by its end results, which may affect the lives and livelihoods not only of the community to which they may be responsible but to the people of the world at large. They cannot be behindhand, so they "give ideas their head" and they politically back and heavily endow scientific "cults." (Recently it was nuclear physics; then it was solid-state physics, with its implications in electronics; now it is space research; and presently it will be DNA.) The privileged disciplines can recruit heavily, and an imbalance occurs in science. What was once natural philosophy becomes a series of crash programs, with spectacular results. But the unacceptable alternative would be Neo-Scholasticism, or a reversion to medieval obscurantism, in which experiment would be discouraged while the Meaning of Man was being reappraised.

Somehow, wisdom and science must be reconciled, and that can only be done if people are prepared to understand the nature and methods of science—not necessarily the specialized *expertise* of the career scientists—and the implications of science.

The contents of this book have been organized to show both the evolution of science and some of the conflicts between "culture" and "science." Unlike much written about science today, this is a study in depth. It is also a salutary reminder that, while most of the great scientists may be alive today, science itself has been a historical process of lend-lease—that we have, though we tend to forget it, leased or borrowed much from civilizations that may, for the present, be scientifically and technologically overshadowed by the achievements of science in the European tradition.

If we look at the "European tradition" that produced the eruptive breakthrough to present-day accomplishment, we find that it is comparatively recent—just about as old as the United States. When Benjamin Franklin was in London fighting for the repeal of the Stamp Act, he was consulted by Matthew Boulton of Birmingham about the practicability of a steam pump to hoist the water from the tailrace of a factory millstream back into the millpond. Franklin, for once, was unable to suggest the answer. If he had, then Boulton might have inquired no further and might never have turned to James Watt, with the resulting partnership that gave the steam engine, and steam power as a motive force, to the Industrial Revolution. And without the prosperity of that revolution during the nineteenth century, first in Britain, then in Western Europe, and then in the United States, science and technology would not have burgeoned. There was the wealth produced by industry, to produce the education, to produce the research, to produce new industrial processes, which required more research, which in turn produced more industrial prosperity and subsidized academic opportunities. In the twentieth century, from the bases secured by the first Industrial Revolution billions of dollars of hardware and research equipment can be thrown into space.

Some will say, and this book will show, that this approach is truncating history. Was not Western man the heir of Greco-Roman culture and of the science that went with it? Indeed he was and the heir of much more—of the earlier civilizations, of the Chinese, of the Hindus and of the Arabs. But the question is, What is meant by "science"? Much that is claimed as the achievements of "science" today are (if we make the distinction and it is questionable whether we should) the results of "technology."

The distinction between "science" and "technology" can only be Platonic in the sense of Plutarch's prescription of Plato's attitude to Eudoxus and Archytas when, by experiments and recourse to instruments, they solved problems the theorists considered insoluble:

. . . Plato inveighed against them with great indignation,

as having corrupted and debased the excellence of geometry, by causing her to descend from incorporeal and intellectual to sensible things, and obliging her to make use of matter, which requires much manual labor, and is the object of servile trades; then mechanics were separated from geometry . . . being a long time despised by the philosopher . . .

Plato's enthronement of theory over practice continued to tyrannize Western thinking for over 2,000 years. True, there were rebels like Roger Bacon, William of Occan, Paracelsus, Leonardo, and Galileo, who invoked the eye as well as the inward brain and insisted upon experimental evidence.

During this time, science, as a pure exercise of reason, which was often divorced from the senses and certainly divorced from "the object of servile trades," was a discouragement to progress. It was also evidence that culture and science are not separates but powerfully interact one with the other.

Around 250 B.C. Ctesibius invented a perfectly good pump fitted with valves, cylinders, and pistons, which would have been capable of mechanically raising water to much greater heights than the devices that existed then or for many centuries afterward. Yet there is no evidence of its being used for draining mines or irrigation.

Nearly 2,000 years ago, Hero of Alexandria invented a steam engine that was quite practical and embodied the principles of both the turbine and of jet propulsion—all those centuries before Parsons (turbine) and Whittle (jet). The basis of his invention was a hollow sphere of metal with two right-angled tubes set in it, the outlets of which pointed in opposite directions. There was a cauldron from which the steam entered the sphere through tubes that acted as the axis. The force of the steam escaping through the angular tubes made the sphere revolve. In his *Mechanica* he showed a complete understanding of a transmission system. By employing a handle, which revolved a cogwheel, which acted as a winch for a multiple-pulley system, which dragged on a lever, which was hinged on a fulcrum, he had a device that lifted a weight far in excess of the muscle effort of the man who turned the handle. He discovered that hot air expanded and could effectively drive water from a cistern. This water entering a bucket served as a weight which, descending, turned spindles. They were merely toys, or magical appurtenances of the temples. The progenitor of the steam engine and his technique of expanding air were just conjuring tricks. The altar fires could be used mysteriously to open doors and disclose the gods. The engines were not put to practical use because this was an age of slavery; muscle-power was abundant and mechanical power was unnecessary. Hero's discoveries were, in his time, "uneconomic."

Similarly, the Romans who, because of their great aqueducts, we regard as great water engineers, never understood the science of hydraulics. Perhaps because of the limitations of their lead pipes they never thought of transporting water under pressure, relying instead on gravitational flow. Although the elemental ideas of watermills existed in Roman times, and were described by Vitruvius in the days of Emperor Augustus, they were never put to effective use (and, indeed, to the end of the eighteenth century the largest waterwheels for industrial use never exceeded ten horsepower). Again the explanation was that in a civilization where musclepower, in terms of slave-owning, was a "status symbol," mechanical methods were unnecessary, and without the need, there was no encouragement to investigate the scientific laws on which such developments would be based.

In the early seventeenth century Francis Bacon laid the foundations of modern scientific research. He described the scientific method, which is still valid today, and insisted upon proof by experiment to the point that in stuffing a goose with snow, to preserve it, he died of pneumonia. The Royal Society of London and the Paris Academy, in the 1660's, were concerned, in their original inquiries, with mundane things like the manuring of the soil or aids to navigation. In the eighteenth century the Royal Institution, which was to provide the laboratories of Davy and Faraday and the breakthrough in chemistry and physics those two promoted, was set up for "feeding the poor and giving them assistance . . . connected with an Institution for introducing and bringing forward into general use new inventions and improvements, particularly such as relate to the management of heat and the saving of fuel, and to various other mechanical contrivance by which domestic comfort and economy may be promoted. . . ."

The final liberation from Plato's intellectual aristocracy of science came in the next century with what A. N. Whitehead has called "The greatest invention of the nineteenth century . . . the invention of the method of invention."

"The method of invention" is an excellent definition of

technology. It does not preclude the standard definition "the science, or systematic knowledge, of the industrial arts," but it applies precisely to the role of the trained technologist of today, and to the teams of technologists who, by systematic application of research and of scientific "laws," have replaced the inspired "hunch" and, largely, the lone inventor. They are substituting industrial science for industrial arts. Weaving, for instance, may be an industrial art that can be enhanced by science, but the man-made fiber is woven in science itself. The craft of a woodworker can be improved by a lathe, but the plastic that can be die-pressed (replacing the craftsman) into a television cabinet is not just a new material; it provides a new technique.

Science and technology are part of the same spectrum and they merge in that spectrum to an extent that nowadays it is difficult to dissociate them. With that proviso, one might categorize:

Pure (or academic) science is the pursuit of knowledge for its own sake, an insatiable curiosity about the facts of nature, without any utilitarian object whatsoever.

Fundamental applied (sometimes called basic) science is the study of a problem such as the behaviour of metals or gases from which people may eventually develop special steels for a jet engine or launch a rocket into space or produce thermonuclear energy. It provides the indispensable information for further progress, but valid for many purposes in many fields.

Applied science, which tackles a specific program to find a specific answer, e.g., not the behaviour of gases in general but how a gas will behave in a type of jet engine.

Technology, on the basis of fundamental knowledge and experimental checks, develops the know-how and shows how scientific facts can be made to "work for their living" in an industrial process.

Technics, which should be included in the modern spectrum of science, is the actual industrial operation, vested, say, in the process engineer or the qualified technician.

The academic and basic scientists are "The Makers-Possible"; the applied scientists and the technologists are "The Makers-to-Happen"; and the technicians "The Makers-to-Work."

And nowadays, with operations research, market research, quality control, etc., the commercial scientists might be called "The Makers-to-Pay."

Another point of relevance, as between science and technology, is time coincidence. A scientific discovery, or a technological invention, depends on the man, the method, and the moment. The man may have the intuition, the insight, or the shrewd observation. He must have the method, the scientific training, to test and try the observation. But the moment is not always his to command.

Leonardo's principles for a flying machine were aerodynamically sound in the mid-sixteenth century, but the moment was deferred until the invention of the internal combustion engine. James Watt's steam engine would never have proved itself efficient if Wilkinson, the cannon-borer, a fellow member with Watt of the Lunar Society of Birmingham, had not, at that moment, perfected a lathe to accurately turn the bore of his cannons and also the precision cylinders for the steam engine.

There was the paradoxical case of Thomas Alva Edison who had over a thousand patents to his credit but only one scientific discovery. This was the "Edison effect," which by force of habit he patented but failed to follow up. It was a phenomenon he observed while he was developing his electric lamp, using a carbon filament. The carbon vaporized when too much current was passed through and deposited a fine soot on the inside of the lamp. He noticed, however, that there was a "transparent shadow," a clear line in the soot directly opposite one of the legs of the carbon loop. He decided that the carbon was being shot off from the far leg of the loop and was being impeded by the near leg. He put a metal plate between the legs of the loop and was able to detect the current passing and to prove that it was flowing in one direction only—like traffic down a one-way street. And there he left it, to be taken up twenty years later by John Ambrose Fleming, who invented the diode, and Lee de Forest, who added a grid and completed the modern radio valve. The moment had not been for Edison because he made the observation thirteen years before J. J. Thomson discovered the electron that made the "effect" comprehensible and the valve feasible. And with that valve, or radio tube, the development of radio communications became possible, so that Edison's "effect" extended, through radioastronomy, to the edge of the universe.

It is an oversimplification to say that economic and social forces determine the advances of science. That does not explain why Faraday, in Britain, and Joseph Henry, in the United States, should have discovered electromagnetic induction—radio, in our terms—simultaneously, with no interchange of information. Or why Gowland Hopkins, the biochemist, should have persisted all his life, despite the headwagging of his colleagues, in an interest in butterfly wings—to be confirmed by the discovery of "pterins" (butterfly wings), which are basic chemicals in molecular chemistry and the living cells. There is, apart from forces, a kind of "climate" in which scientists do get "hunches," often coincidentally, which confuses priorities. Nevertheless, economic and social forces unquestionably determine the frontal movements of science, and, by a concentration of men and means, encourage spectacular advances in the branches of science. Indeed, the role of the gifted amateur or the lone inventor has practically disappeared. Most science is the result of group research, under creative leadership but still the work of teams.

Academician Peter L. Kapitza, of the USSR, examined the future of science in the *Bulletin of Atomic Scientists* (XVIII, 4, April 1962):

> When I think over the developments in science which I have observed over my lifetime, I am amazed above all at the general attitude towards science. In my youth, we spoke of *pure science*, science for the sake of science. This is no longer the case. Science today is judged as a necessary part of the social order. The state gives increasingly wider attention to science as an essential function, on a similar footing with the army, the police and judiciary. This was not so fifty years ago; private initiative dominated science then.
>
> We speak of the division of science into fundamental and applied, but this division is artificial and it is difficult to know where fundamental science ends and applied begins. It is a division based more on administrative needs than on subject matter. Langmuir, for example, worked in industrial plants but made fundamental discoveries while solving technical problems of electric lamps.
>
> State expenditure in science continues to increase as scientific research expands. Large and complex tasks include the construction of accelerators and large reactors and exploration of outer space. The solution of such tasks ceases to be an individual matter and becomes a group concern. The question of the creative group work continues to be timely. . . .
>
> At one time the theater consisted only of actors; direc-

tors were negligible figures. Now, however, particularly in films where thousands or tens of thousands of actors occupy the scene, the chief role is taken by the director. Such directors, or producers, are needed in science. What do we require of a director? His role is creative, not administrative. He must understand the play, must comprehend what is created, must correctly assess the performers, give good roles to good actors and distribute the forces properly. He must create a great film.

The director of a great project, even although he does not himself work creatively in science, can be a great man. I do not know why the director of such a magnificent technological achievement as the satellite is not worthy of the Nobel Prize, even if he did no scientific work. Just as Eisenstein and René Clair are great artists as well as great directors, so too the organisers in science can be great artists in their fields. We are in a period of scientific and technical development where organisers of science must be given a role. We know cases where a good actor is also a good director—Charlie Chaplin, for example. Correspondingly, there was the British physicist, Ernest Rutherford, a great scientist as well as the creator of a great laboratory. . . .

He argued that man's survival is a condition of his proper use of science.

"If we compare the weight of an animal's head, the instrument of creative work, with his extremities, the instruments of physical labour," he wrote, "we get an interesting result. Let us take the ichthyosaurus, an animal with a tiny head and a giant body. Such an animal had no future. The future belonged to Man whose head weighed approximately 5 to 10 per cent of his whole body. We perceive that nature dedicated more to the spiritual as compared with the physical part of man than many states do at the present time."

Another Soviet academician, Nikolai Semenov believes that half of mankind in the future will be engaged in creative scientific work. Liberated by technology from the drudgery of providing the necessities of life, one half of mankind will be engaged on social duties and the other half will be engaged on the material developments, doing those tasks where an individual approach to solving problems is necessary.

While social and economic forces react upon science, so

science reacts upon social and economic progress, and political thinking.

Woodrow Wilson has pointed out that the American Constitution was based on a theory of political dynamics that was "an unconscious copy of the Newtonian Theory of the Universe." One might query the "unconscious." There was a Scot named William Small who had been Professor of Natural Philosophy at Williamsburg. One of his students was Thomas Jefferson, who wrote in his autobiography that "Small probably fixed the destinies of my life." Small was a close friend of Benjamin Franklin, who introduced him to Matthew Boulton. It was Small who suggested to Boulton that, to solve the problem of the steam pump, he should get into touch with James Watt, the "philosophic artisan" (or, as we would now say, "laboratory technician") at Glasgow University. There can be little question that Newtonian physics influenced the thinking of the makers of the American Constitution, with its system of checks and balances. So Small, the natural philosopher and expounder of Newton, left his *imprimatur* not only on the United States but, as the scientific godfather of the steam engine, on the Industrial Revolution as well.

The Industrial Revolution produced its social convulsions and its political optimists and pessimists. In reaction against William Godwin's *Political Justice,* which looked to the machine to bring humanity to a state of perfection (if only human institutions would allow it), the Reverend Thomas Malthus produced his *Essay on Population* (1798). He used mathematics to confound Godwin's utopianism. He attacked the idealistic theory because it ignored the fundamental traits of human nature and particularly the "principle" of population: that population would outrun the means of subsistence; that population increases in geometrical ratio while subsistence only increases in arithmetical ratio.

Malthus, apart from the controversy that still rages around his name, linked nowadays with birth control, had a profound influence on political economics (earning for it the title of "the dismal science"), on social legislation, and on scientific thinking. His arguments were used to justify poverty; as J. L. and Barbara Hammond said (in *The Town and Country Labourer*), "Malthus put a cushion under the conscience of the upper classes"—if the condition of the poor were improved, they would just multiply and die of starvation. But the scientific chain reaction was the more important. Both Charles Darwin and Wallace independently were influenced by Malthus in their approach to evolution. Darwin wrote: "I fortunately happened to read Malthus' *Essay on Population* and the idea of natural selection through the struggle for existence at once occurred to me." And Wallace wrote of Malthus' *Principles of Population,* "Its main principles remained with me as a permanent possession and twenty years later gave me the long-sought clue to the effective agent in the evolution of organic species."

In the sequence, when the *Origin of Species,* Darwin's work on evolution appeared in 1859, Friedrich Engels wrote to Karl Marx: "Darwin whom I am reading is splendid . . . this is the book which contains the basis in natural history from our point of view."

The ferment of scientific ideas in the mid-nineteenth century produced, among other things, "Marxism." This was "scientific socialism," which applied the logic of science to the forces of history and of economics. In a sense, Karl Marx's "laws" were a product of the social and intellectual forces to which he was applying them. Ideas and institutions, law and politics, even religious concepts and artistic expression are parts of the social superstructure, inevitably changing with the gradual changing of the economic foundation. By the very nature of technological development, production units of ever-increasing size are necessary, bringing together ever greater masses of workers in one enterprise and ever larger amounts of capital per labor unit—thus, according to the Marxist argument, only the community at large will finally be able to provide the organizational framework of production. This, of course, is what has been embodied as a political system and has produced the ideological antithesis between capitalism and communism, in effect, dividing the world in two. What is essentially true is that technological progress, although its speed can be influenced by political, legal, religious, or other developments in the superstructure, is virtually irreversible. It may not be, as some philosopher-pessimists like Jacques Ellul think, a closed system, but it is subject to less and less conscious influence; it is a case of rationalizing a development after the event. But it is a part of the process, exaggerated by present-day science, by which man, since he knapped his first flint, has improved his control over nature, with varying degrees of effectiveness. This material approach, through the perfection of technology, depends on physical experiment and its mathematico-philosophical interpretation. The store of knowledge grows and technology

is carried forward by it. To the extent that the social consequences of this irresistible movement can be foreseen the
Marxist claim to forecast social evolution is soundly founded.

Whatever the overtones of the ideological conflict, which
is concerned more with practice than with theory, Academician Kapitza (*ibid.*) is surely right in saying that there is a
lack of objective approach to the social sciences:

> Take Marx's works for example. They were written a
> hundred years ago and unquestionably are basic in the field
> of sociology. Marx was able to discover a number of laws
> in the construction of society! he was able to show the
> influence of economic factors on the development of so-
> ciety. The laws of Newton are taught in secondary schools
> in capitalist countries—why are not Marx's sociological
> laws also taught? They are as valid for human societies as
> Newton's laws are valid for science.

Many may dispute their determinist validity, but at least
people should know what they are disputing. It is possible
to study Marxism without accepting all its tenets.

Out of the same ferment of ideas and, considerably out of
the works of Darwin, provoked by Malthus, came the application by Sigmund Freud of scientific principles and method
to the mental and emotional states of Man. Again the
"schools" may dispute about the details of Freud's ideas, but
no one can dispute the revolution in thinking and attitudes
he produced. He did apply research methods and measurements to the problems of "how the mental apparatus is constructed and what forces interplay and counteract in it." This
led to a radical approach to neurosis, psychosis, and to the
normal mind.

Around the same period (at the beginning of this century)
Pavlov's work on neurology profoundly influenced experimental psychology. His discovery of techniques for creating
"experimental neuroses" in dogs did much to pioneer the
scientific approach to the study of human mental disorders.
As always, and as is proper in science, some of his work is
disputed by later workers (but sometimes by those who are
just the "schoolmen" of the subject), but he and Freud broke
through the barriers of prejudice and obscurantism as surely
as Vesalius did when, defying the pontiffs, he explored the
anatomy of the human body. Because of them and because of
new drugs and new methods science has made available, and

because of a new attitude socially engendered, the stigma of mental illness has been removed and the mentally sick can be treated and regarded like the physically sick.

The social sciences are still "underprivileged." Never more necessary than they are today—to deal with the confusions and conflicts the exact sciences are themselves producing through technological innovation—they are still struggling for status. It is complained by many in the exact sciences that the social sciences have borrowed the terminology but not the discipline of the natural sciences; that they use scientific jargon that loses its reference. This is rather condescending of those who either invent or borrow terms from each other which, in the transfer, lose their original meaning. The impeachment might apply all around, for there is certainly a need for a terminological reappraisal—terms are calculated to confuse not only the layman but scientists of different disciplines as well.

Experimental scientists are not natural philosophers. Einstein once said: "When I study philosophical works, I feel I am swallowing something which I don't have in my mouth." Present-day scientists need something to bite and chew upon. A famous neurophysicist was asked the question, "What is the difference between the electronic brain and the brain that conceived the electronic brain?" His answer was, "Ask a metaphysicist." But the philosophers are also out of their depth in the rising dam of scientific discovery. Indeed it is difficult to imagine who could encompass the amount of new knowledge that is flowing in. It is estimated that some three million original scientific papers are contributed to scientific journals or delivered at scientific meetings every year. Wisdom is being drowned in a Niagara of knowledge.

Most scientists, either by their training or by the disposition that took them into that training, are not socially conscious. They do their job. They produce results. They want to test those results even on a megaton scale. They do not take responsibility. That, they say, is up to others. On the other hand, a growing number of scientists have developed a new awareness and are perturbed. As individuals, and across the barriers of politics and suspicions, they meet and discuss. They are earnest in their efforts to achieve a mutual understanding that can become a common understanding. This is only one type of bridge. There is another—across the public and to the decision-making people.

That bridge must be built from either side, to meet in the middle. This requires, from nonscientists, some effort to know what the nature of science is, and the articles that follow are intended to help.

PART ONE

The Origins of Science

Prehistory and Antiquity

THE PREHISTORY OF SCIENCE;
ARCHAEOLOGICAL DOCUMENTS*

V. Gordon Childe

I

The following article assumes (1) that modern science, as a body of knowledge based on individual experience but transmitted and accumulated socially and verified by successful application to the attainment of socially approved ends, is the offspring of the traditional lore of preliterate hunters, peasants, and craftsmen, and (2) that part of this lore can be deduced from such results of behavior as have fossilized in the archaeological record. To understand what follows the reader must bear in mind the peculiarities of that record and the methods adopted by prehistorians for its interpretation.

The fossilized results of behavior available for study comprise in the first place artifacts—natural or artificial substances, the shape or structure of which has been modified by human action—but also food refuse, materials transported by man from the positions in which they occur in nature, natural situations utilized (or neglected) by man and other phe-

* Journal of World History, I, 4; II, 1.

nomena. The records suffer from two major defects: firstly, many kinds of behavior (gestures, spoken words, etc.) do not fossilize at all, producing no durable results; secondly, all organic substances, save bone, horn, ivory, and shell, have normally vanished. As a result not only artifacts of wood, sinew, hide, and similar materials, but also vegetable foods are virtually unrepresented; how great a gap that leaves can be gauged by a glance at the diet of any savage community today. Subject to this limitation, the surviving data can yield evidence as to the selection of materials for use and of food for consumption, the processes employed in procuring and processing them and even the uses to which they were put.

Archaeology claims to be a science and therefore deals only with abstractions. Its data are always and necessarily members of a class, termed in archaeological jargon "types." Of course no two handmade artifacts are even as nearly identical as a pair of factory products. But the archaeologist as such is no more concerned with the unique features of a particular statuette than is the zoologist with the peculiarities of an individual race horse. Scientists must regard these as examples of the class "Tanagra figurine" or "*Equus caballus*" and leave the appreciation of their individual merits to the connoisseur or the punter. An isolated stone tool or the debris of a single repast remains just a potential archaeological datum. Only when other tools are discovered of the same form, fashioned by the same technique, or even made from the same distinctive rock does the former become significant; the remains of meals may turn into archaeological types if it appears that the same limited selection from a wider range of available foodstuffs recurs at several sites.

Archaeologists classify their types on three bases—functional, chronological, and chorological. The first yields the broad division into axes, adzes, bracelets, earrings, dwellings, temples, and so on. But within each division prehistorians can recognize many types of ax, adze, dwelling, temple, etc. These differences may be due to progressive improvements or to mere changes in fashion with time. In that case they help to define archaeological periods that are nothing more nor less than the periods of time during which selected type-fossils were current and which are represented by assemblages containing the selected types. For fortunately archaeological phenomena are found "associated," that is, observed occurring together under conditions that indicate use at the same time, and such assemblages of associated phenomena turn up at a plurality of sites. Such a recurrent assemblage containing the same type fossils is termed a "culture."

Archaeological periods are defined by more or less abstract types and are indeed constituted of the assemblages or cultures in which such occur. With the aid of very abstract types the archaeological record is divided into the familiar Paleolithic, Mesolithic, Neolithic, Paleometallic ("Bronze"), and Neometallic (Iron) Ages. By taking rather less abstract types the first age has been further subdivided into Lower, Middle, and Upper, while further subdivisions of each age can be defined by concrete types. But archaeological time exhibits seriation but not duration. By purely archaeological means it has been proved that the several ages and their subdivisions everywhere and always follow one another in the same order if they are represented at all. Archaeology must appeal to astronomy, geology, physics, or the written record to establish the duration of its periods, and, when the latter are thus measured against an independent time scale, it often appears that their borders do not coincide everywhere. For instance a "Tudor" house in Ireland may have been built much later than such a house in England, though in both countries a Jacobean house will be later than a Tudor one. In this article, however, this peculiarity of archaeological time should cause no confusion.

Now "association" implies not only "use at the same time" but also "use by members of the same society"—of a group of persons capable of cooperating and communicating with one another. In fact in the same period and often in one and the same ecological province we often find quite different assemblages distinguished one from the other by apparently arbitrary divergences in types of artifact serving much the same purpose—e.g., of ax, bracelet, or dwelling—and often by similar divergences in the food eaten or the sites selected for habitation. Such observed arbitrary differences are attributed to divergencies of tradition between distinct, though contemporary, communities. Distinct but contemporary cultures therefore should represent distinct societies; "cultures are peoples," as Kossinna put it.

Hence, if, as assumed, archaeological data result from the application of accumulated information or knowledge, the accumulation and transmission of that knowledge must have been effected by social tradition. Theoretically, of course, three quite distinct kinds of behavior might leave a mark on the archaeological record. In what is often termed *instinctive be-*

havior an external or internal stimulus automatically releases in the organism a set of bodily movements and adjustments that may be very complex, as in building a cocoon or a nest, but may still be quite independent of any previous experience on the part of the reacting organism itself. On the contrary *learned behavior* involves at least a modification of instinctive behavior as a result of the reacting organism's own individual experience. Notoriously there are two ways of learning— by *trial and error* and *example*. A rat can learn to escape from a maze and so can an electronic machine. The rat cannot transmit this acquired characteristic to its biological descendants while the machine has no descendants at all. The information thus acquired remains *private* to the experiencer. Kittens and even chickens can, however, learn, by imitating their parents' reactions, certain modes of behavior, provided the appropriate stimulus is present in sensation to both parties simultaneously. Distinctive of human learning alone is the use of *precepts* (i.e., symbols) that refer to situations not actually present and that need never have been present in the learner's experience. It will be convenient to postpone for discussion with reference to concrete archaeological data the defence of the assumption that archaeology can distinguish between imitative and preceptual learning. It suffices here to remark that both processes convey information that is *"public"* in contrast to that acquired by trial-and-error learning.

Plainly the symbols used as precepts in the last-mentioned kind of learning must be to some extent conventional and must mean or refer to abstractions. It still seems convenient to call the meanings of such symbols "concepts" or "ideas" and to distinguish behavior involving their use as conceptual in contrast to behavior at the perceptual level. Reasoning has been defined as "operating with symbols in the head instead of going through a physical process of trial and error." In that case only behavior at the conceptual level would deserve the epithet "rational."

2   Men are born into this world equipped neither with special bodily organs for securing food, avoiding predators and preserving body temperature nor, it would seem, with

specific instincts enabling them automatically to remedy these deficiencies. Our species' biological success in the evolutionary struggle for survival has been achieved by man's learned capacity to control and make fire, and to fashion tools of wood, stone, bone, metal, and other materials not produced from his own body. It is precisely the realization of this capacity that has created the archaeological record itself. The oldest section of this record is not only immensely long —of the order of 500,000 years in terms of astronomical and geological estimates[1]—it also consists almost entirely of assemblages of stone tools, only exceptionally (as in the cave of Chou-kou-tien near Pekin or on a buried land surface at Olorgesailie in Kenya) associated even with food remains or other kinds of archaeological data. In it therefore we cannot properly distinguish "cultures" in the sense defined on p. 36. But we can recognize contrasted assemblages of stone tools, distinguished by form, technique or material, to which the name *"industries"* has been given.

All creatures deserving the generic name of man from Sinanthropus[2] on seem to have used fire, presumably for cooking—bones from his home at Chou-kou-tien are scorched or burned—as well as providing warmth to have operated on naturally fractured bits of stone to make them fit his requirements better and to have collected and selected stones suitable for this treatment. Now it is certain that human infants today do not know how to kindle fire or make tools as a caterpillar knows instinctively how to spin a cocoon. There is no sort of reason to suppose that Sinanthropus or any other early hominid was more richly gifted by nature than its descendants. They had to learn how to control fire and how to use it, how to modify the shape of bits of stones, and what sorts of stone were most amenable to such treatment. They had to learn how to procure their food—*Sinanthropus* successfully hunted deer and less regularly other beasts from hyenas to elephants—and indeed what to eat. For men are omnivorous; the stimuli that release the appropriate appetitive reactions are not specific.

All this must have been learned in the first instance by

[1] Throughout this article the chronology set forth by F. E. Zeuner in *Dating the Past* (London: Methuen, 1960; New York: Longmans, 1961) has been followed.

[2] Since for an archaeologist man is "a toolmaking primate," this and other fossil species are cited without prejudice to the hotly debated question of their genetic relationship to *Homo sapiens*.

trial and error. It is, however, extremely unlikely that each generation of hominids had to find all this out for itself. Much more probably each generation learned from its seniors what to do and how to do it. In that case there must have been a social tradition inculcating precisely the appropriate behavior. Such a tradition constitutes at the same time a body of public information drawn from the private experiences of individual hominids but somehow imparted to other members of the species. It must be termed a rudimentary science.

The social character of this germinal tradition becomes clearer at a slightly later stage. By the middle pleistocene it is possible to distinguish three divergent traditions in stone working and in one at least to recognize the reproduction of standardized forms in hundreds of thousands of examples and over thousands of generations. There are two obvious ways of making sharp-edged cutting tools from a core—a lump of flint or other stone. You can chip bits off the core until it has been given suitable edges and the desired shape; the result is termed a *core tool*. Alternatively you can detach from the core flakes that can themselves serve as tools.

It should here be insisted that both procedures demand both great dexterity and considerable familiarity with the properties of the stone utilized. Just bashing two stones together is not likely to yield a usable flake or core tool. To produce either the blow must be struck with precisely the right force and at the correct angle on a flat surface—the striking platform. The latter must in turn make an acute angle with an adjacent side of the lump and the blow must fall at the proper distance from the edge thus formed. That Lower Paleolithic tool-makers knew how to do all this is shown by thousands of well-finished tools and still better by failures. For, besides "mishits" due to clumsiness, we have cases where it is obvious that the correct blow had been struck at the right place to produce a certain flake, but the flake had snapped off short owing to some internal flaw in the core that could not have been detected by the operator at the start.

That this knowledge was not instinctive is shown by the selective application of one or other of the foregoing procedures in distinct assemblages or industries. All over Africa, western Europe, southwestern Asia, and the Indian peninsula we encounter industries characterized by an absolute predominance of core tools, termed hand axes. In central and southeastern Europe, on the contrary, hand axes are rare; we find instead industries, generally classed as Clactonian, consisting mainly of flake tools. Such industries occur in western Europe too, but normally in strata (i.e., geological subperiods) in which hand axes are unrepresented. Finally in eastern Asia are assemblages of rough "chopping tools" that display no preference for either of the foregoing procedures. To this last-named cycle belong the tools made by *Sinanthropus* and apparently those by the nearly related *Pithecanthropus* of Java. Thus, though no cultures can yet be distinguished in this section of the archaeological record, divergences in segregated industries disclose three distinct traditions. Standardized forms are still more informative.

It is no doubt highly improbable that so many hominids in the long Lower Paleolithic Age should each by individual trial and error have selected flint or the nearest available microcrystalline stone and independently hit upon the same method for shaping it. This improbability recedes into impossibility when the stone is shaped to a standardized form. Now museum collections today contain literally tens of thousands of hand axes, all conforming to a single pattern, all fashioned by the same sort of procedure and all fashioned from material possessing similar flaking qualities.[3] There is no statistically significant probability that such agreement could result from the independent and unaided efforts of trial and error made and repeated by the thousands of hominids over many generations from England to the Cape. Both the pattern and the technique for its production were surely inculcated by social tradition; members of each generation learned from their seniors both what to make and how to make it. Of course the tradition thus established was the fruit of individual private experimentation, but the knowledge gained thereby was communicated and thus made public. To this extent it qualifies as rudimentary science. There seems no good reason to restrict this designation to the knowledge applied in the manufacture of standardized hand axes which most conclusively justify its use; it can reasonably be applied to toolmaking in general.

Now the manufacture and use of tools mean the application of acquired information not only about the properties of stones, but also about the capacities of the human body and in particular of the hand. As most early tools are unspecialized and must have served a variety of purposes, it is hard to estimate how much of this information had to be acquired.

---

[3] Of course a substantial variety of standardized forms are comprised under the blanket label "hand ax." This statement applies to each of these types.

The uses to which most Lower Paleolithic tools seem best adapted—scraping, sawing, and chopping—as well as the manipulation of the raw material by percussion might be just refinements of innate instinctive reactions shared by the hominids with other primates. That seems much less likely in the case of boring, which requires a twisting movement of the wrists. And yet some Clactonian flakes seem to have been adapted by secondary chipping to act as borers.

What is true of the "geological" and "mechanical" knowledge applied in toolmaking should hold good also of fire production, and of the very extensive knowledge of the habits of game animals and also of weather and the seasons deducible from Lower Paleolithic hunters' success in the pursuit of game as large as elephant, as formidable as the tiger, and as elusive as gazelle. Here may be recognized a germinal sort of chemistry, zoology, etc.

Finally advancements in toolmaking must reflect enlargements of the public information applied. In fact during the long Lower Paleolithic period the changing form and finish of stone tools bear witness both to increasing skill in operating old techniques and to the discovery of new methods of working—for instance the replacement of the "anvil technique" by the baton method for shaping Acheulian hand axes. Improvements in finish, presumably resulting in enhanced efficiency, are observable in the course of time in both flake and core tools. Hand axes at least can be arranged in typological series—that is a logical progression in which each stage is distinguished by ever more finely and accurately trimmed specimens—that can be shown to correspond to a chronological succession—i.e. the better finished specimens as a whole prove also to be the later in time. Moreover, many of the later hand axes appear to be more delicately and elaborately flaked than would seem requisite for bare efficiency. It really looks as if some Acheulian men were aiming at producing something that was not only useful but also pleasant to handle and symmetrical to look at—in a word, beautiful.

In any case not all Lower Paleolithic tools were improvised when the need arose. On the contrary there is evidence that, where suitable raw material occurred in nature, stocks of flake or core tools were manufactured for future use. There is further a little evidence that Acheulian man could firmly fasten together two or more separate artifacts to form a *composite tool*—in fact, a bolas. This hunting device consists of two or more stone balls attached to a rope so that when hurled through the air it will entangle the legs of the quarry. Roughly shaped stone balls are in fact far from uncommon; at Olorgesailie such are reported to have been found *in situ* grouped as they would have been left from a bolas when the "rope" (presumably a strip of hide and in any case an artifact) had decayed. If the inference from the group of stones to the shaped and knotted thong be accepted, the following paragraphs would become almost superfluous, but there exists no direct evidence for composite tools till Upper Paleolithic times.

By reference to the established fact of the manufacture of standardized tools we must try to answer certain inevitable, if somewhat metaphysical, questions as to the nature of the "knowledge" applied, the means of communication employed, the level of behavior deducible from the observed results. Concretely, does the production of a standardized hand axe by detaching flakes from a larger core necessarily imply a "concept" of the result to be obtained, the use of precept to supplement example, conceptual as against perceptual level behavior? Does the successful repetition of the proper blow indicate a "knowledge of cause and effect"? And is a typological series, like that drawn up for hand axes, "the expression of a sequence of ideas and concepts"? Could not the pupil learn just by carefully observing and imitating the movements of the master how to detach flakes from a core? Having been shown a standard hand axe, could he not recognize it when he had so reduced the core by imitating the master's blows? In saying that such an operator "knows how to make a hand axe," need we mean more than that he recognizes a hand axe when he sees one and that by imitation and repetition he had made habitual a very complex set of muscular reactions that are released on the presentation of a stimulus—a visible lump of suitable stone?

I suggest that these questions, framed in terms of individualistic psychology, are from a sociological and historical standpoint irrelevant if not meaningless. The standardized tool is itself a concept fossilized. It is an archaeological type just because it is one embodiment of an idea that transcends not only each individual instance but also each individual hominid who makes a concrete reproduction of it, in a word a social concept. To reproduce the model is to know it, and this knowledge is maintained and transmitted by a society. Whether this group of intercommunicating and cooperating hominids were just a lineage or a tribe, it was larger and more durable than any of its members, and so the knowledge it shared was more comprehensive and enduring than the percepts and memories of any individual and may be said to constitute a supraorganic world of ideas existing "in the heads of society." The means of communication employed may not indeed be precisely deducible from surviving results of behavior; the relatively insignificant progress in control over the external world during this vast period may be a good argument against attributing to Lower Paleolithic men any system of symbols so flexible as that provided by phonetic language. Still, at the worst the pattern hand ax shown to the apprentice is not just a sign that releases a train of habitual reactions leading to the satisfaction of a natural appetite, but also a symbol the meaning of which, i.e., its use and the method of manufacture, has been communicated by society.

The fact of communication itself presupposes a patterned world of ideas in the heads of all society's members and, insofar as the communicated information can be successfully applied, this pattern must to some extent correspond to that of the external world. We cannot indeed directly infer at this stage the structure of the pattern in "society's heads." If acting on the principle "Do A, and B will happen" be equivalent to acting on information categorized under causality, then use of the category is revealed in the Acheulian flint-workers' behavior. Still, could he have verbalized the maxim, it might well turn out to be of the type "Tip the guardian and he will turn on the lights" rather than "Turn the switch and the lights will come on!" (most probably an undifferentiated confusion of both formulas).

3   The Middle Paleolithic stage (corresponding to the Last Interglacial and the First Maximum of the Würm Glaciation in Europe) is not marked by any revolutionary progress in the manufacture of tools, but provides some data for the clarification of just those metaphysical issues touched upon in the last paragraph. For from it survive in inhabited caves assemblages illustrating aspects of behavior other than eating and flint-knapping and the skeletal remains of some of the actors. Of special relevance to the organization and communi-

cation of information, oddly enough, is ritual behavior now unambiguously attested. The bodies of Moustierian men, whether belonging to the extinct Neanderthal species or to the potentially more adaptable variety represented in Palestine and parts of Europe, were interred in an artificial hollow dug in the cave floor and disposed in a flexed attitude and in some cases allegedly accompanied by a joint of meat or a couple of implements. Such formal burials are known from several caves in western Europe and in Palestine and some caves contained several burials, not all simultaneous, so that the rite must have been traditional. The observed behavior cannot be the response to any external stimulus, but must have been prompted by quite abstract ideas. Its repetition proves the communication of these ideas by the use of symbols that must have been purely conventional. Similar conclusions can safely be drawn from the special ceremonial treatment accorded to skulls, notably at La Ferrassie (Dordogne) and at Monte Circeo near Rome, and quite probably from many plausible instances of cannibalism.

Hence Middle Paleolithic men, even the bestial looking Neanderthalers, could communicate with each other by the use of conventional symbols—not demonstrably *spoken* words. By their aid, of course, each member of a Middle Paleolithic society participated in a world of ideas transcending his private experience and indeed all sensory experience are as eternal as his society itself. But it is only the existence of a world of ideas that is relevant to the history of science and not the eschatological or superstitious parts of its contents that happen to be most explicitly disclosed in the durable results of overt behavior.

However, new techniques in the manufacture of stone tools do point in the same direction. Middle Paleolithic flake tools (the core tradition did also persist) were generally made from cores, prepared with greater care than the Lower Paleolithic Clactonian ones. Now a prepared core is really a secondary tool—an artifact fabricated not to satisfy any immediately felt need, but for the manuufacture of instruments that should satisfy such needs if and when they arose. May it not be fairly inferred that cores were prepared to yield suitable flakes in order to achieve an ideal or conceived end? Moreover in the so-called Levalloisean technique, normally employed by Middle Paleolithic societies in North Africa and southwest Asia and by some in Europe too, the precise outlines of the flake desired were blocked out on the core.

I cannot imagine how this were done unless the operator had an abstract idea of what he wanted to produce; for the unstruck core resembles the result rather less than a blueprint resembles a machine. The repeated reproduction of geometrically similar flakes at many places and over many generations then shows that the idea was traditional and social.

4   With the Upper Paleolithic, beginning in Europe with the mild interstadial that interrupted the Last Glaciation, the whole character of the archaeological record changes radically. Not only does it now reveal an enormous multiplication of specialized and standardized tools and techniques, and the use of materials hitherto unrepresented, it also presents richer and more varied assemblages of associated artifacts, and those allow both insight into aspects of human behavior hidden at earlier periods and a finer discrimination of "cultures." The prehistorian can now be sure that he is dealing with a great number of societies, distinguished by divergences in their traditions of stone-working, of burial, of art, and even of diet. Owing to the unevenness of archaeological exploration and to local deficiencies in the record, the content and spatial boundaries of many of the cultures that should represent such societies are still imperfectly determined. Their chronological relations are often doubtful. The very number of cultures that ought to be distinguished even in an area so well explored as Europe is still fluid; for instance after fifteen years' research the single "Aurignacian" that Dr. Garrod sketched in 1938 as stretching from Palestine to France seems to be dissolving into a series of related groups. Much more than before are we now dealing with a plurality of distinct traditions in which knowledge was accumulated, separate "sciences" if you like.

The best known Upper Paleolithic tools in Europe and southwestern Asia are blades, made from prismatic or pyramidal cores, prepared even more carefully in advance than the Levalloisean. But in eastern Asia and much of Africa Moustierian or Levalloisean traditions persisted alone. By new and old techniques alike ingenious new secondary flint tools rendered possible the fabrication of efficient implements from bone, antler, ivory, and shell—materials previously utilized only casually. This new or improved equipment in turn opened the way to the invention of propulsive engines. Finally, application of these enlarged productive forces not only greatly enhanced success in the chase, but also opened up a hitherto untapped reservoir of food—the life that swarms in rivers and along the coasts. Of course all these material advances are reflections and consequences of the enrichment of the stock of information accumulated by Upper Paleolithic societies.

It seems likely that the detachment of blades and the manufacture of certain Aurignacian tools presupposed the discovery of a new technique of flint-working—pressure as opposed to percussion—and it is certain that many of the thin missile points, distinctive of the Solutrean, are pressure-flaked. To fashion tools or other artifacts out of bone, antler, and ivory you must know the distinctive properties of these materials, which are different from those of cryptocrystalline or microcrystalline stones on the one hand, of wood on the other. Bone, antler, and ivory can be given a tough point or edge only by grinding and polishing, a technique subsequently applied to edging fine-grained stone. Objects of all three materials might be perforated, and often this was done apparently by drilling rather than percussion or boring—a technique requiring different muscular movements and equipment than those employed in boring. Unless the bowdrill were used, the spindle would be rubbed between the palms of the hands. In either case men were producing rotary motion—a sort of motion rare in terrestrial nature though destined to play a decisive role in modern technology.

Construction, in the sense of joining firmly together two or more distinct pieces of material, suggested by the dubious Lower Paleolithic "bolas" (p. 41), is now well-attested for the Upper Paleolithic: sections of blades with blunted backs and square-trimmed ends were undoubtedly mounted end-to-end in a grooved piece of wood to form a composite knife; bone points have their bases split, notched or beveled obviously for attachment to a wooden shaft. Even a missile with a foreshaft can be inferred from surviving parts. Needles again point to tailored garments of fur or hide or tents composed of sewn skins. Positive evidence for constructed dwellings is afforded by excavations in South Russia and Siberia. They were roofed with skins supported on a framework of antlers over an excavated area. The skins, of course, have perished completely, but the stone scrapers so common on all Paleolithic sites can confidently be interpreted in the light of ethnographic evidence as used for the preparation of hides, though not of course exclusively.

Composite tools involving separately moving parts are already machines embodying quite abstract concepts and serving remote ends. The spear-thrower is a device using the lever principle to increase the range of missiles. It is attested archaeologically first in the Magdalenian of France by specimens carved out of reindeer antlers. Spear-throwers may, however, have been made earlier in wood; for from the recent distribution of the device many ethnographers infer that it was more ancient than the bow-and-arrows. In the archaeological record the latter is actually represented earlier by arrowheads, rather doubtfully in the Aterian of North Africa and quite certainly in the Spanish Solutrean. North of the Alps and Pyrenees the first plausible evidence is provided by actual wooden missiles with microlithic flint points from Hamburgian sites in the Late Glacial of North Germany. Feathered missiles figure even earlier in Franco-Cantabrian cave-paintings, for instance at Lascaux. The paintings may of course depict thrown darts rather than an arrow shot from a bow, but in any case show that the value of fletching missiles was already known by the early Magdalenian or Gravettian phase in France. The bow of course ingeniously utilized the resilience of certain woods to store up the muscular energy exerted in spanning it so as to release the whole at once, and this might easily be mistaken for a nonhuman motive power. The same principle must have been used for traps, which have naturally failed to survive.

The bow can also be utilized to actuate the drill spindle; if the bowstring be looped around the spindle, moving the bow backward and forward provides a more efficient method of converting linear into rotary motion than rubbing between the palms of the hands. There is indeed no sort of evidence for the use of the bow drill in Pleistocene times. The great popularity of "drill patterns" (patterns of dots drilled into bone or antler) in the North European Maglemosean has plausibly been regarded as evidence for the bow drill's use in early post-Glacial times, well before the novelties of the Neolithic Revolution had penetrated to northern Europe and probably before their emergence in the Near East.

The new missile weapons themselves would have guaranteed the huntsmen's success. At the same time the location of Upper Paleolithic encampments illustrates that familiarity with the habits of game that could only be inferred earlier; the great midden heaps of bones of gregarious herbivores left by the Gravettians, for instance, in France, Austria, Moravia, and South Russia are situated on natural routes for the herds' seasonal migrations and, particularly in the last-named area, point to an appreciation of the advantages offered by accidents of the terrain that could be utilized in canalizing the movement in a collective hunt. Fishing opened up a quite new supply of food that Moustierians had conspicuously failed to exploit. Was their failure due to ignorance of the food value of fish or to lack of equipment for catching them? Both deficiencies in any case were remedied by the Aurignacians, and their ultimate successors in Europe, the Magdalenians, must have owed their prosperity in no small measure to salmon runs up the French rivers every summer. The only piece of undoubted fishing tackle that survives is the bone gorge. Simple fish weirs may plausibly be inferred. Small sharp bones found in some caves may have formed parts of composite fishhooks, but that is just a guess. True fishhooks (of bone), fish spears (leisters), and nets with floats are, however, attested from the Mesolithic. Clark has recently drawn attention to the possibility that the Magdalenians of France dried the fish caught in the summer for consumption during the winter as was done by the Amerinds of the northwest Pacific coast.

In addition to discovering fresh sources of food, and inventing equipment for exploiting these, at least one Upper Paleolithic society had found out a new method of kindling fire to supplement frictional methods that must have been employed much earlier; the Magdalenians sometimes used flint and pyrites, a process that gave rise to the familiar flint-and-steel appliances after iron-smelting had been discovered.

Not content with fashioning composite tools at least one group of Upper Paleolithic men went on to produce an artificial substance that does not occur as such in nature. Several groups are known to have modeled in clay, though the results can be preserved only in most exceptional circumstances, as in the deep cave of Tuc d'Aubert. A molded lump might easily have fallen into the fire and been baked hard. Apparently an intelligent mammoth-hunter at Dolni Věstonice (Moravia) noted the result of such an accident and repeated it deliberately. In any case at this encampment small figures of animals were modeled in a mixture of clay and ash and then fired in a hearth. Thereby, of course, a chemical change was affected, the heat driving out a molecule of water from the hydrated aluminum silicate to leave pottery that is no longer plastic and will not disintegrate in water. This much the mammoth-hunters of Dolni Věstonice had recognized. There is no evidence that the discovery was put to any more practical use nor that it was communicated to any other community even within the East Gravettian culture to which Dolni Věstonice belongs. Pottery had to be rediscovered at the end of the Ice Age, perhaps more than once!

Of crucial importance is the first evidence for the discrimination and use of the numerical and metrical properties of objects. The construction of any composite tool, for instance fitting flint blades into a wooden handle in making a knife, inevitably involves measurement—that is the comparison of two or more objects in respect to magnitude alone, ignoring for this purpose all other sensible properties. That in itself is no mean feat of abstraction. Whether the parts to be fitted were compared directly or by reference to a third object, an independent measure—a finger or a hands breadth—is naturally unknown. The use of a socially defined standard is of course highly improbable so early. Counting, which demands even more abstract thinking, is also safely deducible from strips of bone or ivory notched along one edge. These so closely resemble tally sticks in recent use that they may be assumed to have had the same function. On this assumption dead mammoths or reindeer were regarded as units, sufficiently identical to be compared with equally identical notches on a strip of bone in respect of number alone. Whether or not Paleolithic Europeans had conventional names for any natural numbers, they could count and so did use "the category of number," whatever Levy-Bruhl might have said!

While art is traditionally contrasted with science, the celebrated manifestations of artistic capacity that survive from Upper Paleolithic times are indirectly relevant to this article in several respects.

1. We have already remarked indications of esthetic feelings in Lower Paleolithic behavior. Upper Paleolithic men not only perforated shells and carved bracelets and noseplugs of mammoth ivory, but also to decorate themselves or their weapons or cave walls collected and used substances—colored earths, amber, jet—that at the time did not serve for the satisfaction of any biological need directly or indirectly.

2. The pictures incised on slabs of stone or pieces of bones

and ivory and painted or engraved on cave walls illustrate a surprising capacity to reproduce in two dimensions what is perceived as three-dimensional. They illustrate therefore some practical knowledge of the rules of perspective and optical laws. In the same way tubular bones, with one or more lateral perforations and with one end polished, and also perforated phalange bones have been most plausibly interpreted as musical instruments or at least whistles. If such interpretation be correct, their manufacture documents knowledge of some properties of vibrating columns of air, in more pompous terms, of some acoustic laws.

3. The carvings in the round, bas-reliefs and paintings and engravings provide direct information as to the contents of the artists' knowledge and some hints as to its structure. At least in the Franco-Cantabrian province the delineation of animals is so true to life that a zoologist can recognize the exact species intended. Indeed, the best have all the qualities of portraits. They betoken very close and sympathetic observation of their subjects and also a remarkably vivid but extremely concrete memory (the execution of masterpieces in the complete darkness of deep caves suggests to me kinesthetic as much as visual memory). The subject, always an animal of importance in the food quest, is, however, completely objectified and isolated from its environment, which is never even suggested. And no picture is a photographic reproduction of the two-dimensional image of the beast that the artist might have seen reflected in a still pool but rather represents the beast as perceived, though never conceptualized. In one school, for instance, the horns of bison are shown as if viewed quarter face though the rest of the animal is in strict profile. Still one of the main charms of Franco-Cantabrian animal portraiture is its immediacy. In violent contrast to the lively and naturalistic portrayal of animals, birds, and fishes stand the comparatively rare representations of the human figure. None is naturalistic; none could be mistaken for a portrait of a human individual; most have no faces at all. The human figures in fact give the impression of caricatures, and this is true of the so-called Venus figures of Eurasia and of the many representations of men and women in the southeast Spanish rock-shelter art that may not be Paleolithic at all and in its still less datable African analogs. Now a caricature is also an abstraction. We are then faced with the antinomy that animals (at least in the Franco-Cantabrian school) were depicted concretely and naturalistically, humans on the con-

trary abstractly; a faceless Venus figure represents not a real living woman, but the idea of the female. Inevitably Durkheim's footnote—"the notion of class is founded on that of the human groups"—springs to mind.

4. In addition to these conventional human figures Upper Paleolithic artists have left more enigmatic marks that must be purely symbolic. Some are symbols the referents of which —e.g. sex organs—are obvious enough though they hardly exhaust the meanings assigned to them by a lost social convention. Others seem purely geometric, but surely had had some symbolic signification. One variety, though undecipherable, is relevant in another context. Painted blobs and still more cuplike depressions—"cup marks" pecked out on rock —appear to implicate some continuity in tradition between the Upper Paleolithic and the Middle Paleolithic on the one hand and the Neolithic on the other. At La Ferrassie (Dordogne) such cup marks not only adorn an engraved slab found in the Aurignacian level but occur lower down in the same cave on the underside of a block used to protect the skull in Moustierian burial 6. (It is irrelevant whether Neanderthalers themselves made the latter marks or merely selected a stone that bore natural cup marks.) The same symbols are of course quite common in the Neolithic and Paleometallic (Early Bronze) Ages, again often in connection with burials.

5. The practice of a useful craft, no actual products of which are the least likely to survive, can be deduced from another geometric pattern in the Upper Paleolithic repertoire. The maeander or Greek key pattern was very accurately engraved on objects of mammoth ivory from Mezin in the Ukraine. The pattern is quite complicated and was in fact relatively seldom used in prehistoric art. Yet Dr. Weltfisch has recently shown that it arises almost automatically from a fairly simple kind of basketry weave. Of course it is *a priori* likely that Paleolithic communities had discovered how to plait twigs and grasses, but the basketry pattern from Mezin is the nearest approach to direct evidence till the Mesolithic; from that period wicker fish traps or weels have been preserved in north European peat bogs. Incidentally, simple basketry patterns automatically illustrate geometrical propositions that were utilized at least by the oldest literate communities; the chequer pattern, for instance, is a visual statement of the formula for the area of a rectangle.

Finally the cave art provides the most convincing argument for supposing that Paleolithic societies, like savage communi-

ties on a comparable technological level today, organized
their information on what are generally called "magical"
lines. What motive could have inspired the execution of
elaborate portraits of game animals in very inaccessible positions in the remotest recesses of dark tortuous caves? Perhaps
beliefs such as, "As surely as the artist's brush strokes create a
painted horse on the cave wall, so surely will there be an
edible horse for us to hunt," or "As I draw this dart trans-
fixing the bison I have depicted, so shall our darts pierce the
prey in the chase outside." If Paleolithic societies did act on
some such beliefs, it is certain that faith in the casual efficiency
of the pictorial wounding of a painted bison did not deter
the huntsmen from inflicting deadly wounds on living bison.
Magical causes are not substitutes, but supplements, for physical causes or rather preliterate societies have not succeeded
as well as modern scientists in isolating efficient causes.

So, if only for its magical content, the information accumulated by any Paleolithic society must have been ordered by
very different categories to make a very different pattern from
those characterizing the worlds of science and even of common sense today. Nor can we assume that the pattern was the
same for all Paleolithic societies save insofar as it comprised
as a component a pattern such as scientists find verifiable.
For, however close the abstract similarity of the categories
employed by the simpler societies of today, the whole tendency
of recent anthropology has been to discredit theories of
unilinear evolution whether in material culture, social organization, or noumenological beliefs. If then we admit with
Durkheim, as I am convinced we must, a historical evolution
of the rules of logic, we are not thereby entitled to assume
one single "primitive logic" from which our logic has been
born. "Each civilization has its organized system of concepts
which characterizes it."

This brings us at once to the question as to how far information acquired by one society could be or was communicated to others. By Upper Paleolithic times the wealth of the
archaeological record is such that we can recognize a very
substantial number of contemporary or successive societies,
sharply distingushed from one another by contrasted traditions in flint-working and by divergent types of tools and
weapons, styles in art, fashions in personal adornment, burial
rites, and so on. And the diversity was certainly greater than
a prehistorian can hope to detect.

The comparatively rapid divergence of traditions expressed

in the multiplication of archaeologically distinguishable cultures presumably reflects an at least equal divergence in the symbolic means of communication whereby the traditions were maintained. It is thus in itself a positive argument for the use of phonetic languages by Upper Paleolithic societies. For phonetic symbols (being-time series) are much less probable and much less mimetic than gesture symbols. Their meanings, that is, are much more purely conventional than most of the signs used in known kinetic languages. The same inference might be drawn from the accelerated tempo of change in the archaeological record. The Upper Paleolithic on Zeuner's chronology occupies some 80,000 years as compared with the 400,000 or more assigned by the same author to the Lower and Middle Paleolithic. Moreover, the environmental changes—in Europe an interstadial and two readvances in the last Glaciation—were far less violent than the alternations between Glacials and Interglacials that divided up the longer period. The observable changes are indeed relatively small compared with those detected in the same area during a single millennium of the Neolithic, but are nonetheless much more conspicuous than anything detectable in a comparable interval at earlier stages. In France, for instance, Magdalenian VI is technologically and artistically further from Aurignacian I than is Micoquian from early Acheulean. Insofar as this apparent change in tempo be not due to the accidents of the archaeological record, it might reasonably be attributed to the increasing use of a more flexible system of symbols with which to "operate in the head" as a substitute for physical trial-and-error processes. (Of course a priority of kinetic over phonetic language, of bodily gestures over spoken words, is absolutely undemonstrable and must remain one of two equally plausible guesses.)

It is thus very probable that there were at least as many distinct languages as there were archaeological cultures. The babel of tongues would inevitably impose graver obstacles to "international" intercourse than it does today.

Now opportunities for such "international" intercourse are attested even in the Old Stone Age by bones of Atlantic fish in the caves of Grimaldi on the Riviera and by Mediterranean shells found on settlement sites in the Dordogne and on the Middle Dnieper. Archaeologists hope to be able to trace also the diffusion of ideas, at least of discoveries and inventions, from one society to another by the distribution of distinctive types and techniques over several archaeological provinces.

The Solutrean has been thought to offer evidence of such diffusion and also for continuity of tradition between Middle and Upper Paleolithic. The culture is characterized by delicate lanceheads or even arrowheads, made on thin flakes trimmed all over one or both faces by shallow flaking. The trimming could in most cases be effected by an improved version of the Acheulian baton technique but in some types pressure flaking must have been used as well. Some at least of the flakes thus trimmed have been made from disc cores of Middle Paleolithic (Mousterian) type rather than prismatic or pyramidal blade cores. Now in France and Spain Solutrean implements and techniques appear somewhat abruptly in layers separated from the Moustierian by deep deposits containing blade tools distinctive of the Aurignacian and Perigordian or Gravettian cultures. At the same time there is a marked decline in the bone industry and in works of art. It really looks as if the Solutrean were introduced by well-armed invaders. But still such cannot have annihilated the established populations since the artistic tradition is not completely broken and in the uppermost Solutrean horizons many flints are exactly like those of the latest Gravettian save that they are retouched in Solutrean technique. Finally this technique itself disappears locally, and in the Magdalenian we witness a revival of Aurignacian and Gravettian traditions, as if the diffusion of Solutrean types and techniques made no permanent contribution to the technical traditions accumulated by glacial societies in western Europe.

In central Europe and south Russia on the contrary the local Solutrean seems to follow directly on a local Moustierian, that is distinguished from the better known Franco-Cantabrian by a more frequent use of bifacial trimming on flake tools as well as on small hand axes. At Kostienki this Solutrean is followed by a true blade culture, known also in central Europe, agreeing with the French Gravettian in a use of bone, the production of works of art and even in the forms of flint implements, but distinguished in its flint work by some bifacial retouching rather in Solutrean style. Again the North African Aterian is essentially a Levalloisean industry, practiced in one instance at least by men of Neanderthaloid physical type, but including leaf-shaped lanceheads of Solutrean shape and trimmed all over both faces. Finally Solutrean techniques of bifacial working of flakes were used for the production of Yuma and Folsom points, the oldest well-defined flint types

of the New World, and very widely indeed for the production
of arrowheads in the Old World Neolithic.

Now typologically it is easy to derive Solutrean types and
techniques from some Acheulian-Moustierian hybrid, a *Moustérien à tradition acheuléenne*. But the same development may
have taken place independently at several places, so that the
Solutrean cannot be very confidently invoked to prove diffusion of technical knowledge. To France such knowledge
was most probably brought by a migration, but there it
seems to have had no lasting effect in practice. Nor are
other archaeological evidences for the communication of
ideas across cultural frontiers much more conclusive.

In England isolated Magdalenian objects found in a few
caves associated with types of the native Creswellian culture
could easily have been brought by actual visitors from France,
with which Great Britain was still linked by land, and in
any case the devices they illustrate were not demonstrably
incorporated in the native culture nor reproduced locally.
On the other hand, needles, which appear in Europe first in
late Solutrean or Magdalenian contexts, were made also on
the Yenesei and the Angara in Siberia, and even at Choukou-tien near Peiping in China, and in both regions drilling
was applied to bone or stone, but the associated flint tools
in no case are made of blades and indeed resemble Moustierian
more than Magdalenian or even Solutrean types. Needles
and drills in fact belong to local Siberian and Chinese cultures, otherwise quite distinct from any European assemblage.
Prehistorians assume, at least as a heuristic device, that
needling and drilling were diffused, but cannot yet establish
whence they were diffused and so that they were in fact
diffused at all.

If then we attempt to sum up the useful information accumulated and applied in practice at the end of the Pleistocene period, we must not imply that it was organized as
a body of knowledge, communicable to, and shared by, all
Paleolithic societies. The applications, which alone can be
observed, are doubtless embodiments of traditional lore accumulated and maintained by distinct social units and presumably expressed in equally distinct conventional symbols if
not encased in divergent logical frames too. That some of
this information was nevertheless pooled is at best a deduction from the observed distribution in the Mesolithic or
Neolithic of devices and techniques like bows-and-arrows,
geometric microliths, needles, harpoons, pressure-flaking, drill-

ing, well beyond the bounds of the particular archaeological cultures amongst which they are observed in the Paleolithic. But this argument applies solely to information that was translated not only into action, but also into substantial instruments of action.

Equally useful information about the habits of the mammoth and the woolly rhinoceros, accumulated and successfully applied by Paleolithic societies, has, in default of writing, vanished totally. We have no clue how widely similar information about more permanent phenomena was shared among contemporary societies or transmitted to their cultural heirs.

The following incomplete list of the material embodiments of information that have survived in the archaeological record purports then only to present the "applied science" of some Paleolithic societies that was eventually replicated by, if not communicated to, a substantial proportion of our species. If it assumes diffusion, it carries no implication as to any symbolic form in which such applied science was transmitted.

scraper (hides)	wedge	missiles
awl	?chopper	
needle	mallet	spear-thrower
knife	spoke-shave	bow-and-arrow
graver (stone),	arrow-shaft	harpoon
	straightener	gorge
bone, wood)	hammer	
saw (bone)	punch (flint)	
drill bit (bone,		whistle
stone)	sinew-frayer	flute
borer (bone,		
stone)	strike-a-light	
polishing stones		tally stick
(bone)	lamp	
plane (wood)	paint-grinder	two-dimensional drawing

Only appliances that actually survive have been included: traps, frictional devices for fire production, etc., though confidently inferrable, are deliberately omitted. The words in parentheses indicate the sort of materials to which the tool was probably applied.

5   "Mesolithic" denotes no new cultural stage but just a continuation of the Paleolithic into the Geological Recent or Holocene till the effects of the Neolithic Revolution become

evident. At the same time the "Mesolithic" section of the archaeological record is very poorly defined save in northern Europe, western Europe, Crimea, Palestine, and perhaps the Sudan, though in the first-named province its documentation is exceptionally rich. Hence the Mesolithic can conveniently be treated as an appendix to the Upper Paleolithic with which it is sometimes combined under a single designation Miolithic.

We may note first the following embodiments of applied science to be added to the list just given:

chisel (woodworking)	hook (fishing)	sledge
adze (woodworking)	leister (fishing)	paddle
? ax (woodworking)	weel (fishing)	boat
	net and float (fishing)	

The development of an efficient kit of woodworking tools is reliably attested for the early post-Glacial only in northern Europe. It may be regarded as an adjustment to the spread of forest over regions formerly covered with open steppe, bare tundra or ice sheets, but no similar adjustment is detectable in the equally well-wooded regions of Atlantic Europe. The flint adze—or ax—blades expressing this adjustment are edged by one or two transverse flakes, an ingenious process termed the *"tranchet"* technique. A rather similar technique is illustrated on certain Acheulian hand axes termed "cleavers" that are common in Africa and the Indian peninsula, but rather rare in Europe. Later adze blades made by the true *tranchet* blow occur in Palestine, Egypt, and even the Solomon Islands, posing a knotty problem for diffusionists. East of the Baltic, where large flint nodules were scarce, adze blades were made of fine-grained rock edged by the grinding technique applied to bone and antler in the Upper Paleolithic. The result is of course the polished stone celt, the ubiquitious type fossil of the Neolithic, but this does not imply that this tool was diffused from Mesolithic northern Europe. Indeed a stone chisel or wedge, thus sharpened, is known already from a late Paleolithic site on the Don.

"The domestication of the dog," deducible from its skeletal remains or dog-gnawed bones from all provinces, need not be an application of any novel kind of information though it is a potential source of such. Dogs presumably just attached themselves to men's encampments without becoming dependent on human foresight for the provision of food and water or for protection against predators. Men did not therefore need, and had little opportunity for acquiring, such

intimate acquaintance with the sexual and other habits and
organs of their canine companions as was demanded and
offered by the care and breeding of cattle, sheep, and goats.
The domestication of the dog is in itself not the first step
in stockbreeding. It did, however give the opportunity of
learning how to direct and control a really living instrument
that could be made useful in the chase and eventually in
rounding up gregarious animals like sheep and even for
pulling sledges.

II

We now come to that section of the archaeological record
that lies between the "Neolithic revolution"—i.e., the first
emergence of farming and village communities—on the one
hand and on the other the invention or adoption of writing
or the replacement of bronze by iron for industrial purposes,
whichever be the earlier. Admittedly a substantial part of this
section in Eurasia runs parallel to the written records of the
urban civilizations of Egypt and southwestern Asia. Of course
the trade and therewith the technology of these literate civilizations affected the illiterate barbarians far beyond their narrow political frontiers, but applications of their learned
sciences can be recognized and discounted so as not to distort
the prehistoric character of our picture. The initial stage is
naturally extremely vague; "the industrial revolution" covers
perhaps a dozen decades; "the Neolithic revolution" must
have occupied at least as many centuries. From Braidwood's
"stage of incipient agriculture" so little direct evidence is
available to control ingenious speculations that for a factual
survey—and that is the aim here—it remains a postulate. Our
survey begins with village communities cultivating cereals
and keeping for food some domestic stock.

Nor can the record hereafter be usefully divided for the
present purpose into self-contained volumes. No doubt the
adoption of intelligent metallurgy does mark a real cultural
horizon at which a new volume might begin, as it does in
traditional archaeological periodization. But in practice it is
too often impossible to state on which side of this boundary

a given technical or scientific event falls. In Europe, for instance, plows and even wheels may have been produced without the aid of metal tools. But even if they were, it can be argued that their European makers were laboriously imitating with stone tools what had been originally created by carpenters enjoying the advantage of saws and other metal instruments. Accordingly, a chronological arrangement, such as was adopted in the first part of this article, cannot be attempted here.

The archaeological record left by the last 7,000 years is less incomplete and enormously richer than that of the preceding Paleolithic age. More survives of man's handiwork if only because it has been exposed for a shorter time to the corrosive action of weather, biochemical change, and earth movements. Though the painful gap left by the decay of organic materials is still felt, more lucky accidents have preserved actual remains of woodwork, textiles, or plants, while imprints of cereals in pottery or of timber posts in the earth often preserve data for the reconstruction of a rural economy or an architectural pattern. At the same time, from the Neolithic revolution on, men have learned to make or do an astonishing variety of new things.

As a consequence of this enrichment, the record discloses an increasing number of distinct societies, expressing their individualities by arbitrary divergences in traditional patterns of behavior that fossilize, and presumably accumulating their several collective experiences in equally distinct traditions. A group of Neolithic farmers, being self-sufficient and yet less mobile than a band of hunters, would be more likely to develop idiosyncrasies of behavior in isolation. At the same time there is more abundant evidence of opportunities for intercourse between the societies thus distinguished and so for pooling traditional lore. Even before the rise of urban civilizations in the valleys of the Nile, the Tigris-Euphrates, and the Indus, and even in regions beyond their influence the distribution of substances far from their occurrences in nature can be traced on quite a large scale, and now not only shells or attractive stones, but also material for implements like obsidian or rocks specially suited for the manufacture of axes and querns were thus transported by human agency. The habitual use of copper or bronze for weapons and tools was nowhere possible without regular trade bringing supplies, often from a considerable distance, and even manufactured goods were seen caught up in this commerce. Well before 2000 B.C., objects manufactured on the Indus were transported to the valley of the Tigris, and after 1500 B.C., actual Aegean manufactures turn up in England while ornaments "made in England" have been identified in Mycenaean and Minoan graves.

The speed of technological progress in the 4,000 years here surveyed, in comparison with that in the preceding 40,000, is breathtaking. It is scarcely comprehensible unless the results of observation and experimentation were being accumulated not only in the narrow oral tradition of each local peasantry but in a larger pool to which, however indirectly, most such societies had access and could themselves contribute—a rudimentary kind of supernational science in fact. Inevitably much of the applied science of prehistoric times must of its very nature be confined at least to a single ecological province. For instance, most of the agricultural techniques based on experience gained in Egypt or Syria would be inapplicable among the temperate forests of upper Eurasia. But after all, even today universities recognize such geographically restricted branches of science as tropical medicine and tropical agriculture. But if the traditional techniques for cultivating them were by their very nature tied to an ecological province, the cereals themselves were subject to no such restriction. Nor is any such limitation discoverable on the practices of weaving, potting, and metallurgy nor on the use of wheeled vehicles, sailing boats, the balance, and so on. Whether the discoveries and inventions involved therein were diffused or made independently several times, the knowledge on which they are based, and which is based upon their use, was in fact the common property of a very large number of distinct societies; for they are not peculiar to, or distinctive of, any one "culture" in the archaeological, partitive sense.

A second peculiarity of this volume of the archaeological record is that it can be divided into relatively short and well-defined chronological sections. It discloses a wider range of phenomena, modifications of which can be conveniently used to define stages or periods in local sequences. The intercourse between distinct societies just noted in turn offers opportunities for correlating stages in several local sequences into more comprehensive periods. Finally prospects are opened up of measuring these archaeological periods in terms of centuries or years and so of transferring them into a global chronological frame within which phenomena in one locality can be compared with contemporary events in another. Varved clays laid down annually by the melt waters from a glacier afford a very indirect method of connecting archaeological events with the series of tropic years, but the available results seem too unreliable for use here. A more hopeful chronometer is the decay of the radioactive carbon isotope, C14, that has been absorbed by any organism during its life. When grave technical difficulties have been overcome, it should be possible to calculate to within a few decades how many years ago any piece of organic material incorporated in an archaeological deposit ceased to form part of a living thing and absorb C14. In 1954 very few revelant deposits have been thus dated, and the figures given must still be taken with reserve. Yet the central date of 4750 B.C., for Jarmo, a site considered by botanists to reveal a very early stage in the domestication of cereals, seems to be of the right order of magnitude and has been used as a basis for estimating the beginnings of the Neolithic revolution and so of the section here surveyed.

If the beginning of our period be fixed rather precariously by atomic physics, the written records of Egypt, supplemented by Babylonian documents, define at about 3000 B.C. its end on the Nile and on the Tigris. Our survey does not stop short there, but even in regions that remained illiterate for another two millennia the historical chronology based on the Oriental records can be extended thanks to the trade relations indicated above; by 1500 B.C., the greater part of Europe from Britain and Sweden to Sicily and Greece can be brought into the frame thus provided. So we can form a much better idea of the rate of change and the speed of the accumulation of information than can be gleaned from the geological and climatic changes that were alone available in the previous article.

Thirdly, the sheer volume of documents is now too great for it to be practicable, were it relevant or necessary, to catalog the natural substances, known to one or many preliterate societies, to enumerate instances illustrating the selection of materials (e.g. of stones for axes or querns) with the aid of accumulated experience or to list the instruments, including, for instance, wheeled vehicles, invented in the light of such knowledge. The present article must be limited to presenting evidence under the following heads: (1) behavior directed to the attainment of remote ends and guided by tested inferences from collective experience—sowing and planting, selective breeding, the production of artificial substances, mining; (2) metrical and numerical operations.

2   The Neolithic section of the archaeological record as
here defined begins with the cultivation of wheat and barley
and the domestication of sheep, goats, cattle, and pigs. Explicit
data to document the preceding stage of incipient food production or to control directly theoretical speculations as to the
priority of agriculture or stockbreeding are nonexistent at
present. We begin near the culmination of a revolution in
thought as much as in economics. Food production is behavior guided by socially accumulated experience in the
expectation of results to come some months later. The act
of sowing in particular expressed by implication a faith in
the predictive value of socially transmitted information and a
belief in at least one of the uniformities of nature. The last
vestige of anything that could be explained as sign behavior
has been left behind; the cultivator is reacting to purely conceptual and social stimuli.

Concretely the cultivation of cereals presupposes the knowledge—i.e., the belief confirmed by social experience—(1)
that any suitable seed planted will germinate after some weeks,
(2) that it will produce a plurality of like seeds, (3) what
to plant, and (4) what conditions are essential to germination
and ripening. The application of this basic information must
evoke further observations leading (5) to some selection
among the sports that would arise under artificial conditions
and to the elaboration of some technique of cultivation or
rural economy. The latter will vary with the locality, but in all
environments will demand rules for the discrimination of the
most suitable soil, the invention of some instrument for tilling,
the determination of the appropriate season for planting, and
the invention of suitable methods to counteract soil exhaustion. In support of these general deductions space permits the
presentation of evidence on only a few specific points.

The cereals cultivated at Jarmo in Kurdistan—*Triticum
monococcum,* and *dicoccum* and two-rowed barley—are not
only the oldest known, but stand nearer than any grains
hitherto examined to wild ancestors, and these latter are confined to southwestern Asia. Accordingly, as all other Neolithic
farmers in Eurasia and Afrasia cultivated the same grains,
the cultivated cereals were diffused and so the knowledge

of what grains to cultivate was embodied in a single tradition common to all Neolithic farmers though items were added to it or dropped from it locally. The apparent absence of *T. monococcum* from Egypt and its rarity in western Europe may be attributed to selection, while hexaploid wheats may have started as sports, perhaps in more than one center, and been favored by deliberate selection. It is presumed that plots were tilled with hoes or dibbles before the invention of any sort of plow, but as all three implements could be made entirely of wood the presumption is undemonstrable. The use of a plow is attested by the oldest written documents from Egypt and Mesopotamia, soon after 3000 B.C., in the Aegean, about 2000 B.C., in the "Early Bronze Age" of Upper Italy, in the latest "Neolithic" in the Swiss lake dwellings, in Holland and Denmark.

The problem of soil exhaustion does not of course arise in riverine irrigation cultivation. Some solution, most likely a systematic alternation between tillage and pasture, may be inferred from the permanent occupation of the earliest villages, attested by tell formation, in Iran, Syria, the Levant, Greece, and the Balkans where "dry cultivation" was presumably practiced: it can only result from deductions from observations accumulated over several generations. Throughout the temperate forests of Europe shifting agriculture prevailed during the local Neolithic phase and persisted locally much longer. The creation of rural economies adapted to these or other local conditions is too specialized a theme for this article.[4]

Neolithic farmers in southwestern Asia, northern Africa, and Europe already kept all the useful food animals that men have found domesticable. To a variable degree this was the result of mostly unconscious experimentation; in early historic times the Egyptians did actually experiment in the domestication of gazelles, oryx, and other beasts without permanent result. To some extent too domesticated breeds are the results of selection. In the case of cattle, herdsmen would be able to keep under control most easily the smaller and more docile members of the herd that in a wild state could hardly survive. So too they would kill for meat the most troublesome and pugnacious heifers. Thus without much forethought a tractable but relatively small breed would be established,

---

[4] For lack of detailed evidence, whether botanical or archaeological, no reference will be made to the cultivation of flax, beans, peas, nor to the vine, olive, or other fruit trees.

and early domestic kine of the *Bos brachyceros* stock are miserably small when compared to contemporary wild cattle (*Bos primigenius*). In this process no exception based on experience is implied. That may, however, be inferred from the results of sheepbreeding; for fleecy sheep seem to be artificial products of a selection that must have been deliberate. Wool-bearing sheep, though still unknown in Egypt, had been established in southwestern Asia by 3000 B.C., and had probably reached temperate Europe by 2000, though as late as 1500 the wool used for cloaks in Denmark was still mixed with so much sheep hair that some investigators imagined that deer hair had been deliberately added to the wool.

Selective breeding implies familiarity with the reproductive processes of the animals bred. In fact, observations on flocks and herds must have given herdsmen information about sexual physiology denied to huntsmen. Quite probably it was their observations that revealed the role of the male in human reproduction that is not understood by all surviving hunter tribes even today.

The production of artificial substances is as distinctive of the Neolithic stage as food production itself. It is equivalent to the deliberate causation of chemical changes by thermal or other agencies and thus indicates the recognition of uniformities in nature of the same kind as those expressed in chemical laws though of a low order of generality. The trains of action involved, often very complicated and prolonged, must have been initiated in the confident expectation of remote results, inferred from collective experience embodied in traditional rules. It is implied in food production itself insofar as cereals were converted into bread; for bread and even flour are substances that do not occur in nature though no more artificial than several dishes that might appear on food-gatherers' menus.

Though cereals may at first have been merely popped or parched, saddle querns or other kinds of grain rubber are found on nearly all Neolithic sites and point to the production of flour. The latter may have been eaten as a kind of gruel, but "bread ovens" are conspicuous in all early villages in Hither Asia, Greece, the Balkan peninsula, southeast and central Europe, and served to convert flour into something more unlike any natural material than most savage dishes. Heat alone was presumably the first agent of transformation. A biochemical reaction was, however, being deliberately invoked to "raise" the bread by the beginning of the written record in Egypt and Mesopotamia.

By that time too, fermentation was being used to produce an alcoholic liquor from barley. It has indeed been rather perversely suggested that barley was first cultivated in order to produce beer. There is of course no direct evidence pointing in that direction; on the contrary, half-baked loaves of leavened bread were used in making beer in ancient, as in modern, Egypt. The fermentation of grape juice to produce wine was practiced in the Near East by 3000 B.C. Late Neolithic lake dwellers in Austria are believed to have made a sort of cider, probably from crabapples, while the fermentation of a sort of cranberry wine may perhaps be inferred from the contents of vessels found in Danish barrows of the Middle Bronze Age, c. 1500 B.C.

3 Pottery is produced by the decomposition of hydrated aluminum silicate by heat. At least one tribe of Paleolithic mammoth-hunters had observed this transformation (pp. 48-49) but the practical application of such an observation for the manufacture of vessels demanded the further discovery of the need to add a temper to the pure clay. Some of the earliest Neolithic farmers in Cyprus, Palestine, Kurdistan, and Baluchistan made no pottery (though the early Cypriotes molded and tried to bake vessels of untempered clay) while some Mesolithic hunter-fishers in the Sudan and in Denmark may have discovered the technique for themselves without the aid of immigrant farmers. Otherwise all farming communities represented in the archaeological record did make pots though the art was not demonstrably diffused along with the bases of food production. All potters knew what would happen when they heated tempered clay to over 450°C. Many could also predict the result of chemical changes in the impurities of the clay or in minerals deliberately added thereto, and used this knowledge to embellish their products. For instance, the Mesolithic and Neolithic pottery of the Sudan and later wares from Egypt, Cyprus, North Syria, Anatolia, Greece, and southeast Europe were made from ferruginous clays or more often coated with a hematite slip. Exposed to the air while hot, the iron is oxidized to the red ferric form, while in contact with glowing ashes or the products of incomplete com-

bustion it is reduced to the black oxide (Fe_3O_4). In the fabrics named, the firing was so conducted as to produce an attractively variegated surface—the interior and rim black, the rest of the exterior red, or *vice versa*. Throughout southwest Asia and southeast Europe vases were often painted with mineral colors, and here again the potters knew how to make allowance for the changes in the color of the paint and ground that should result from reactions to the ambient atmosphere during firing. Even in the IVth millennium, kilns, inspired probably by bread ovens, were constructed to give a higher temperature and allow better control of surface color by a regulation of the air supply; good examples are known from Sialk III and Susa and, later, but still "Neolithic," from Olynthus in Macedonia and Ariusd in Transylvania.

Quite a number of other artificial substances—brick, plaster, faïence—were regularly made by prehistoric societies if usually with a limited range in space. But of all, metal, and particularly copper, had the most far-reaching consequences, technical and economic, and metallurgy was the most abstract and comprehensive of the prehistoric applied sciences; quite justly has the use of metal been made the differentia of an "age" by archaeologists. Of course, copper, like gold, is not strictly an artificial substance (for it occurs albeit rarely as native copper). Metallurgy—I mean intelligent metallurgy—is the culmination of a series of discoveries, namely: (1) that copper is malleable; (2) that annealing restores malleability; (3) that copper is fusible and can therefore be cast; and (4) that the metal can be obtained from oxidized ores by heating with charcoal—i.e., smelting. It is far from certain that casting (3) precedes smelting (4); the temperature of fusion, 1085°C, is higher than that required to initiate the chemical process of reduction (c. 750°C) and could not be obtained without the employment of charcoal that would also serve as a reducing agent. In any case, owing to the rarity of native copper in the Old World, supplies of the metal sufficient for its industrial use could only be obtained by smelting.

The extractive side of metallurgy demands substantially more theoretical knowledge and technical experience than the foregoing phrases reveal. The metallurgist must have learned by experience or by instruction to recognize from superficial indications what sort of rock should contain ore and which of the minerals embedded in the lode should yield copper when heated with charcoal. As the various copper ores, though generally brightly colored, are otherwise dissimilar in appearance, their classification is highly abstract. Smiths and smelters must likewise know the properties of charcoal and how to produce it; for charcoal itself is an artificial substance made by the partial combustion (really distillation) of wood in a confined space. Then a blast or forced draft was essential for fusion if not for reduction. On ethnographic analogies bellows would be expected, but there is no archaeological evidence for such till late in the third millennium, though the nozzles (*tuyères*) should survive—and do from the Late Bronze Age. Earlier Egyptian pictures show the use of blowpipes—but only by goldsmiths. Probably the draft of a vertical potter's kiln would generate sufficient heat, and furnaces were modeled on such kilns till bellows were invented. Then the first product of smelting would not be recognizable as metal—a regulus—but a spongy mass needing refining by quite complicated further operations.

The malleability of copper may well have been discovered independently at several places where native copper occurs or did once occur—in Ireland, Spain, "Hungary,"[5] the Urals, Iran, and elsewhere—and native copper was actually melted, though not quite certainly shaped by casting in "Hungary." But it is not at all likely that the very abstruse processes involved in smelting and casting—what is here termed "intelligent metallurgy"—were discovered more than once in the Old World. Yet conclusive arguments for diffusion are lacking. The earliest types of metal weapons, tools, and ornaments are not significantly improbable. The oldest copper utensils—such as axes—are indeed very similar everywhere. Still, after all, they are just metallic copies of widespread stone forms, and moreover on close inspection it is generally possible from the form alone to decide whether a given copper ax were made, say, in Egypt, the Balkans, India, or Ireland! The first specialized type to be at all widely diffused is the knotheaded pin—found in Gerzean Egypt and at Sialk IV in Iran and later in Cyprus, at Troy II, and in central Europe. Still this device is not very improbable and is not certainly among the first products of intelligent metallurgy in Egypt or Iran. So we cannot argue without qualification that it was introduced into either region by the founders of metallurgy. That can, however, be asserted of central Europe. There knotheaded pins together with other and more specialized Levantine orna-

---

[5] "Hungary" is here used to denote the whole area of the Middle Danube basin that before 1914 formed the Kingdom of Hungary.

ments were among the earliest products of the Unětician bronze industry.

Secondly there are indeed reasonably good grounds for believing that intelligent metallurgy was practiced east of the Tigris well before 3000 B.C., not before 2,000 B.C in Ireland and Bohemia, only five centuries later still around the Urals and in China. But at the moment it is impossible to prove, however likely it may seem, that metallurgy began in Anatolia, the Aegean, or even the Iberian Peninsula later than in Mesopotamia and Iran. If only through the lack of an independent chronological frame of reference, I cannot show that the further a metallurgical center be from any focus, so much the later its starting point. I believe that the very considerable body of information indispensable for the extraction and casting of copper was accumulated in a single tradition and so diffused. But I cannot prove this—nor yet whether such tradition, if any, should have included from the start two other complexes of discoveries—the reduction of sulphide ores and alloying—that were essential to the full development of the Bronze Age.

The first ores to be smelted were presumably oxides, carbonates, silicates—"oxidized ores." But the commonest copper ores are sulphides, and these cannot be smelted by heating with charcoal till they have been oxidized by a preliminary roasting in a current of air. Operators smelting sulphide ores must be able to predict the results of two quite independent chemical reactions. It is hard to determine how early the exploitation of sulphide ores began. Spectrographic analysis, on which our knowledge of the impurities in ancient metal objects is largely based, does not disclose the presence of sulphur, and in any case traces of this element may not be unimpeachable evidence of production from sulphide ores. The fact of mining and the discovery of roasting places put beyond question the extraction of copper from the sulphide ores of the eastern Alps at least by the Late Bronze Age and possibly as early as 1700 B.C. Dikaios' recent discoveries at Ambelikoú B prove the exploitation of Cypriote ores, today exclusively sulphides, in the IIIrd millennium. Hence the discovery of the technique in Hither Asia may well go back to 2500 B.C. at least.

The first age of metals has been known as the Bronze Age since Thomsen created the accepted archaeological period names, but the term is a misnomer. Unalloyed copper was extensively used throughout the period thus designated. Till 2000 B.C. most "bronzes" from Egypt, Crete, and the Levant, when analyzed, turn out to be made of unalloyed copper. After that date unalloyed copper was commoner than bronze in Anatolia as late as the Hittite Empire, and around the Urals was used exclusively till the Iron Age. Nor can the use of unalloyed copper be held to denote a universal stage in the development of metallurgy as suggested by the popular term "Copper Age"; no such "age" at all has yet been detected in China. Finally absence of tin need not imply ignorance of bronze but only lack of resources for securing supplies of a relatively rare element.

The production of bronze ultimately involves the knowledge (1) that copper will combine (form an alloy) with other metals; (2) that an alloy is easier to cast and yields a more efficient casting than unalloyed copper; (3) some properties of the suitable metals and their ores; (4) the superiority of tin; and (5) the best proportions to use.

Historically the earliest deliberate alloy of copper, known from the archaeological record, is an alloy containing lead, used for the manufacture of small ornaments in the Uruk period of Mesopotamia (3500-3000 B.C.). Such an alloy was too soft for industrial use, but owing to its low melting point was eminently suitable for small *cire perdue* castings. Soon after 3000 B.C. bronzes with a variable tin content begin to turn up in Mesopotamia, Jordan, North Syria, western Anatolia, the Aegean, and in the Indus cities. Objects of metallic tin have been found at Thermi in Lesbos (before 2500 B.C.) and in a sepulchral cave in Tuscany not much later. Some specimens from Ur and Troy already contain 10 percent of tin. This proportion was apparently established as the standard alloy around 2000 B.C. and was used in the first regular bronze industries to be established soon after in central Europe and Britain (but not in Ireland) and, about 1300 B.C., in China. It seems then likely that the value of the tin-copper alloy was discovered in southwest Asia quite early in the IIIrd millennium and was soon recognized from the Indus to the Mediterranean, and that the best proportion had been determined by 2000 B.C. Thereafter the relevant knowledge was diffused to Britain and China. Incidentally, the establishment of a standard alloy implies accurate measurement and the use of a balance or bema by illiterate technicians.

Where was the alloying carried out? Plainly not at the copper mines where the ore was smelted. Ingots of unalloyed copper are known, but none of tin (save one from Falmouth in Cornwall of uncertain antiquity but in no case older than

1500 B.C.). The alloying might have been carried out by the
manufacturing smiths or by an unidentified group of middle-
men standing between them and the primary producers. (Alternative alloys of copper with antimony or arsenic instead
of tin were notoriously used in some regions, but they are
of only local significance save perhaps as indicative of an
abstract idea of alloys in general and of experimentation inspired thereby.)

In addition to copper and tin, silver and lead were extracted and utilized in prehistoric times, though by a more
restricted range of societies (during the IIIrd and most of
the IInd millennium only in southwest Asia, eastern Russia,
and the Mediterranean basin). The metallurgy involved is
significant in the present context. Silver is generally found
in ores combined with lead or more rarely copper, so that
reduction yields only an alloy. The separation of silver requires a second chemical reaction dependent upon its resistance to oxidization being greater than that of the baser
metal. The process of separating silver from lead, known as
cupellation, is in fact so difficult that Forbes has argued
that all early silver is really a naturally occurring silver-gold
alloy, electrum. However, analyses, though far too few, provide no confirmation of his hypothesis while the use of lead
even for sizable vessels in protoliterate Mesopotamia is explicitly against it. Moreover, Louis Siret, himself a mining
engineer, found evidence that the noble metal was efficiently
extracted from argentiferous copper ores in southeast Spain
during the Bronze Age. Knowledge of silver and its refining
was being applied in Hither Asia before 3000 B.C., in the
Aegean and India a few centuries later, and somewhere toward
2000 B.C. had spread to Spain.

Corporate groups of operatives severally engaged in producing, or manufacturing, articles of copper, tin-bronze, and
silver-lead respectively each applied systematically and successfully traditional rules based on accumulated observation
and experimentation in the execution of relatively long-term
projects. Their traditional lore was public in the sense that
all engaged in or at least directing the operations were privy
to its generalizations and might contribute thereto, but not
in the sense that the basic principles of agriculture or pot-
making were known to all members of a Neolithic or later
village community. Metalworkers were normally full-time
specialists; the several branches of metallurgy were "mysteries" into which their practitioners had been initiated wheth-

er by adoption or apprenticeship. Whether initiates constituted a "craft clan," a sort of "guild," or some other form of corporation is irrelevant. Any such corporation must have been at least originally to some extent "international." The suggestion that "the brand of Cain" was an "internationally" recognized badge to guarantee some measure of personal security to craftsmen who would, as Homer puts it, "be welcome everywhere," but would lack the protection of local kinship organizations, is frankly alluring. No metalworkers' graves have been recognized in the extensive cemeteries of the Early and Middle Bronze Age in Europe as if such craftsmen were not incorporated in the tribal societies whose members enjoyed the prerogative of burial in these cemeteries. At Ugarit in North Syria bronzeworkers appear about 2000 B.C. as votaries of distinct deities.

If the accumulation, maintenance, and diffusion of metallurgical traditions by corporations be admitted, we must still postulate a diversity of corporate bodies and so of traditions. On the one hand, the manufacturing and extractive branches of the industry probably remained distinct. A village coppersmith need know no more of the sources of metal and of the chemistry of smelting than did a European village blacksmith in the eighteenth century. In India and Africa iron smelting and smithying are no doubt usually combined, but there is no evidence for such a combination in the Bronze Age; smelters are known near mines and foundries in centers of population. Even where the first smiths seem to have been immigrants and began by reproducing foreign types (Asiatic types in central Europe, Irish or central European types in Denmark) they soon set about producing distinctive local variants thereon and novelties as if they had settled down to work in one tribal territory. By the beginning of written history in Egypt and Mesopotamia smiths had already been absorbed in the territorial states. The manufacturing branch thus tended to lose any international character.

On the other hand the extraction and working of the several different metals are likely to have been conducted by distinct corporations.

4   Coppersmiths, silversmiths, goldsmiths were necessarily masters of bodies of traditional lore, but of a much more concrete kind than that demanded by the extractive

processes. Prospectors and smelters were applying what may
be fairly termed chemical and petrological "laws." Predictions based on a rudimentary stratographical geology guided
the operations of miners, but this inductive procedure is more
obviously exhibited by Neolithic flint miners than by ore
miners of the Paleometallic stage. The latter only followed
lodes from surface outcrops by vertical or horizontal cuttings,
though using such ingenious techniques as "fire-setting,"
Neolithic miners sank shafts through ten feet or more of
solid chalk to reach layers of flint nodules for the existence
of which there were no surface indications at the shaft mouth.
They must have observed an exposure of the flint-bearing
layer in a ravine or on a scarp and correctly inferred that it
continued below the surface into the hillside.

Applications of geometry, which are certainly not inspired
by the sophisticated science of literate societies, are not easily
documented. An accurate right angle could hardly be laid
out without invoking "Pythagorean ratios" or some equally
subtle "geometrical theorem." Now "rectangular" houses or
tombs were often built by Neolithic and Paleometallic barbarians. Many are frankly irregular. But in some cases, for
instance in the Danubian Neolithic province, the two long
sides, though 70 feet or 100 feet in length, are so nearly
parallel as to raise a doubt whether they could have been
laid out "by the eye" alone. Schröder and Helm have pointed
out a number of buildings in this province in which the long
sides approximate to 7/4 of the short sides (q i.e., to an
approximation to $\sqrt{3}$ of the latter length) or to some multiple thereof. They have suggested that the rectangular areas
were laid out by constructing an equilateral triangle with the
short side as base, continuing the two remaining sides to
double that length and joining their extremities. (The result
is of course a rectangle whose diagonal equals twice the
short sides.) The longer houses would consist of two such
rectangles end to end. It may indeed be questioned whether
the archaeological data—merely the holes for posts in the
earth or rows of undressed stones—are accurate enough, or
the number of instances sufficient to demonstrate the use
of such geometrical constructions by Neolithic illiterates. Yet
the oldest surviving monumental buildings of literate societies
seem to surpass in precision what could be obtained by the
eye; the discoverable error in First Dynasty mastabas (of
mud brick) over 135 feet in length is of the order only of
0.25 percent to 0.50 percent.

The application of these "geometrical theorems" inevitably required operations with circles. Prehistoric men could of course draw circles with the aid of a pegged string or a forked stick. Such "compass-drawn circles" in fact frequently decorate objects of bone, metal, and clay, while a miniature adjustable compass, constructed on the beam principle, actually survives from the Middle Bronze Age of central Italy. About 1500 B.C. Stonehenge illustrates on a grand scale the accuracy obtainable with a pegged length of rope by illiterate Britons. More abstruse principles must have been invoked to secure the even spacing of the wooden posts encircling Dutch and English barrows of slightly later date, to judge from the marks of temporary "ranging rods" that the meticulous excavations of Glasbergen and Case have lately revealed. In a word, not a few of the properties of space that Greek geometers integrated into a deductive science were known and used by preliterate architects and builders a thousand or two years earlier.

A similar conclusion might be drawn from the perforation of thick stone ax and mace-heads; for they were regularly drilled from both sides so accurately that the two perforations met symmetrically in the middle to form a single hole. Miscalculations are surprisingly rare though enough have been found to prove that the method was in fact employed. Neolithic toolmakers probably achieved these successes with the aid of some mechanical device rather than any abstract theory.

Measurement in the sense of spatial comparison is, as we saw, involved in any construction of composite tools, as well as of houses and clothes. Neolithic and Paleometallic societies had advanced to the construction of "machines" with independently movable parts like looms and wheeled vehicles. The requisite measurement could still be effected by direct comparison of the component pieces or at least by the use of personal standards—the maker's finger, foot, forearm, or span. The conversion of such personal units into conventional standards sanctioned by a whole society had of course been effected in Egypt and Mesopotamia by the time the written record begins in those countries. Attempts to define inductively older standards by comparing the measurements of numerous prehistoric artifacts and structures are liable to be vitiated by the imperfect state of the documents concerned. According to Mond and Myers both the "royal cubit" (of 2.68 inches) and the "Persian" or "sacred cubit" (of 3.11 inches) were recognized by Egyptian architects about the time of the

"Union of the Two Lands," but it may be doubted whether reliable documents are yet numerous enough to establish statistically the recognition of prehistoric standards recognized over a wider area.

Accurate comparison in respect of weight requires the invention of a balance or bema. As remarked on p. 69 this may be inferred from approximations to a standard proportion of tin to copper in the bronze used by various preliterate smiths. Scales are of course attested by actual specimens, representations, or weights in all early literate civilizations, including the Minoan, Mycenaean, and Indic. But in barbarian Europe the first two sources are missing and the earliest undoubted weights belong to the end of the Bronze Age and are hardly older than 1000 B.C. In Egypt on the other hand, stone prehistoric objects have been quite plausibly interpreted as weights and approximate well to multiples of the beqa of 13.625 grams though the series is hardly so complete as to yield indisputable inductions. With the same reservation the Daric standard may likewise have been current in Hither Asia in prehistoric times while a third system was developing in India. Though attempts to derive the historic Egyptian and Indic systems from a common prehistoric source are not considered convincing, all three systems were occasionally used in the several countries in all three states and eventually among barbarians beyond their frontiers.

Weighed quantities of gold, silver, or copper served as standards of value in the many exchange transactions that characterized the ancient urban civilizations, but such of course could not be recognized archaeologically. In central Germany and northwestern Europe certain symbolic double axes of copper may very likely have served as ingots and have been thought to represent multiples of a standard unit of weight. But the distribution of the known weights is not really statistically significant and the units might be almost anything between 500 and 600 grams! So too, no plausible highest common factor has been found for the weights of the torques, used as ingots in the central European-Italian metallurgical province and probably also in north Syria. In Europe at least it looks as if copper was valued in numbers of pieces rather than by weight. This might be regarded as an assimilation of the valuation of metal to the system of pricing in terms of cattle inferred for prehistoric Indo-European peoples from philological and historical data. In the Mycenaean-

Minoan civilization, where the balance is directly attested, this prehistoric ox-standard was ingeniously equated with 25.5 kilograms by weight of copper, multiples of this unit being cast as ingots in the shape of an outstretched ox hide.

Some hint of the concept of number among prehistoric societies may be drawn from the foregoing facts taken in conjunction with the oldest written numerals. Numeral notations with a regular periodicity are as old as writing in Egypt, Mesopotamia, Crete, and China. But in the oldest Sumerian documents (the "pictographic tablets" from Uruk and Jemdet Nasr) the symbol next higher than 10 stands either for 60 or for 100 according as to whether jugs of beer or grain are being counted or measured. Perhaps then the symbol stood not for an abstract number, 60 or 100, but for a conventional unit of measure, itself equivalent to 6 or 10 lower units each with conventional designations. If so, any quantity was conceived as a sum of discrete bits that could be counted. Of course in the case of measures such units are arbitrary and generally conventional, but even so for laying out a right angle a length of rope can easily be divided by folding into twelve or thirty equal parts.

A correct estimate of the tropic year's length would doubtless be very useful to farmers. Much ingenuity has been spent in trying to prove that stone circles and other megalithic monuments were in fact used, if not designed, as astronomical instruments for fixing a date in the tropic year. It really does seem likely that Stonehenge was orientated to the midsummer sunrise, but even here there is no agreement as to how an observation was taken, and in the case of other monuments not even plausible orientations have been discovered. So too the preliterate Egyptians were credited with having established a calendar year of 365 days by 4241 B.C. from observations on Sirius, till Neugebauer showed that the same result could be obtained more simply by counting and recording the days between Inundations and averaging the result of fifty years' observation. In the light of a new C14 dates, it now seems extremely unlikely that a calendar based on the heliacal rising of Sirius was introduced before 2776 B.C.

SELECTED BIBLIOGRAPHY

I

A. Arkell, *Early Khartoum*. London and New York: Oxford University Press, 1949.

H. Breuil and R. Lantier, *Les hommes de la pierre ancienne*. Paris: Payot, 1951.

J. G. D. Clark, *Prehistoric Europe: the Economic Basis*. London: Methuen, 1952.

E. Durkheim, *Elementary Forms of Religious Life*. London and New York: Macmillan, 1915.

G. Fruend, *Blattspitzen des Paläolithikums in Europa*. Bonn: 1952.

Dorothy Garrod, "The Upper Paleolithic in the Light of Recent Discovery," *Proceedings of the Prehistoric Society, 1939.*

————, "Southwest Asia and Europe in the Late Paleolithic Age," *Journal of World History,* I (1953).

B. Howe and H. Movius, "A Stone Age Cave Site in Tangier," *Papers of Peabody Museum,* XVI, 3 (1940), and XVIII, 1 (1947).

H. L. Movius, "The Lower Paleolithic Cultures of Southeast Asia," *Transactions of the American Philosophical Association,* 1948.

A. Pannekoek, *Anthropogenesis*. Amsterdam: North Holland, 1953.

R. Pittioni, *Vom geistigen Menschenbild der Urzeit*. Vienna: Deuticke, 1952.

II

A. Arkell, *Esh Shaheinab*. London and New York: Oxford University Press, 1953.

R. J. and L. Braidwood, "The Earliest Village Communities," *Journal of World History,* I (1953).

V. G. Childe, *New Light on the Most Ancient East*. London: Routledge, Kegan Paul, 1952.

————, *The Dawn of European Civilization*. London: Routledge, Kegan Paul, 1950. New York: A. A. Knopf, 1951.

H. H. Coghlan, *Notes on the Prehistoric Metallurgy of Copper and Bronze*. Oxford: Pitt Rivers Museum, 1951.

E. C. Curwen, *Archaeology of Sussex*. London: Methuen, 1937.

P. Dikaios, *Khirokitia*. London and New York: Oxford University Press, 1953.

R. Mond and O. H. Myers, *The Cemeteries of Armant*. London: Egypt Exploration Society, 1937.

A. E. Speiser, *Excavations at Tope Gawra*, I. Philadelphia: University of Pennsylvania Press; London: Oxford University Press, 1935.

SCIENTIFIC SPIRIT IN ANCIENT INDIA*

R. C. Majumdar

It is a well-known fact that the achievements of the ancient Indians in the realm of positive science are very poor as compared with their progress in other fields of intellectual activity, such as literature, philosophy, grammar, art, etc. But this phenomenon is more or less true of all ancient civilizations. Greece is generally regarded as an exception. But there, too, the most remarkable point is not so much the actual progress of positive sciences as the growth of that rational attitude of mind that lies behind at the root of all scientific researches. But while this great trait of Hellenic civilization has been duly appreciated by the modern world, it has failed to note that the same spirit or attitude of mind also characterized the culture of ancient India. For the world has judged India by the many myths and superstitious beliefs that characterized her people and that are reflected in her literature. Few have made any attempt to remove the upper crust of crude and unreasoning faiths and notions and examine the essence of the spirit that lies behind them. In the case of Greece the world has concentrated its attention on the best features and ignored the worst, while exactly the opposite has been done in the case of India. The result is not dissimilar to what we may expect if one compares two pictures—one painting only the best and most magnificent part of a city, and the other depicting only the squalid and miserable slums of another city. Greece has enjoyed the good luck of the first and India suffers from the misfortunes of the last; whereas the fact is that each of the two cities possesses the same characteristic features of having both a splendid and a wretched quarter, side by side.

It has been boldly claimed that for the first time in the history of mankind we find in the Greek philosophy of the sixth century B.C. "the birth of science, that is the application to the world of nature of a rational habit of thought, seeking to disentangle a strand of plain and literal truth from the tissue of mythical fantasy."[1] But at that very age the Eleusinian and Orphic mysteries and various irrational faiths and superstitions inherited from earlier days dominated the minds of the Greeks. Belief in magic and divination, culminating in the unquestioned faith in Oracles, particularly that of Delphi, had the strongest hold on all classes of Greek people, from the highest to the lowest, almost throughout the course of their history.

The period 530 to 430 B.C. has been styled the Age of Illumination in Greece, "an age in which reason was striving to assert her rule in every sphere, and many superstitions, inherited from antiquity, were being challenged and discarded."[2] During this period Athens was the center of Greek civilization and the seat of activity of a famous galaxy of intellectual giants to whom Greece owes almost everything for which her culture has been valued so highly. But what do we find in actual life of the people during this glorious period of "Illumination"? A few facts, based on unimpeachable evidence, may be cited to illustrate it.

The military operations of the Greeks, even the most important and critical campaigns and decisive battles, were guided by the position of the sun and the moon, and other superstitious beliefs; how such a belief in the effect of the eclipse caused the most disastrous defeat of the Athenians at Syracuse during the Peloponnesian war and ruined their prospect of success is well known. The recall of Alcibiades, which ruined the chances of success at an earlier stage of the same expedition, also clearly shows the triumph of superstitious beliefs over rationality.

---

[1] *Cambridge Ancient History*, IV, p. 522.
[2] *Ibid.*, V, p. 376.

Similar irrational beliefs guided the decisions of the great democratic State of Athens. Anaxagoras, a friend of Pericles, who denied that the sun and the moon are divine beings, was prosecuted for being "irreligious." A decree was introduced authorizing the "impeachment of persons who do not conform to the religious observances of the city, or who teach doctrines concerning things in the sky." The General Assembly of Athens, the greatest democracy in the ancient world, condemned Anaxagoras to death, and all that Pericles, the great leader and the uncrowned king of Athens, could do was to aid his friend to escape from Athens. It is worthy of notice in this connection "that in this enlightened age the study of astronomy was forbidden for nearly half a century (up to 403 B.C.) in the city which was the center of Greek culture."[3] During the same age Protagoras is said to have been indicted for irreligion on account of his treatise *On the Gods,* and although he managed to escape from Athens before trial, all copies of the book that could be found were burned publicly in the marketplace.[4] Even Socrates, "the most remarkable figure of the Illumination," was hardly appreciated by the Athenians. He and his circle of friends and disciples became notorious as the "Thinkers" and became legitimate subjects for ridicule by comic poets like Aristophanes. The climax was reached when Socrates, the greatest luminary in the intellectual firmament of Hellas, was condemned to death by the Athenian democracy, as he was found "guilty of not worshipping the gods whom the city worships, and of introducing religious novelties."[5]

These instances, which could easily be multiplied, clearly prove that even the most rational and advanced scientific spirit in any age or in any country may not affect, to any appreciable extent, not only the general masses, but even the majority of higher classes in society. Such a knowledge ought to be a great corrective to those who are apt to belittle the development of rational thought and scientific spirit in ancient India simply on account of the many relics of old faiths and superstitious beliefs of a past age. In any case the examples cited above should, I hope, make it quite clear to all that in order to form a proper estimate of the growth of rational and scientific spirit in ancient India, we must confine our-

[3] *Ibid.,* p. 383.
[4] *Ibid.,* p. 384.
[5] *Ibid.,* p. 391.

selves to the manifestation of that spirit wherever found, and should always remember that their value is not minimized by crude thoughts and beliefs that might be proved to have existed side by side, not only among the masses but even among the majority of the intelligentsia. With these preliminary observations in order to clear the ground, I would now proceed to trace the rise and development of scientific spirit in ancient India.

One may clearly discern the rational and scientific spirit even in the hymns of the *Rigveda,* the earliest written record of ancient Indian culture, and probably the oldest literary work of some dimensions that humanity has bequeathed to us. It carries us back to a period more than five centuries before the faintest beginning of scientific spirit in Greece of which we have any positive evidence. Let us take one hymn from this work generally known as the Creation Hymn (X. 129). It begins with a searching inquiry as to the origin of the world. "What was there at the beginning?" it asks. "What covered all? what sheltered? what concealed?" Then followed the solution. "There was neither death nor immortality, neither heaven nor earth, neither day nor night. Possibly there was water's fathomless abyss, and the germ, that lay covered in the husk, burst forth, and from this spark burst forth all creations. There was only one who breathed breathless by itself, from whom all this creation came, and the gods themselves came later into being." But this was a mere speculation and did not satisfy the author of the hymn. He ends with the question: "Who knows from whence this great creation sprang?" and similar other queries. Similar strain of thought is traceable elsewhere in the *Rigveda,* culminating in the bold conception that this ultimate reality, i.e., God, is one, though the sages describe him differently. These hymns show some advance not only over the crude conceptions of Thales over the nature of the universe, but also over the system of cosmology propounded by Anaximander, who is said to have set the pattern for the whole Ionian tradition of rational thought. We may, in any case, place the beginnings of a rational inquiry into the phenomena of nature, which is the precursor of science, at least five centuries before Greece.

The philosophical speculations on the origin of the universe in later age in India are no less advanced than those of the renowned Greek philosophers on the subject. The formulation of the five primitive elements of nature, namely *kshiti* (earth), *ap* (water), *teja* (fire), *marut* (air), and *vyom* (void or sky), closely resembles the Greek conception of fire, air, earth, and water as primitive immutable substances. The atomic theory of Kanāda has many points in common with that of Leucippus and Democritus. It is admitted that the theories of these Greek scholars brought physical science to a point beyond which further advance was hardly possible in default of instruments of precision. But reference may be made to some theories of Indian scholars that probably mark an advance over Greek thought. Thus Kanāda evolved the theory of sound as being propagated by undulation, wave after wave—a theory that "cannot fail to excite our wonder and admiration."[6] Equally striking is his theory that light and heat are only different forms of essentially the same substance. In summing up the great contributions of ancient Greek philosophers to science, a distinguished scholar has observed as follows: "In Heraclitus, as in some others of the greatest thinkers, the historian is astonished and baffled by finding in his central thought what looks at first sight like an anticipation of the most modern views of physical reality, reached by intuition at one bound which overlaps all the painful process of observation, hypothesis, and experiment required to lead science to a similar standpoint."[7] The same thing may easily be said of Kanāda and Kapila who anticipated him.

As a reaction against the speculative philosophy of Heraclitus Zeno stressed the point that the most important problem was no longer "How was the world made?" but "How was the knowledge of the world possible?" We find in ancient India a similar spirit which heralded the birth of true science. We can trace the gradual stages in the growth of scientific process in India, namely, close and precise observation of facts and phenomena, followed by a systematic effort to classify, analyze, or synthesize them with a view to explain, interpret, or discover some general principles and to coordinate them with the knowledge already gained. The eminent Indian scholar, Dr. Brajendra Nath Seal, has analyzed the method of science followed in ancient India and described, with specific examples, the different processes involved in it, viz. perception, observation, experiment, fallacies of observation, inference, and hypothesis. The ancient Indian writers not only

[6] P. C. Ray, *History of Hindu Chemistry*, p. 1.
[7] *Cambridge Ancient History*, IV, p. 558.

knew these processes but also defined the conditions each of them must fulfil in order to be accepted as satisfactory.

Most of these processes are best seen in the development of Indian astronomy. The sun, moon, and the stars were no longer regarded as gods with mysterious movements, but a careful observation was made of the sky leading to the knowledge of the twenty-seven lunar mansions, the sun's annual motion giving rise to the different seasons, and the reckoning on the basis of a solar year containing twelve lunar months with an intercalary month every third year. All these we find in the Vedic literature proper. The progress in astronomical studies was maintained until the climax was reached in the time of Āryabhata, at the beginning of the sixth century A.D. His famous discoveries, such as the new epicyclic theory, the correct length of the year, the rotation of the earth on its axis, and the true explanation of the eclipse, must be regarded as striking achievements in the science of astronomy. It is interesting to note that he incurred great displeasure of the orthodox section, on the ground that his theory of eclipse was opposed to the scriptural view that the eclipse was caused by the demon Rāhu devouring the sun and the moon. He would probably have lost his life if he were born in Periclean Athens, or thrown into prison if he had flourished in Europe during the Middle Ages, but the orthodox Indians, though they refused to accept his view, neither condemned Āryabhata for irreligion nor prohibited the study of astronomy as was done in Athens. As a matter of fact, freedom of thought and inquiry was a special characteristic of ancient Indian culture, and people were at liberty to express any views about God, man, or earth—even to deny the existence of God or the sacred character of the *Vedas*—without sharing the fate of Socrates or Galileo. This absolute freedom of thought must have been a great factor in the development of the right scientific spirit.

The development of medical science was almost phenomenal in character. The view that diseases are not due to any supernatural causes is exultingly referred to by Farrington as marking an important advance made by the Greeks in the progress of medical science, but such a rational view is met within the Buddhist canonical literature at an early period. The story of Jivaka and the many kinds of diseases cured by him, even though partly imaginary, leaves no doubt about the wonderful progress in the knowledge of anatomy and surgery, and the scientific method of treatment based on close

observation of facts and generalizations. The Buddhist canonical works, the Pali *Mahāvagga* and the *Vinayavastu* of
the Mūla-Saryāstivādins, written in Sanskrit, describe with
fullness of detail the symptoms of various diseases and the
method followed by Jivaka in curing them. Nothing like this
has come down to us from any part of the ancient world,
belonging to an age when these works were composed. A
few episodes in the story of Jivaka are very illuminating.
When he and his fellow students completed their study of
medicine under a renowned teacher they were asked to
collect plants with medicinal properties. Jivaka brought in
a larger number than others, and when questioned by the
preceptor, explained the medicinal properties of those not
usually regarded as possessing them. Another story refers
to the treatment of the king who was suffering from a
peculiar kind of pain, the cause or remedy of which no
physician could find out. Jivaka, after a tedious inquiry,
came to learn of a man who had just died after suffering
from the same kind of pain. Jivaka immediately dissected
the dead body and found some worms in his entrails. After
various experiments he found that the juice of garlic proved
fatal to these worms. So he made the king drink the juice of
garlic—much against his will because the drink was forbidden
by orthodox practice—and the king recovered. Reference is
also made to various types of surgical operations with full
details.

The growth of medical science presupposes a knowledge of
chemistry and helped its development. This subject has been
thoroughly dealt with by the eminent chemist Dr. P. C. Ray
in his classical work on the subject. He has come to the
conclusion that "the knowledge in practical chemistry, prevalent in India in the twelfth and thirteenth centuries A.D.,
and perhaps earlier, is distinctly in advance of that of the same
period in Europe."[8]

The science of botany also made great progress and a
regular classification of plants was made with various subdivisions. The *Vrikshāyurveda* of Parāśara describes the life
of a plant in its various aspects and the author even attempts
to explain the origin of the first organic body. Another work,
the *Upavanavinoda,* deals with the selection of soil, classification of plants, various methods of plant propagation, recipes for nourishment of plants and their treatment in

diseases. Varāhamihira, who flourished in the sixth century
A.D., deals in detail with the plan of sowing trees at intervals,
diseases in trees, the method of curing them, manuring and
improvements of fruits and flowers, even to the extent of
changing their color, scent, and other essential properties.
Udayana notices in plants the phenomena of life, death, sleep,
waking, disease, drugging, transmission of specific characters
by means of ova, and movements toward what is favorable
and away from what is unfavorable. It was also asserted
that plants have a sort of dormant or latent consciousness
and are capable of pleasure and pain, that they are sensitive
to heat and cold, to the sound of thunder, as well as to the
odors, both pleasant and unpleasant.

In physiology and biology the Hindus had advanced ideas
on metabolism, circulatory system, vascular system, nervous
system, foetal development, and transmission of specific characteristics by heredity. As regards physics, reference has been
made above to the theory of atoms and the wave theory
of sound. It appears from the Chinese translation of an old
Buddhist work that the Hindus had a knowledge of the principle of Archimedes.

In arithmetic the Hindus made the epoch-making discovery
of the decimal system of notation based upon the principle
of the place-value of the first nine numbers and the use of the
zero. This has now been accepted all over the world and by
simplifying arithmetical calculations and processes has revolutionized almost every branch of the physical sciences. The
old method of expressing large numbers by means of symbols
was very cumbersome, but Europe was following it down to
the twelfth century A.D., when the Indian system was made
known through the intermediary of the Arabs. The most
striking progress in mathematics was made by Āryabhata, to
whom reference has been made above in connection with
astronomy. His *Āryabhatiyam* refers to some of the important
properties of circles and triangles, which show that most of
the theorems included in the first four books of Euclid must
have been worked out before his time. It describes several
properties of the circle, discusses questions connected with
projective geometry, and gives a value for π far more accurate
than any suggested till then. In algebra simultaneous equations
with four unknown quantities have been solved, and the
problem of finding a general solution of the indeterminates
of the first degree is successfully tackled. Besides dealing with
the rules of involution and evolution, the *Āryabhatiyam* deals

with the arithmetic progression, both of numbers as well as of their squares and cubes. That trigonometry was also cultivated is clear from the use of the sine functions made for solving the problems of astronomy. There is no doubt that in the realms of arithmetic and algebra the Hindus had the lead over the contemporary Greek mathematicians. Reference has been made above to the striking discoveries of Āryabhata in the field of astronomy. The European writers believed that an Arabian astronomer was the first to discover and utilize the sine functions, but the credit should go to Āryabhata. He also worked out the accurate formula to measure the increase or decrease in the duration of two consecutive days. He obtained the correct equation for the orbit of a planet by taking the apse. He postulated an epicyclic theory of his own to explain the variations in planetary motions. His equations of spherical trigonometry to find out the right ascension and declination of any point on the ecliptic are also correct. He accurately expressed the angular diameter of the earth's shadow at the moon's orbit, and knew how to find out the duration of an eclipse and total obscuration. He has laid down rules for determining what part of the moon will be obscured in an eclipse. The length of his year, 365.2586805 days, is nearer its true duration than that postulated by Ptolemy; the same is the case about his longitude of the sun's apogee and sidereal period of the moon's nodes.

Literary and archaeological evidence leaves no doubt about the great progress made in India in mineralogy and metallurgy. Mining operations were extensively carried out as far back as the third century B.C. if not at a much earlier period. Extensive use of gold, silver, copper, lead, and tin in the third millennium B.C. is proved by the excavations at Mohenjo-daro. The famous iron pillar near the Qutb minar on the outskirts of Delhi testifies to the development of metallurgical skill of the Hindus in the fourth century A.D. This huge iron pillar, twenty-four feet in height and six and a half tons in weight, has stood exposed to the tropical sun and rain for 1,500 years but does not show the least sign of rusting or corrosion. Even the simple forging of so large an iron column could not have been accomplished anywhere else in the world, not only at that time but also for many centuries afterward.

Great progress was also made in zoology. We find different scholars making various classifications of animals on the basis of their *vīja* (ovum or seed), or according to the number of their senses, habitat, mode of life, and dietary value.

Owing to military necessity the knowledge of horses and elephants reached a high standard, and the ancient Greek and Roman writers refer to the training of elephants and treatment of their diseases by the Hindus. We have a treatise on elephants, *Hastyāyurveda,* claiming a high antiquity, and systematic treatment of cows, dogs, cocks, turtles, goats, and horses in the *Brihatsamhitā* of Varāhamihira (sixth century A.D.).

Apart from positive results obtained, the scientific spirit of inquiry shown by the Hindus is demonstrated in various ways. They inquired into the properties of matter and arrived at very important results anticipating or foreshadowing some well-known laws of physics. Dr. B. N. Seal has dealt with the theories of motion and ideas on acoustics prevalent in ancient India.[9] The principle of parachute was utilized in devising means of coming down from a great height when no other ways are available. It consists in "jumping down with an open parasol made of skin which descends slowly to the ground on account of the resistance of the air." Attempts were also made to formulate general laws. Thus Udayana seeks to prove that "air has no weight" by showing that a bladder made of thin membrane would weigh the same whether it is empty or filled with air. He also notes that a balloon filled with *dhūma* (smoke or gas) rises in the air, whereas the air-filled balloon comes down. Udayana concludes that neither air nor gas has any weight. Whatever we might think of this conclusion, we have here an important scientific process at work, namely experiment as an independent method of proof or new discovery. Although Udayana stumbled upon the truth that there were gases lighter than air, we have no knowledge whether he or anyone else made any further advance upon his experiment.

Daring nature of the spirit of inquiry is indicated by the following statement of Varāhamihira, mentioned above: "As food is the support of life, and food depends upon rain, it is important to discover the laws of rain by any means." Varāhamihira then proceeds to discuss these laws as propounded by no less than four previous writers on the subject. As an indication of interest in the subject it may be mentioned that rain gauge was known in ancient India. Varāhamihira also discounts the idea, then held by many, that the gems are

[9] B. N. Seal, *The Positive Sciences of the Ancient Hindus,* pp. 129, 153.

the bones of demons. He supports the view that "gems are various sorts of stones which naturally exist in earth." He then describes twenty-two different kinds of gems with their properties.

It would be clear from what has been said above that, since the earliest period of which we have any written record, we can trace a rational spirit of free thought and inquiry in India that triumphed over mythology, theological beliefs, and popular superstitions. This spirit at first took the form of philosophic speculations into the origin of the universe, but soon led to the growth of sciences by observation of natural phenomena, collection and classification of data, practical experiments, and formulation of general laws.

INDIA AND SCIENTIFIC EXCHANGES
IN ANTIQUITY *

J. Filliozat

1   India is frequently regarded as a world of its own,
a world with a civilization in which science played little part.
If the term "world of its own" means that it is a cultural
area of great originality, the former opinion is correct. In
any other sense it is quite mistaken, for India has been in
continual contact with other countries.

The first civilization known to have existed on Indian soil
is that of the great cities found at Harappā, in the Punjab,
and at Mohenjo daro, in Sind, which lie some 450 miles apart
and show signs of belonging to the same culture. Theirs was
a highly developed civilization, its features including large-
scale town-planning—chiefly at Mohenjo-daro, where a far-
reaching network of sewers has been brought to light—and
tremendous fortifications dug up at Harappā; its relations
with foreign countries have supplied the best means of putting a date to it. The script, which is peculiar to this civilization and has not yet been deciphered, appears on a number
of seals, some of which were found in Mesopotamia in
archaeological strata dating from about 2500 B.C. Relations
were maintained with other civilizations, some of them far
distant from India, until at least 1600 B.C.—the approximate
date attributed by Mr. J. F. S. Stone to beads found there,

* Journal of World History, I, 2.

and which are thought to come from Crete. The Vedic Aryas, a detached branch of Indo-Europeans, appear to have destroyed this civilization when they invaded India from the northwest and brought with them, or soon developed, the culture evidenced by the *Rigveda,* the oldest surviving Sanskrit work. This was a culture related to that of the ancient Iranians. The *Rigveda* contains allusions to the destruction of fortresses by the gods of Indra and Agni, which may very well refer to the capture of ancient strongholds such as that of Harappā. The most probable chronology for the Vedic texts agrees with this interpretation.

Much later, in the time of the Achaemenian Persians, India—now Aryanized and Brahmanic—began to suffer a long succession of invasions carried out by most of the nations that lived to the northwest or had reached that area as a result of earlier though not always durable conquests. The other aspect of the situation is that Indian Buddhism and culture were meanwhile being carried into those same northwestern regions, and thence eastward throughout continental Asia and even to Japan, and that—together, this time, with Brahmanism—they were also penetrating overseas, to Southeast Asia and the Indonesian archipelago.

As for Indian science, not only did it develop at an early date, but it played a considerable part in this cultural expansion. It was formerly assumed, in some quarters, that there was no evidence of this fact, and even nowadays the general tendency is to dispute it.

Indian science is often regarded now as an offshoot of the science brought to the East by Greece. From Greece and from the Hellenistic Orient India did indeed receive certain artistic styles—those developed in the Greco-Buddhist art of Gandhara, in northwest India. Sanskrit writings on astrology clearly owe something to the astrology of Alexandria. And it is evident that Islamic science, which took over from Greece, was imported into India as well. Hence the readiness to infer that all seience in India is derived from the Greeks, directly or indirectly; that when the Indians mention the Greeks, it is an admission of indebtedness; that when they do not, they are keeping something back. In any case, so the inference goes, everything they know comes, in more or less distorted form, from the Greeks. And if they do happen to put forward a few ideas not found in Greek writings, this is solely due to the fact that not all the Greeks' ideas have come down to us: but we can be certain the

Greeks had these particular ideas, the Indians being incapable
of conceiving them for themselves or borrowing them from
any other source.

An appreciable number of Indian writers go to the other
extreme and see India as the schoolmistress of the human
race, a role the European romantics attributed to her for a
time. These writers base their claim on traditions that place
the origin of their science and literature in very ancient
times, long before the birth of Greek culture. It was, indeed,
their reliance on the chronology presented in those traditions
and their belief that Sanskrit was the parent of all European
languages that led the romantics to think as they did. But
the remote dates suggested by tradition are disproved by the
findings of historical research, and this gives fresh ammu-
nition to supporters of the theory that Indian science stems
from Greece—exposing India to the charge of making unjustified claims to antiquity and to the suspicion that any
Indian document that makes no reference to sources is a
plagiarism. The mere fact that the traditional chronologies
are ridiculous suggests that Indians are unable to look facts
in the face without bias and can therefore have no talent
for scientific pursuits.

But this attitude is untenable.

In the first place, the ancient chronological calculations
that are now disproved were the result of an ill-fated but
basically scientific attempt to coordinate historical events with
the cyclic progression of astronomical phenomena, which,
unfortunately, had been misinterpreted. That attempt goes
back no further than the early centuries of our era, at most,
and seems to have been made under the more or less direct
influence of Alexandrian astronomical speculation; it is far
from characteristic of the general trends of Indian culture,
although it gained wide acceptance in late Indian tradition.
Other and older chronological computations, though not entirely accurate, are less disastrous, and there is clear evidence of the Indian scrupulousness about facts. It is true
that generalizations take precedence over points of detail;
the cosmic and social order is felt to be more interesting than
a particular event, and a law than an individual phenomenon.
But the generalizations do attempt to be analytical and rational. Being arrived at too expeditiously, the observations
on which they are based are disclosed prematurely, patient
experiment is cut short, and there is a too frequent tendency
to illustrate summary explanations by mere comparisons.

But this form of research did result, at an early stage, in the formulation of theories that, though premature, constituted rational attempts to explain the structure of reality—in other words, of the sciences.

The first signs of an attempt to codify the sciences are found in the most ancient Indian writings—the Vedic and Brahmanic texts—between 1500 and 500 B.C., and relate to astronomy and physiology.

2   The most important astronomical item to be found in the Vedic texts (*Yajurveda and Atharveda*) is a list, already in its final form and destined to become a classic, of twenty-seven or twenty-eight constellations, the *nakshatras,* spread out along the path of the moon (Av. XIX, 7 and 8, 1). This list is largely the same as another, found in Chinese astronomy and called the list of the *sieu.* J. B. Biot, who proved the *nakshatras* and the *sieu* to be virtually identical, believed that Chinese astronomy was more ancient than Indian and that in any case the latter was entirely drawn from outside sources. In this particular instance he alleged as proof of Indian plagiarism that the Indians, unlike the Chinese, had made use of the *nakshatras* for a purpose for which they were not originally intended, and maintained that the invention of an instrument should be attributed to those who know how to employ it. But he had overlooked one use of the *nakshatras*—indeed, their principal use—which was later pointed out by Léopold de Saussure and is perfectly in accordance with the requirements of the Brahmanic rites, these being regulated by the movement of the heavenly bodies; this is to enable the positions of the full moon and the sun in relation to the planets to be calculated simultaneously. For the diametrical opposition of sun and moon at the moment of the true full moon makes it possible, by direct observation of the moon's position in relation to a particular star, selected as a control, in the *nakshatra* through which the moon is then passing, to determine the then invisible position of the sun, by means of the control star in the opposed *nakshatra.* It should be noted that the control stars in the *nakshatras* were chosen not for their exceptional radiance but, so far as possible, because their projections fell

at right angles to the equator or, more simply, because they lay along the same circle of declination.

Contrary to Biot's opinion, the first complete list of *sieu* to be known in China is later than that of the Indian *nakshatras;* but this alone is not enough to prove that India made the earliest scientific use of them; for the most ancient Indian documents give no information on the point. For the time being, however, it is hard to see why they should have been invented before there was any idea of the purpose to which they might be put. In any case, in Brahmanic times the diametrical opposition of sun and full moon was a fact well known to writers, who describe the full moon as "the greatest distance between sun and moon" and the new moon as "the smallest distance" between them (*Gobhil-agrhyasutra* I, 5, 7-8).

It is by no means impossible that the *nakshatra* and *sieu* systems were invented independently by the Indians and the Chinese as they scanned the same expanse of sky for guide marks required for similar purposes. It seems more probable, however, that one country was borrowing from the other, and in the usual way it was China which borrowed from India. But any such transaction must necessarily have occurred at a very remote period, for which there is no proof of contact between India and China. This being so, a number of authors have considered it more likely that the Indians and Chinese borrowed from some third source, assumed to have been "Chaldean" or Mesopotamian, since astronomy is known to have been cultivated in Mesopotamia at an early date. There are, however, no traces of such a system in that part of the world, and had it been known it should at any rate have survived as an alternative to the zodiac, which is a much less precise system for calculating the position of the sun by the heliacal rising and setting of the stars.

However this may be, the *nakshatra* system remained as a basic feature of Indian astronomy, and the introduction of the Greek zodiac in the first centuries of our era, when Alexandrian astrology was adopted, did not affect its use. It continued to be employed as an alternative to the zodiac, constituting a kind of zodiac with twenty-seven divisions instead of twelve. Equal zones of declination were attributed, ideally, to each of the twenty-seven *nakshatras* (the twenty-eighth, whose inclusion in the list is optional, being of zero amplitude). Moreover, likewise after the beginning of the

Christian era, India spread the knowledge of the *nakshatra* system to all the regions to which she successively exported her culture, and to the neighboring countries in the West.

In that direction, we find the Sassanid Persians, the Arab astronomers, and the Copts in Egypt all marking the moon's course of approximately twenty-eight days by that number of asterisms, regarded as "lunar houses." In the case of the Arabs and Copts these are undoubtedly subsequent to the adoption of the *nakshatras* in India, but this does not automatically prove that the Arab scientists borrowed the system from India (passing it later to the Copts). For apart from the fact that the Arab "houses" existed before the Arabs were in direct contact with India (which would not, in itself, be conclusive), the idea seems already to be foreshadowed in a Hermetic Greek text. It may have originated independently among all those who wished to assign some sidereal guide mark to each day of the lunar month. What makes an Indian influence appear probable is the choice, in the majority of cases, of the same control star as the Indians had appointed for each "house"; but the control stars may have been selected at a later date.

In Iran the idea of the twenty-eight lunar houses does not appear until a very late date, after long contact with India and even after the first contact with Arab science. Many authorities consider, however, that a number of ideas may have originated at a remote period, but that the earliest evidence of them was probably lost, like the greater part of ancient Iranian literature. In this particular instance there was even, at one time, an attempt to interpret an Avestaic list of names of beings invoked (*Yasna,* XVI, 3-6) as an early list of twenty-seven lunar houses, despite the inescapable fact that there were thirty names on the list; they were subsequently attributed to the days of the thirty-day month. The use of such names rather than those of stars that are actually to be found in the *Avesta* would seem, on the contrary, to show that ancient—Avestaic—Iran was not acquainted with the lunar houses, much less with the system of the Indian *nakshatras,* no equivalent of which has so far been discovered in the ancient history of any country west of India.

Thus, when Greek astronomy reached India, through the trade and cultural exchanges between that country and the Roman Empire, it was superimposed on an Indian astronomic system devised to meet the needs of the calendar and of the study of cosmic movements, of which the Brahmanic liturgy had for long been seeking to form an idea. It brought new astronomic knowledge and, above all, certain methods of foretelling the future by astrology that had not previously been in use in India. For though the Indian calendar indicated favorable periods, and celestial phenomena were considered to predict various events, the course and conjunction of the heavenly bodies were not yet generally regarded as controlling people's destinies down to the minutest detail. Henceforth, India combined the earlier methods with the new ones, the *nakshatra* system with that of the zodiac that was necessary for astrology, and used both simultaneously. It transmitted them jointly to Indo-China and Indonesia, particularly in connection with Brahmanism. Buddhism made a less extensive use of the astrological system that originated in Greece, because generally speaking it disapproved of the arts of divination and therefore tended to preserve faithfully the calendar based on the ancient astronomy.

The *nakshatras* were not the only characteristic feature of that astronomy. Its concepts regarding the evolution of the universe also included a theory of great cosmic cycles, and at a later stage the use of the trigonometric sine was introduced as a contribution to the mathematical representation of astral positions.

The invention of the trigonometric sine seems to have resulted from the improvement of the tables of chords drawn up by Hipparchus and Ptolemy by the substitution of the half chord of the double arc in place of the chord. This innovation, mentioned for the first time in the *Sūryasiddhānta*, a treatise whose principal sections date from the middle of the fourth century, is specifically attributed to the Indians by the Arab astronomer el-Battanyi, who introduced it into Arab science. It formed the basis for the further development of trigonometry.

The theory of the great cycles of the universe and the ages of the world is much older and is related to Greek and western Asian speculations concerning the "great year," the period within which all the stars make a round number of complete revolutions. It is an attempt to express the law of eternal recurrence in mathematical terms, by measuring the astral cycles. The concept of the "great year," which developed during the Vedic period from the idea of a lunar-solar period of five years, combined with that of four ages of the world that succeed one another with diminishing vigor, gave rise to the notion of a general period comprising shorter periods and divided into successive ages. The duration of these ages, and of the general period, was calculated during the Brahmanic period (*Satapathabrāhmana*) by dividing the ordinary year into 10,800 moments. The year was regarded as a form of the Master-of-things-born (*Prajāpati*) and represented, in the order of the Efficient Word, by 10,800 stanzas of the *Rigveda*, consisting of 432,000 syllables, while its liturgical symbol was an altar of 10,800 bricks. Among the classical astronomers and cosmologists the great period emerged as one of 4,320,000 years (sometimes 4,320,000,000), the basic element of which was a number of sidereal solar years—1,080,000—constituting the shortest period to contain an entire series of mean solar days, the length of the sidereal year being calculated in such a way as to appear to correspond to observed facts, while yielding the result 1,080,000, a multiple of 10,800. Moreover, the properties of the number 108 made it remarkable, for instance as the sum of the phases of the lune multiplied by the number of the *nakshatras* (4 x 27), while 10,800 is the product of the number of Brahmanic divisions of the day multiplied by the number of days recognized as composing the year.

These different numbers are thus seen to justify to the full, for purposes of Brahmanic speculation, the choice made of them and their transmission by Indian scientists to Indo-China under the Khmers. Neither was it in India alone that they were used in calculating the "great year": Censorin (*De die natali,* XVIII) states that Heraclitus and Linus calculated that period as one of 10,800 years, though we are not told why; and according to Berossus the Babylonian great year was a period of 432,000 years, comprising 120 "saroi" of 3,600 years apiece. In the sexagesimal system used in Sumeria the word *šar* has a numerical value of 3,600; but it is only on the strength of later evidence that we find the number applies to a cycle of years. Though we thus have very scanty information concerning these Greek and Babylonian estimates that coincide with certain Indian estimates, it would appear that the former were not in very extensive use in their respective spheres, as they were in India—where, moreover, they are found prior to the fifth century B.C., the time of Heraclitus, and thus long before the third century B.C., the age of Berossus. There are three possible explanations to account for their precise numerical concordance with the corresponding Indian data; it may be the accidental result of similar though independent speculation; it may be due to direct or indirect borrowing from India; or it may be due to borrowing by India, by Heraclitus, and by the late Babylonians from a common source, unknown but presumably located in the Near East in ancient times. I shall return to these possible explanations after completing my account of other and particularly remarkable instances of concordance between India on the one hand and Greece and Mesopotamia on the other.

3   In physiology and medicine it may be noted that the principal Indian theories in the Brahmanic period have equivalents in certain abstruse Greek concepts, and, conversely, themselves display subsidiary features that are prominent in the corresponding fields in Mesopotamia.

As far back as the Vedic texts, previous to 1000 B.C., ancient India was familiar with a pneumatistic theory by which all human activities, both bodily and mental, and all natural activities as well, were attributed to the play of puffs of air originating in the wind, the universal driving power. Not until much later was this doctrine codified and expounded, but the majority of its essential elements, such as the great number of puffs of air acting on the organism, and even their technical names, are already mentioned in the Vedic texts, showing that the corresponding ideas were already in existence. Moreover, these same texts, and those of the ancient Brahmanic period, between 1000 and 500 B.C., are familiar with the concept that the bile is of an igneous nature, and soon afterward we find a theory concerning the part played in the organism by the pituitary gland, which represents the aqueous element. And in the central theory on which the whole of subsequent Indian medicine was based, the breath, the bile, and the pituitary gland became the three associated factors by which that theory sought to arrive at a rational explanation of the operation of the vital functions, and the disturbances to which they were subject, without recourse to supernatural intervention or to any mysterious or magical practices.

The notion that the breath of life circulated in other parts of the body in addition to the respiratory organs was a commonplace in ancient times. It is already mentioned in the Papyrus Ebers, toward 1500 B.C., and Paul Diepgen considered this to be the first emergence of the theory of the *pneuma,* which was widely held by Greek physiologists at an early epoch. Nowhere, however, were its technical details so precisely listed as in India, which carried it systematically to the point of distinguishing different breaths of air as fulfilling particular functions, and had done so from a very remote period, as is proved by the frequent use of such specialized designations in ancient documents. Now there is a Greek text, the Hippocratic treatise on *The Winds,* which, without entering on a detailed description of organic breaths with their own special functions, lays down a pneumatistic theory similar to that of India, inasmuch as it attributes the movements of the universe and of organic life in general to the action of the wind, and above all accounts for the majority of illnesses in terms of perturbations of the breath or wind. This treatise is more restrictively pneumatist than the classical Indian treatises, which allow for the action of the bile and the pituitary as well as that of the breath; but pneumatism in an exclusive form was also professed by certain Indian writers, before the classical doctrine established itself.

As for that doctrine, it has a Greek parallel in the *Timaeus* of Plato, in which the pathological teaching is much closer to this Indian doctrine than to the other Greek doctrines. The *Timaeus* describes a category of diseases attributable to the *pneuma,* the pituitary and the bile, and this general resemblance to Indian medicine in pathogenic explanation is carried into numerous points of detail, such as those relating to the pneumatist pathogenesis of tetanus, the nature of the pituitary and the bile, and the injection of bile into the blood. Certain of these similarities may be fortuitous, but several of them relate to concepts that cannot be formed simply on the strength of observed facts; and it is more difficult to believe that these were invented separately than that they were derived from one and the same school, or arrived at as the result of some knowledge of the trends of research in that school.

Noting these analogies, we are thus confronted with the same problems as those arising out of the resemblances between Heraclitus and Indian astronomy, and in respect of neighboring periods; Plato wrote the *Timaeus* in the last years of his life, which came to an end in 347, and the Hippocratic treatise *On Breaths,* though its date is unknown, is anterior to Aristotle (384-322), who considered it to be by Hippocrates himself, and very probably posterior to Gorgias (circa 483-375), or produced in a circle close to that Sophist. In the sphere of medicine, as in that of astronomy, therefore, we find cases of the concordance of Greek and Indian doctrines belonging to the fifth and fourth centuries B.C.—a period when India and the Greek world alike were busy building up theories. But it is also a period when the Persian Empire was forming a historic bridge between the eastern fringes of the Greek world and the Indus valley by means of its satrapies—a process that in the case of India had begun at least as early as the reign of Darius I, who conquered Sind after having had it reconnoitered by the Greek Skylax in 519 B.C.

It is also in this precise period that we find definite contact between the culture of Babylon and that of India. The Achaemenian Persians employed in their satrapies a number of Babylonian officials who used the Aramaic script. This was an alphabetical script, and a defective one; it did not render all the sounds of the languages transcribed into it, but only the skeletons of the words—which, though sufficient for recognition, did not convey their complete phonetic form. The Indian grammarians, on the contrary, had devised a very precise phonetic system to render all the sounds of Sanskrit, so that the Vedic and Brahmanic formulas could be accurately preserved. Writing, for them, must give an exact rendering of the recognized phonic elements and their combinations. The basic Indian script, known as *brāhmi,* is constructed in such a way as to conform to this aim and does not correspond to any alphabetical system. In northwest India, however, it exists side by side with a special script known as *kharosthī,* the forms of which are derived from the Aramaic script used by the Achaemenid officials, but adapted to a system that tends to imitate that of the *brāhmi.* In other words, this is a transcription in Aramaic characters (substantially supplemented for the purpose) of the learned script of the Indian phonetists. This "Aramaic-Indian" writing could hardly have been developed without cooperation between Babylonian and Indian scholars.

It is also noteworthy that the Indian medical tradition includes a method of prognostic that seems alien to the fundamental, classical concepts of that tradition, but that corresponds to certain ancient and widespread Mesopotamian theories proved to have been known in the Achaemenian Empire at the very time when the Indus valley was being governed by the Persians' Babylonian officials.

An Accadian treatise on medical diagnosis and prognostic has recently been published under this title by M. Labat. It is of considerable importance because it takes the form of numerous tablets from copies that were made at widely different periods, thus proving its great and enduring popularity. Like the other fragments of Mesopotamian medical writing hitherto discovered, it differs from the Greek and Indian treatises in making no attempt to account for the facts by formulating rational theories. It does, however, set forth the results of observations that imply the possession of some objective experience of pathological facts. In this respect it is a forerunner of the Hippocratic treatises on prognostic (*Prorrhetic I, Coan Prognoses*), which are also in the form of catalogs of symbols. Nevertheless, it gives the chief place to divinatory signs relating to illness. For instance, at the very beginning it describes a series of omens it declares to be of value in prognosticating and diagnosing certain forms of possession, and which are based on the encounters made by the healer on his way to the patient's dwelling. These are, of course, purely divinatory and have nothing to do with medicine. The Indians, too, in addition to their rational medical teachings—which are based on examination of the patient, on experience of morbid phenomena, and an attempt at a natural representation of physiological and pathological mechanisms—have a method of prognostic by divination the very principle of which is alien to those teachings, though it coexists with them. And this method is similar to that described in the Accadian treatise. It, too, makes use of signs encountered on the way to visit the patient, and even includes those based on the circumstances in which the sick man's messenger arrives to summon the doctor. There are further similarities in the method of describing the clinical symptoms, which is much the same in the Accadian treatise as in the parts of the Indian treatises that list those symptoms—the majority of which are, in both cases, unfavorable. Analogies also occur in regard to the view of possession as a "seizure," more especially in the diagnosis of the forms of "seizure" of young children, according to the age at which the disturbances first appear.

Similarity of beliefs about possession is not in itself exceptional, in view of the great frequency of such beliefs in all parts of the world; India mentions "seizure" by female demons as far back as the Veda and quite independently of any medical teaching. But the fact that Indian medical teaching includes, and in a place of its own, a method of prognostic which is alien to its own ordinary nature but conforms to Accadian tradition, inevitably suggests that India was borrowing from Mesopotamia in this respect. And we know for certain that the Accadian treatise in question was in use in the Achaemenian Empire, for one of the tablets it comprises is dated from the eleventh year of the reign of Artaxerxes— 453 B.C. The relations we know to have existed between Babylonian and Indian scholars at this period lends considerable plausibility to the idea of an influence that would be the most satisfactory explanation of the resemblances pointed out here.

All the astronomical and medical data, whether Greek or Mesopotamian, that it has been possible to compare with ancient Indian data thus date from the Achaemenian occupation of the Indus valley. We can now proceed to consider how the similarities may have arisen.

4   The precise and restricted nature of the chief points of resemblance (correspondence of figures, igneous nature of the bile, association of breath, bile and pituitary gland as physiological and possibly pathogenical agents) renders unlikely any extraordinary accumulation of coincidences between independent trains of scientific thought. It is very likely that India was the borrower in the case of the divinatory method of prognostic set forth in the Accadian document of the Persian period. But this could not be the case with regard to the concepts also found in Heraclitus, the Hippocratic Collection, and the works of Plato, since those concepts were established in India, or present in all their elements, at a time when Greek science had not yet begun its great progress.

It has sometimes been suggested that the Greeks, Babylonians, and Indians may have drawn from a common source, but this is a purely gratuitous hypothesis, since there is no trace of an older source and we have no historical information to suggest that India on the one hand and the Greeks and late Babylonians on the other hand had access to a common foreign tradition. We are thus left with the hypothesis that the Greeks and the late Babylonians borrowed from India at the very time when the Persian Empire included parts of Greece and India and had entrusted their administration to a body of Babylonian-educated officials who were undoubtedly in touch with Indian scholars.

But the nature of scientific borrowing is extremely variable. It sometimes takes place on a vast scale, when a whole culture is adopted by a group that had none of its own, or has abandoned its former traditions. That is certainly not the case here. Babylonian and Greek science have far more original features than they have points of resemblance to Indian science. Borrowing may also be sporadic and restricted. It may relate not to definite results and established doctrines but to trends of research which, though followed separately, lead nevertheless to the same conclusions. In such cases all that is necessary, at the beginning, to create a spirit of emulation and lead to the elaboration of analogous theories is for a group of scholars to come across brief hints and fragmentary indications of the theories being investigated by another and distant group. And it is evident that under Persian rule there were extensive opportunities for such transmission of brief hints and fragmentary indications between the Indian and Greek worlds.

True, the majority of writers consider that there can have been no real contact between Greeks and Indians until Alexander's expedition established them. Indeed, direct contact on a large scale certainly did not exist before the Macedonian army set foot in the Indus valley. And when it is observed that even their occupation of that region left the Greeks very vaguely informed about Indian doctrines, it is natural to assume that they can have known nothing at all about them when they had no possibility of making inquiries on the spot. But it must be remembered that in spite—or rather, because —of their military occupation of India, Alexander's Greeks were in no position to gather information about Indian science when they were on the spot. They were aware that it existed, they may on occasion have made use of it, but the difficulties created by language barriers, even where interpreters were available, prevented them from mastering the Indian theories in cases where they would have liked to do so. Moreover, India was never in a hurry to reveal herself to her conquerors; there were Europeans there from 1497 onward, but only a handful of them discovered the country's culture and its vast body of literature, and that not until more than a century later. The failure of Alexander's expedition to establish any useful scientific exchanges between Greeks and Indians does not prove anything.

What could not be achieved by a brief contact resulting from brute force could have come about far more easily through the slow, peaceful trickle of information to all parts of the Achaemenian Empire. And we need not necessarily assume that it made its way solely thanks to the officials whose long association with Indian scholars led to the creation of the hybrid Aramaic-Indian script. It is a well-known fact that there were Greek doctors at the court of Susa and that Greeks traveled as far as India in the service of the Great King—Skylax, for example, explored it for Darius—and all this gave the Greeks further opportunities for study. It is doubtful, indeed, whether Ctesias, the Greek doctor who concerned himself more particularly with India, ever collected any worthwhile information about Indian science, for the surviving fragments of his writings are full of fantastical stories. But evidence that certain Indian medical practices were known to some of the authors of the Hippocratic Collection is afforded by the treatises *On The Nature of Women* and *On the Diseases of Women,* which refer to several of them. We also know that in the time of the Persians there was at least one regular route along which Indian merchandise traveled to the northern part of the Greek world, to the shores of the Pontus Euxinus. The existence of this land and sea route, which passed by way of Bactria, the Oxus, the Caspian Sea (into which the Oxus still flowed, though its course later changed and led to the Sea of Aral), and the Cyrus, and thence along the Phasus into the Pontus Euxinus, was noted at the time of Alexander's expedition by Aristobulus and later, under Seleucus and Antiochus Soter, by Patrocles, before being rediscovered, much later, under Pompey. There is no need to suppose that such information about Indian ideas as reached the Greek physicians and Heraclitus had traveled along a trade route so far to the north; but the existence of that route provides evidence, too frequently overlooked, that India had active contacts with the West even before Alexander's time.

It may be objected that trade caravans do not necessarily propagate scientific ideas. But it was thanks to trade contacts far more than to the rare diplomatic missions (which in any case traveled along the trade routes) that Greek astrology was brought to India in the first centuries of the Christian era. Furthermore, the Indian scientific ideas found in the writings of Heraclitus, the Hippocratic treatises and the works of Plato are of a very simple description and may easily have been conveyed together with the practical teachings of Indian therapeutics, whose arrival in the Greek world, at the same time as Indian drugs, is demonstrated by the treatises *On the Diseases of Women* and *On the Nature of Women.* In any case the existence of regular trade relations must have greatly facilitated the conveyance of ideas, which, as we have seen, can be disseminated by quite sporadic contacts and along routes much longer and less direct than were available in this particular instance. For example, we find that at Newminster, England, Indian astronomical methods were being employed in 1428, having reached Europe by way of the Arab scientists, nearly seventy years before Vasco da Gama and the new series of European invasions of India— the first since Alexander. Moreover, shortly after Alexander's day the Greeks themselves thought it was quite credible that an Indian should have brought Indian philosophical ideas direct to Athens at the height of the Achaemenian period, seventy years before Alexander's expedition; Aristoxenes of Taranto, who lived about 320-300 B.C., describes a supposed conversation between Socrates and an Indian philosopher in his circle. The statements attributed to this philosopher are very plausible, but might have been invented by Aristoxenes, since he was writing after Alexander's time; and the anecdote is generally regarded as fictitious because the presence of an Indian in Athens before Alexander's campaign is held to be impossible; but it did not seem so to Aristoxenes, a contemporary of what are described to us as the events that brought about the first possible encounter between Greeks and Indians.

We thus have the authority of history, as well as our own observations of points of concordance in scientific and technical matters, to justify the supposition that India, which by the Vedic period (we know nothing about the ideas held in the more ancient civilizations on the Indus) had created a science of astronomy and a physiological and medical science, played a definite part in the scientific exchanges of antiquity and was particularly assisted in doing so by the international exchanges resulting from the prolonged inclusion of the nations concerned in the Achaemenian Empire.

There is usually a greater disposition to attribute another role to India—apart from the credit that country often receives as the alleged inspiration of Pythagoras, Democritus, and others, a reputation it has enjoyed since the Hellenistic period, but that rests, so far, on evidence that is too vague. India is frequently credited with the invention of the zero and the so-called "Arabic" system of notation. Arab evidence on the subject is sometimes challenged—wrongly, it would seem, for the system in question was widely used in India long before the inception of Arab science. The earliest epigraphic evidence of it dates back to A.D. 595-596, it had reached Cambodia by the seventh century, and its use was already implicit in the method of extracting square roots that was taught in the fifth century by the astronomer Āryabhata. All the same, the invention of zero cannot be attributed to India. The ancient systems of notation employed in India, as known to us from inscriptions beginning in the middle of the third century B.C., do not use nine figures and zero, whereas the latter was in use in Mesopotamia at an earlier date. The idea may have been brought to India by the Babylonian officials employed by Persia, who were in touch with Indian scientists. But zero does not make its appearance in India during the period immediately following the contact with those officials, which suggests the alternative and perhaps more likely explanation that zero was reinvented during the earliest centuries of the Christian era by the Indian scholars who, about that time, began to elaborate various systems of representing numbers—by figures, by signs, by letters, or by symbolic words, according to whether they were seeking to express themselves in scholarly verse or in the form of actual mathematics.

However this may be, India was undoubtedly the first to popularize the system of notation that has become that of modern times, for it was from India that this spread, in the late classical period and in the Middle Ages, as far as northern Mongolia and Tibet, throughout Southeast Asia, to Indonesia, and to the Arab countries, whence the Arabs carried it into Europe.

It is thus entirely erroneous to suppose, as has so often been done, that India was the passive recipient of Babylonian and Greek scientific theories—the latter only after Alexander's expedition—and used them without acknowledgment. India was an original, active, and expansive center for the elaboration of scientific theories, and by no means an isolated center.

It communicated easily with the Near East in ancient times, before Alexander, during the Persian era. Later it carried its doctrines to an area even wider than that covered by Greek science, giving a generous welcome to the latter and spreading it jointly with Indian teaching. It is not even certain whether in the early centuries of the Christian era, when India borrowed largely from the teachings of Alexandria, it did not compensate by supplying some of its own scientific knowledge, for we have conclusive proof that the Brahmanic doctrines, those which, in principle, India guarded most jealously, were known—in succinct form, but with remarkable accuracy—as far away as Rome in the third century. St. Hippolytus, or another author of his milieu, in his *Refutation of All Heresies,* written about the year 235, summarizes them—though he had never visited the East himself—in a manner that fully conforms to the teaching of the Brahmanic *Upanishads;* and though his summary includes particulars that had been common knowledge since Alexander's time, it is based on new and much more accurate information, transmitted from the Deccan and unknown to the ancient writers. India must now be accepted as one of the great centers for the elaboration and exchange of scientific theories since the days of antiquity.

TRANSLATED FROM THE FRENCH
BY DAPHNE WOODWARD

SELECTED BIBLIOGRAPHY

J. B. Biot, *Études sur l'astronomie indienne et sur l'astronomie chinoise.* Paris: 1862.

L. de Saussure, *Les origines de l'astronomie chinoise.* Paris: 1930.

R. P. Festugière, *La révélation d'Hermès Trismégiste,* I. Paris: 1944.

J. Filliozat, *La doctrine classique de la médecine indienne.* Paris: 1949.

M. Labat, *Collection des travaux de l'Académie internationale d'Histoire des Sciences.* Paris-Leyden: 1951.

O. Neugebauer, *The Exact Sciences in Antiquity.* Copenhagen: 1951.

S. Piggott, *Prehistoric India.* Harmondsworth: Penguin, 1950.

J. F. S. Stone, "A Second Fixed Point in the Chronology of Harappa Culture," *Antiquity,* XCII (December, 1949), pp. 201-205.

It communicated study, with the Magi, Logos in philosophers before Alexander during the Persian era. Indian carried its doctrine to an area even older than that reveal by Greek expression put to the familiar welcome to the labor. An appealing in height with transcending. It is not even certain whether in the early stages of the Christian era, since India, but round history, from the teachers of Alexandria, it did not communicate by supplying some of its own scientific knowledge, but we have conclusive proof that the intellectual exchange, those spent in appositive India quoted not laboriously were known in Sanscrit form, but with remarkable exchange... as far back as to the third century St. Hippolytus or another author either utilised in his Refutation of all Heresies, written about the year 230, summarizes them — though he had received what the Peri had himself — in a manner fully conforming to the teaching of the Brahmans, Upanishads, and though his summary includes particulars that had been common knowledge since Alexander's time, it was based on new and much more recent information, transmitted from the Deccan and unknown to the ancient writers. India must now be accepted as one of the great centers for the elaboration and exchange of scientific theories since the days of antiquity.

TRANSLATED FROM THE FRENCH
BY DAPHNE WOODWARD

SELECTED BIBLIOGRAPHY

J. D. Bibl. Bidez, ... Les mages hellénisés et set l'astronomie grecque, Paris, 1930.

L. de Saussure, Les origines de l'astronomie chinoise, Paris, 1930.

R. R. Festugière, La révélation d'Hermès Trismégiste, I, Paris, 1944.

... un doctrine classique de la pensée... Indienne, Paris, 1943

M. Labat, Collection des hymnes de ... mésopotamie, ... d'histoire des Sciences, Paris-Leyden, 1951.

O. Neugebauer, The Exact Sciences in Antiquity, Copenhagen, 1951.

S. Piggott, Prehistoric India, Harmondsworth, Penguin, 1950.

J.E. Staton, "A Second Fixed Point in the Chronology of Harappa Culture," Antiquity, XGII (December 1959), pp. 201-205.

PART TWO

The Development of Science

The Middle Ages

SCIENCES IN CHINA FROM THE FOURTH TO THE END OF THE TWELFTH CENTURY *

Kiyosi Yabuuti

I. THE PERIOD OF THE NORTHERN AND SOUTHERN DYNASTIES

Unable to bear the oppression of the different races in northern China, the Chin Dynasty transferred the capital to the lower reaches of the Yang-tzū River in A.D. 317, and, thenceforth, the tract along the river came under the rule of the Eastern Chin. At the same time, many different races were in conflict and, at last, in 386, the Northern Wei Dynasty was established and obtained control of northern China, thus causing the direct confrontation of north and south. The Wei Dynasty had existed for about 150 years, but was for some time divided into the East and West Weis; soon afterward, Northern Ch'i from Eastern Wei and Northern Chou from Western Wei were established and later still the Sui Dynasty was set up by one of the commanders of Northern Chou, which again brought the whole of China under its authority. In the same manner in 420 the Sung Dynasty[1] emerged from the Southern

---

[1] This dynasty is different from Sung after the T'ang Dynasty.

Journal of World History, IV, 2.

Dynasty that upheld the tradition of the Chinese. After the Sung, the Ch'i, and Liang Dynasties fell, the Ch'ên Dynasty took control. This latter was overthrown in turn by Sui at the end of the sixth century.

Throughout the long period from the fourth century to unification by the Sui Dynasty, the northern part of China, which had been the stronghold of the Chinese from far back, came successively under the control of the different northern races, and the Chinese themselves migrated to southern China along the Yang-tzū River. Consequently, the cultivation of southern China was remarkably improved and, as the administration in the south was chiefly in the hands of aristocrats in the old tradition, classic studies were continued. Indian Buddhism, first introduced in the time of the Second Han Dynasty, had gradually increased its influence; large numbers of Buddhists passed through Hsin-chiang province, the translation of various Buddhist scriptures was under way, and huge stone caves were made at Ta-t'ung and Lung-mên during the Northern Wei Dynasty. All this exerted a great influence upon both north and south, and consequently the power of Buddhism became greater in China than that of Taoism, which had hitherto been dominant. Later, during the Sui and T'ang periods, the influence of Western civilization with Buddhism as its core grew more remarkable. In the north, the land had been devastated by a series of disturbances. With the Northern Wei period, however, the strong agricultural policy was extended, and such excellent technical books on agriculture as *Ch'i-min-yao-shu* were compiled. Needless to say, the Chinese were the representatives of civilization even when under the control of the different northern races, and although they carried the cultural tradition to the south, there was a sharp difference between north and south. From the middle of the sixth century, however, unification of the two regions began, and this was consolidated by the Sui Dynasty.

A. *Mathematics and astronomy*

Chiu-chang-suan-shu or *Arithmetic of Nine Sections,* the basic Chinese work on mathematics, was compiled in the Han period, and in A.D. 263 was annotated in detail by Liu

Hui of Wei of the Three Kingdoms, who was himself a creative mathematician and the author of *Hai-tao-suan-ching.* Subsequent mathematical works still surviving include *Sung-tzŭ-suang-ching,* *Chang-ch'iu-chien-suang-ching,* *Wu-ts'ao-suang-ching,* and *Wu-ching-suan-shu.* Except the last two, however, information as to the authors and the date of compilation is vague. The last two are supposed to have been written by Chên Luan of Northern Chou, one of the annotators of the ancient book on mathematics, *Chou-pei-suang-ching,* and the author of books on astronomy. He was a Buddhist priest, but there is no evidence that he was especially influenced by Western civilization. These mathematicians were not so outstanding as those represented by the *Chiu-chang-suan-shu* or *Arithmetic of Nine Sections,* but it is important to remember that the indeterminate equations were first given in *Sung-tzŭ-suang-ching* and *Chang-ch'iu-chien-suang-ching.*

The most remarkable mathematical works are rather those of Ho Ch'êng-t'ien, Tsu Ch'ung-chih, and Tsu Huan-chih, southern scholars and well-known astronomers. Ho Ch'êng-t'ien devised "T'iao-jih-fa" in order to indicate one synodic month by fractions; Tsu Ch'ung-chih originated "Chui-shu," a method no longer employed. His work on the circular constant, however, was a great achievement. According to *T'ien-wen-chih* in *Sui-shu,* he calculated the circular constant as $3.1415926 < \pi < 3.1415927$, with $\frac{22}{7}$ as the rough circular constant and $\frac{355}{113}$ as the exact one. The latter accords with the result obtained by a Danish scholar in the sixteenth century, but it is not known how he reached this. Tsu Huan-chih, a son of Tsu Ch'ung-chih, was the first man to succeed in calculating the volume of a sphere, and both father and son helped advance the work begun by Liu Hui. Though Liu Hui had already used the idea of limit of an infinite series, Tsu Huan-chih adopted the geometrical method in cubing the sphere and utilized an idea similar to the integral calculus of today. The achievements of these two scholars rank high in the history of Chinese mathematics.

In China, the calendar had long been regarded as the symbol of political unification. Just as Gregorius XIII in the sixteenth century provided Roman Catholic countries with a revised calendar, so the calendar officially adopted by any dominant state was used even by countries only nominally under her control. Though it was usual for a new calendar to be introduced with each change of dynasty, it sometimes happened that calendar reform was undertaken during the same dynasty. The calendar in those days showed solar and lunar eclipses as well as the division of months and days. On the ground, however, that these forecasts of astronomical phenomena were necessarily uncertain, "astronomical tables" were frequently revised and new calendars based upon those tables officially issued. During the period under consideration, many astronomical tables were made and the following were among the most important.

First, in Northern Liang, in the northwest, Chao Fei devised an astronomical table called *Hsüan-shih-shu,* and the calendar derived from this was in use from 412 to 439. A lunisolar calendar was used in China, and before the time of Chao Fei, a "metonic cycle" with seven leap months in nineteen years had been employed, this nineteen-year cycle being known as a "chang." Chao Fei, however, adopted a method involving 221 leap months in 600 years, and he named this "P'o-chang-fa." He was thus the first to adopt a method of intercalation other than the metonic cycle; Tsu Ch'ung-chih of the Southern Dynasty followed suit and it became the basis of various methods of intercalation in subsequent astronomical tables.

Ho Ch'êng-t'ien of Sung made the splendid astronomical table called "Yüan-chia-li" in 443 and suggested the first day of each month be fixed by true syzygy instead of mean syzygy. Liu Hung of the Second Han period had already discovered the irregularity of the lunar movement, particularly in regard to the equation of motion, and Ho Ch'êng-t'ien tried to incorporate it into the calendar, though without success. The calculation of the new moon by true syzygy or "Ting-shuo-fa" was adopted in the T'ang period.

The irregularity of the solar movement was discovered by Chang Tzŭ-hsin, the northern astronomer who lived from the end of the North Wei Dynasty to Northern Ch'i and made his observation by "Hun-i," or an armillary sphere, for more than thirty years.

After Ho Ch'êng-t'ien, in accordance with the P'o-chang-fa of Chao Fei, 144 leap months in 391 years were inserted in the astronomical table or "Ta-ming-li" of Tsu Ch'ung-chih, and the precession, first known by Yü Hsi of Eastern Chin, was also adopted. According to Yü Hsi, the numerical value of precession was $\frac{1}{50}$ degree. Tsu Ch'ung-chih, however, amended this into $\frac{1}{47}$ degree. Precession was thereafter frequently used in astronomical tables.

As mentioned above, there were some differences between

the astronomical tables of the Northern and Southern Dynasties, and from the astronomical point of view, the Southern table was superior. Although some of its features were not exactly theoretical, there were many metaphysical modifications in the Northern table. Ch'ên-wei-shuo, or theory of divination, which had grown stronger after the Second Han period, was favored by scholars of the Northern Dynasty with the result that it was associated with astronomy. In the north, too, the Buddhists took part in the compilation of the calendar, and, at the same time, there were many astronomers among the Taoists.

During the reign of Huan-ti of the Second Han, a priest, An-Shih, who was believed to be a son of the King of Parthia, translated *Shê-t'ou-chien-ching* into Chinese and introduced the old astronomy of India. Afterwards, *Mo-têng-ch'ieh-ching*, another manuscript version of the same work, was also translated into Chinese. According to *Hsü-kao-sêng-chuan*, Ta-mo-liu-chih translated the twenty volumes of Brahminic astronomy in obedience to an Imperial command during the reign of Chien-wu-ti of Northern Chou. Besides these, some books on astronomy and mathematics were also translated during the northern dynasties. *Hui-yüan-chuan* of *Kao-sêng-chuan* recounts that Ho Ch'êng-t'ien studied Indian astronomy, but there is no sign of its influence in his surviving astronomical table. Nor is there any trace of Indian influence elsewhere in the field of astronomy, although in astrology it gradually grew stronger.

B. *Medical science and pharmacology*

Among the ancient books of medical science, *Nei-ching* including *Su-wên* and *Ling-shu* written in the Ch'in-Han period should be noted. This touches chiefly upon fundamental medical science, and explains the functions of the human body by the principles of Yin-yang and by the theory of Wu-hsing, or theory of five elements, and also refers to the causes of diseases. It reveals the theories of physiology and pathology in ancient China, according to which man comes into existence with two spirits of Yin-yang, which symbolize heaven and earth and replenish air and food. The five viscera—heart, liver, spleen, lung, and kidney—not only perform their particular physiological functions but have their special spirits and are the center of mental activities. Besides these five viscera, there are the six internal organs: gall, stomach, large and small intestines, urinary bladder and "san-chiao."

The book describes in fair detail the anatomical structure and the physiological functions, but deals very little with the nervous system. It argues that disease is mainly due to a disordered spiritual state or the work of evil spirits such as wind, cold, warmth, and heat, entering the body while it is off guard. Finally, it indicates how to diagnose disease by pulse and how to cure by medicine, depletion, acupuncture, and moxibustion.

In contradistinction to this ancient work is *Shang-hang-lun*, a clinical study written by Chang Chi, otherwise known as Chang Chung-ching of the Second Han. He divided diseases into two kinds of Yin and Yang according to the degree of pyrexia and each of these into three classes according to the place and condition of the symptoms. "Shang-han" was the principal disease belonging to Yang—a fever marked by intense pyrexia and rigor and including typhoid fever and other infectious diseases. About 200, when Chang Chung-ching was a child, this fever killed more than a hundred of his relatives and this later decided him to write his treatise.

Wang Shu-ho of the Chin period was a scholar who revised *Shang-hang-lun* and the author of *Mo-ching*, a famous book on diagnostics. He divides the pulse into twenty-four kinds by its place and characteristics. Huang-fu Mi, who appeared after the time of Wang Shu-ho, wrote *Chia-i-ching* which refers in detail to acupuncture and moxibustion, both specifically Chinese methods of treatment. These were the important books on medical science written in the period of the Northern and Southern Dynasties. In these periods, knowledge of practical cures developed into the basis for medical science in the Sui-T'ang period but no outstanding books represented this period.

Chinese pharmacology is known as "Pên-tsao" (used from the end of the First Han), the term presumably deriving from the fact that herbs (tsao) were extensively, although not exclusively, employed as medicaments. Significant books on pharmacology include *Shên-nung-pên-tsao-ching* compiled by T'ao Hung-ching (A.D. 452-A.D. 536) and a number of works compiled under the name of "Shêng-nung," the father of medicine. This latter revived the tradition of old pharmacology and revised *Shên-nung-pên-tsao-ching* which listed

365 kinds of medicinal substances representing the days in a year and divided into upper, middle, and lower levels, according to the tradition. According to *Shên-nung-pên-tsao-ching,* the 120 "upper" substances represented the elixir of life, the 120 "middle" substances were for the preservation of health, and the remaining 125 were curative. To these were added by him another 365 which were used supplementarily by noted physicians. The account of this second group was given the name of *Ming-i-pieh-lu,* which was not only a compilation of the old pharmacology but became the basis for subsequent developments. The book refers in detail to the properties of each medicine and explains when, how, and where the various herbs should be collected and how they should be prepared and administered.

C. *Agricultural techniques*

From the beginning of the fourth century, northern China was devastated by war, and much land rendered unfit for cultivation, while, on the other hand, many farmers had no land of their own to cultivate. The leaders of the Northern Dynasty had devoted their energies to increasing the population and encouraging agriculture. Specifically, the distribution of land according to age and sex was decided in the ninth year of T'ai-ho (845), a sort of nationalization of land, giving a fixed area to each farmer.

In spite of this, however, aristocrats and other influential men owning slaves were able to retain considerable property, so that distribution was not in fact carried out very equitably. Since northern China had relatively little rain, german millet and ordinary millet were the principal crops, while in the yellow land belt, dry-farming was devised to make the best use of water absorbed into the ocher. *Ch'i-min-yao-shu,* compiled by Chia Ssū-hsieh of the Northern Wei, explains the technique of this dry-farming. The date of compilation of this book is uncertain, but is thought to be between 530. and 550. It is one of the most advanced works on agricultural technique and exerted a great influence on later developments. The technique of aquatic rice cultivation, subsequently of paramount importance, was still in the early stages and is only sparsely treated. German millet is described as the most important food, but after the end of the Northern and

Southern Dynasties, the cultivation of wheat increased substantially with the result that many water mills were built on the northern rivers, a method which grew more prosperous in the period of T'ang.

After the middle of the T'ang period, the technique of aquatic rice cultivation improved, and not only irrigative devices but new farm implements were invented about this time. Moreover, with the Sung period, a new variety of rice was imported and a wide tract along the Yang-tzū River was developed where conditions were especially suitable for rice cultivation. Although there were plenty of swampy places, the large-scale project of land reclamation by drainage had taken place, and agricultural production increased remarkably. Ch'ên Fu of Sung described the technique of aquatic rice cultivation in detail in 1149.

II. Sui-T'ang Period from the End of the Sixth to the Beginning of the Ninth Century

The Sui Dynasty, which dissolved the antagonism between the Northern and Southern Dynasties, worked on the excavation for an enormous canal, which, along with the construction of the Great Wall, is considered among the greatest Chinese engineering achievements. Not all the work on this canal connecting north and south was done during the Sui Dynasty, however; but by repairing waterways which already existed and by excavating a number of canals which passed through from north to south, it was brought to completion. As a result, not only could rice produced on the Yang-tzū River be transported to the northern capital, Ch'ang-an, but of the advantages being handed down to the T'ang period, the canal played an important role in the unification of all China.

In the Sui Dynasty, various changes suited to the unified country were introduced. For example, a system of K'o-chü made official position hitherto open only to the sons of aristocrats accessible to the people in general, but it thereby increased the tendency to concentrate studies on the classics of Confucianism, and thus obstructed free research. Moreover, as the Sui Dynasty fell within forty years, the changes were mainly completed in the T'ang period.

A. *Astronomy and mathematics*

In the beginning of the Sui period, the calendar was based on the astronomical table partially revised in accordance with the method of Ho Ch'êng-tien, and Liu Ch'ao was the most prominent astronomer of the time. He had acquired a thorough knowledge of the astronomical works in the Northern and Southern Dynasties but his own table was essentially original. He reasoned Ting-ch'i or true seasonal points by accepting the irregularity of the sun's motion discovered by Chang Tzŭ-hsin, and improved the calculation method of true syzygy. As a result, calculation of solar and lunar eclipses was remarkably improved. As to the value of precession, he improved Tsu Ch'ung-chih's and adopted as accurate a value as once in seventy-six years. Although the astronomical table was not used in the calculation of the calendar, it provides an example of the tables used in the T'ang period. Ting-ch'i's method was not used until the Ch'ing Dynasty. Li Ch'ung-fêng completed *Lin-tê-li* in the early years of the T'ang Dynasty; although he based it on Liu Ch'ao's table, he unfortunately ignored precession. He did, however, devise a way of expressing fractions of all astronomical constants by a common denominator and this represented a considerable saving of time in calculation. Other excellent astronomical tables in the T'ang period were I Hsing's *Ta-yen-li*, Hsü Ang's *Hsüan-ming-li,* and Pien Kang's *Chung-hsüan-li.* In *Ta-yen-li,* an approximate correct value was found for the irregularity of the sun's motion and the method of calculating the day of true syzygy was improved. While Liu Ch'ao had already developed a method of interpolation in equal intervals for this purpose, I Hsing expanded this to unequal intervals. His method was identical with that of Gauss' interpolation formulae in disregarding the third difference and over.

I Hsing also found that the conditions of a solar eclipse varied according to the observation site and devised a method of calculating these differences. When *Hsüan-ming-li, Chung-hsüan-li,* etc. were put into circulation, most of the improvements related to the method of calculation, and Chinese astronomical tables founded on the traditional method apparently came to an end in the T'ang period.

Buddhism flourished greatly in the T'ang period and as the

country prospered, the visits of Indians and then Westerners increased, with a corresponding increase in the influence of Western culture. At the same epoch Christians of Nestorian faith arrived and made a fairly large number of converts. In the field of science, Indians achieved great success. A number of them occupied high positions in the Royal Astronomical Observatory in China and some even became directors of that institution. Nonetheless, there is no Indian influence apparent in the traditional Chinese astronomical calculation methods and instruments: it is seen rather in astrology. *Hsiu-yao-ching* translated by the priest Pu-k'ung in 859 is the book which introduced Indian astrology and commentaries based on Indian astrology were added to the calendar. In the T'ang period, too, Sunday began to be entered on the calendar as the word "mi." The word is the phonetic translation of "mīr" in Sogdiana, and it was introduced by Manichee who came to China. In the calendar were rules of conduct prescribed for Sunday according to astrology. And when printing began in the T'ang period, the printing of the calendar was one of the first works. The oldest printed calendar in existence can be assumed without doubt to be the one printed in 877.

In the reign of Hsüang-tsung of the T'ang period, Ch'ü-t'an-hsi-ta, an Indian, who was appointed director of the Royal Astronomical Observatory, translated an Indian astronomical book into Chinese, and called it *Chiu-chih-li*. It explained calculation by the method of the third period of Indian astronomy. Astronomy in this period, influenced by the Greek, had reached a fairly high level. In India, besides the sun, the moon and five stars, two invisible stars called "Rāhu" and "Kētu" were thought to exist; all these heavenly bodies were collectively known as "the nine planets," or "navagrāha"; the translation by Ch'ü-t'an-hsi-ta was named after these planets. It is noteworthy that explanations of the Indian numeral and sine-table, originating in Greece, were given in this book, but they did not exert any influence on existing mathematics and astronomical calculation in China.

Many improvements were made on astronomical instruments in this period, notably an armillary sphere made by Li Ch'un-fêng. In the reign of Hsüan-tsung shadows of a pole and the altitude of the North Pole in the "twenty-four chi" or twenty-four seasonal points were observed in every district in China. It was known that the altitude of the North Pole differed according to districts, and I Hsing and Nan-kang

Yüeh were the first persons to measure the meridian arc of
the earth based on these facts. By first selecting a flat area in
Honan and then measuring the distance between two points
which lay approximately on the same meridian, I Hsing obtained the value of 365.4 Chinese li to a degree of latitude.
But he had no clear and accurate knowledge of the shape
of the earth and therefore could not go further in trying to
calculate the dimension of the earth.

In the field of mathematics, a method of interpolation for
astronomical calculation had been originated in the Sui period.
The noted mathematicians in the T'ang period were Wang
Hsiao-t'ung and Li Ch'un-fêng. Wang Hsiao-t'ung used cubic
equation in his *Ch'i-ku-suang-ching;* Li Ch'ung-fêng, who won
fame as an astronomer, annotated a number of old mathematical books. Schools of mathematics were set up to train
special officials and ten classical mathematical works, including Wang Hsiao-t'ung's, were adopted as textbooks. Since
examination problems were limited by these textbooks, there
was little likelihood of creative mathematicians arising in the
school system. Unlike the position of astronomy, there was a
strong tendency in mathematics to respect the ancient tradition and hence no new mathematical studies were undertaken.

B. *Medical science and pharmacology*

Medical literature in the Sui period is characterized mainly
by a complete survey of medicine in the Six Dynasties. Various methods of medical treatment were acquired through
experience, developed in the period of the Six Dynasties, and
in the Sui period were brought to completion. As a result, the
voluminous medical books entitled *Ssŭ-hai-lei-chü-fang,*
amounting to 2,600 volumes, were compiled, and at the time
represented the greatest body of medical literature in the
world. Among works still existing is *Ping-yüan-hou-lun* which
was by the Imperial ordinance compiled by Ch'ao Yüan-fang
and others in A.D. 610. This not only records symptoms but as-
cribes illness to five *miasmata* (evil spirits) and various demons. Despite this mystical element it nonetheless gives the impression that clinical knowledge had greatly increased. Though
descriptions of medical treatment are comparatively brief
and medicinal substances not mentioned, it expounds acu-
puncture-moxibustion and a sort of calisthenica. The influ-

ences of Taoism and Indian medicine are both apparent. Specifically, the theory that there are four elements, each of them involving 101 kinds of illness, derived from Indian medicine.

Ch'ien chin-fang and *Wai-t'ai-pi-yao* by Sun Ssū-miao and Wang Tao respectively are the representative medical books in the T'ang period and deal mainly with methods of medical treatment. The former was thoroughly acquainted with books on Taoism and Buddhism and since he regarded human life as more valuable than a thousand gold pieces (Ch'ien chin), he named his book *Ch'ien-chin-fang*. In his emphasis on medical ethics he merits comparison with Hippocrates. He was not a man of originality but rather one who took up the methods of medical treatment completed in the Sui period, and gave a full account of the quality, usage, and prescription of the substances required for such treatment. Wang Tao was a man of the Hsüang-tsung era, and his book, being compiled on the basis of the earlier *Ping-yüan-hou-lun,* goes into details about prescriptions of medical substances as well as the nature of diseases and pathological theories. Many quotations from Chinese medical books occur in *Isinpô* selected by a Japanese, Yasuyori Tanba, in 984, and in this regard, it is of value for any study of medicine in the Tang period since so many of the original works have been lost.

Hsin-hsiu-pên-tsao was written by Imperial command and under the direction of Li Chih, its compilation was completed in 659, chiefly by Su Ching. It was intended to supplement *Shên-nung-pên-tsao-ching* which was compiled one hundred years earlier.

Since T'ao Hung-ching lived in the southern district, his knowledge of medicinal substances was mainly local but *Hsin-hsiu-pên tsao* added 100 substances to the former book. It is thought that it contained illustrations of medicinal substances, probably in color, and this shows that writing had become scientific and observation of medicinal substances sharp. This book listed medicinal substances from Arabia and several Western countries, indicating that the import of various products from the West had increased conspicuously. For instance, it mentions theriaca, a well-known drug of which the chief ingredient is opium, then imported from the Near East. In this connection, it is certain that the use of opium as a drug was not then practiced in China.

Some information about T'ang drugs can be obtained from the remains of the treasure at Shôsôin in Nara City, Japan. It is a storehouse in which many valuable articles, mostly mementoes of the Emperor Shômu in the Nara era, are kept, including not only medicinal substances but various utensils, implements, garments, porcelains and so forth. There are many articles brought directly from China, among which those imported from the south or from Persia in the T'ang period are included. The medicinal substances number more than sixty, and besides the Chinese products are several introduced from Persia. Further study of this material is being carried out by a number of Japanese scholars at present, and it is expected the results will be published in the near future.

Alimentary therapy had been highly regarded in China from ancient times as can be seen in the list of dietary experts in *Chou-li.* In succeeding years, the Taoists continued to seek the elixir of life by way of diet and, at the end of the T'ang period, Mêng Shên, disciple of the prominent doctor Sun Ssū-miao, wrote *Pu-yang-fang;* later, Chang Ting of Wu-tai, supplementing it, published *Shih-liao-pên-tsao.* Part of an old copy of this book is in the possession of the British Museum.

C. *Printing and paper-making*

Printing originated in China. The art of printing can be traced back to the era of Empress Wu, that is to the end of the seventh century. At first, it was used to meet the massive demands for Buddhist literature, dictionaries and so on, but, about the period of Wu-tai, the sacred books of Confucianism were printed. In the succeeding Sung period, printing became so popular that it was carried out by ordinary individuals as well as by the officials, and it developed until it could run as an independent enterprise. During the years of Ch'ing-li (1041-1048) an artisan named Pi Shêng invented type made of hardened earth and glue to replace the block printing so far used. The process consisted of fixing type on an iron plate with melted wax and placing sheets on the plate as in block printing. As its technique remained crude, type printing never became as popular as block printing in China, although the use of metallic type was later successful in Korea.

The invention of paper is likewise due to the Chinese, dating back to about 100. Various materials for paper-making were used, including, according to the writings of the early Sung period, fibers of paper mulberry, bamboo, mulberry tree, etc. It would seem that the use of many different materials for paper-making and increased production was already under way in the T'ang period, and at the same epoch a unique event had occurred in the history of paper-making. In the tenth year of T'ien-pao (751) in the reign of Hsüang-tsung of T'ang, when the army under the command of Kao Hsien-chih was defeated by an Arabian army in the Turkistan district, a number of Chinese paper-making artisans were captured. Paper-making factories were set up employing these prisoners and from these the knowledge of paper-making eventually spread over Europe.

III. Wu-Tai, Sung Period from the Beginning of the Ninth to the End of the Thirteenth Century

The period of Wu-tai succeeded that of T'ang and lasted some fifty years. It was followed by the Sung Dynasty which unified the whole of China and which came into being in 960. About this time, however, the Liao Dynasty had been formed in the northeastern district of China, and for some time menaced the Sung Dynasty. No sooner had the Liao Dynasty been overthrown by a joint operation of the Chin Dynasty in the northeastern district and Sung in the south, than the former attacked its ally and in 1126 succeeded in capturing K'ai-fêng, the capital city. Consequently, Sung moving its capital to Hang-chou in the south, China was divided into two. Chin established its capital at Pei-ching and occupied the whole stretch of northern China.

It is customary to call the first displacement of central authority of the Sung Dynasty to the south, Northern Sung and its later retreat to the south, Southern Sung. After the rise of the Mongolian race, Yüan took Chin's place, while Southern Sung, losing its power gradually, continued to exist until the end of the thirteenth century.

It was during the Sung period that Neo-Confucianism emerged and gave an impetus to study of the T'ang period and preceding periods. In this Neo-Confucianism, "Ko-wu-chih-chih" ("after scrutinizing the reason for things, seek after deeper knowledge") was emphasized. Although this precept was purely ideal and although it had never been intended to encourage empirical science, yet the natural philosophical thought which accompanied Neo-Confucianism exercised great influence on medicine. Learning spread with the popularization of printing, and the progress of urban culture was conspicuous, but originality in science was little in evidence except for a number of remarkable technical achievements. In the short time from the end of Sung to the beginning of Yüan, considerable advance was seen in the fields of mathematics and, particularly, medicine.

A. *Astronomy, cartography, and mathematics*

Nineteen kinds of astronomical tables, apart from some unofficial ones, were compiled throughout the 300 years of the Sung period, accompanied by as many revisions of the calendar. Even in the Liao and Chin Dynasties, calendars based on Sung methods were used. Most astronomers in the Sung period avoided making new observations of astronomical phenomena but were merely content to modify constants, such as the length of the year, etc. However, as soon as the astronomical phenomena proved to be too much at variance with the existing records, the compilation of new tables became necessary.

The most prominent astronomer of the Sung period was Liu Hsi-sou of Northern Sung. He compiled *Ch'ang-shu* (a kind of chronological table) from the beginning of Han to the end of Wu-tai, and contributed to the compilation of Chinese chronology. About the same period, Shên Kua, whose scholarship was widely recognized and who was conversant in other sciences, wrote *Meng-ch'i-pi-t'an*. In this he pointed out the defects of the existing Chinese luni-solar calendar and became the first proponent in China of the solar calendar, which was, however, adopted only after 1912, under Western influence.

While no remarkable advance was made in regard to astronomical tables, it was in the Northern Sung period that an armillary sphere was constructed, and the position of fixed stars accurately determined. For astronomical as well as astrological reasons, the determination of the positions of fixed stars and the drawing of star charts had been practiced from ancient times in China. In the Sui period, a certain Tan-yüan-tzū composed a long poem, *P'u-t'ien-ko,* in which knowledge of the constellations was incorporated. Among the determinations of the positions of stars in the Sung period, one conducted during the Huang-yu era (about 1050) was particularly noteworthy. There still remain minute records of about 340 stars based on these determinations, that is records of right ascension differences which refer to the standard star of twenty-eight hsiu and the north polar distance of these stars, and from the latter it is easy to calculate a star's right ascension. Besides such a star catalogue, a star chart appears in Su Sung's *Hsin-i-hsiang-fa-yao.* It was based on the measurements made during the Yüan-fêng era (1078-1085), a little later than the Huang-yu era, but it is not known how far the positions of plotted stars are correct, for the original edition no longer exists. In Soochow an astronomical chart engraved in stone seems to have been based on measurements made during the Yüan-fêng era. Many charts were originally drawn for the royal prince by a scholar called Huang Shang, and it is one of these that, during the Ch'un-yu era (1247), was engraved.

Mainly for astrological reasons, all heavenly phenomena, beginning with lunar and solar eclipses from olden times, had been observed and recorded. This tradition continued through the Sung period. From these records it was found that a new star (nova—now presumed super nova) was observed in 1054 and consequently these records are attracting the attention of many modern astronomers. In general, as Chinese records of observation have been kept from remote ages, they can be said to be quite valuable.

Su Sung in his *Hsin-i-hsiang-fa-yao* explained by means of a chart the new astronomical instruments made by himself in the Yüan-yu era (about 1090). He was a man of extensive learning and compiled a book on pharmacology, made a water clock, an armillary sphere, and further, by using the water clock as a motor he made a celestial globe with its stellar system revolve, reproducing the conditions of the sky ever undergoing changes.[2] No doubt, this kind of device existed fairly long ago. In the T'ang period I Hsing and Liao Ling-tsan had made it, and further in the beginning of Sung

---

[2] Exhaustive study on the instrument of Su Sung has been carried out by J. Needham and others. See J. Needham, L. Wang, and D. Price, *Heavenly Clockwork* (London and New York: Cambridge, 1960).

a work by Chang Su-hsün of Shu existed. When Chin captured the capital of Sung in 1126 and brought back many astronomical instruments and books to the north, the advancement of astronomy in Southern Sung declined.

As stated already, an important survey was carried out in the Hsüang-tsung era, and a little later Chia Tan (730-805) published *Hai-nei-hua-i-t'u* and other works on geography in the seventeenth year of Chân-yüan (801). Even though the map no longer exists, it is known that it was a full-sized one of three "jo" (about 360 inches) in width by 3.3 "jo" in length, drawn on graph paper to a scale of one inch to 100 Chinese li. Not only China proper, but also Tibetan districts were included, and as it was useful to national defence, the author received courteous treatment from T'ang's prince. As to existing maps, these are Yü-chi-t'u and Hua-i-t'u which were carved on stone. These are known to have been carved in 1137 because of appearance of the words "7th year of Fu-chang" (1137 is the seventh year of the Fu-chang era of the Ch'i Dynasty which lay between Chin and Sung). Yü-chi-t'u is a map of all China of three "shaku" (about thirty-six inches) by three "shaku," and in a scale of one inch to 100 Chinese li. These graph-paper maps were originated by P'ei Hsin (224-271) of Chin and imported into Chia Tan.

Little creative study is found in mathematics of the Sung period. The wars of Wu-tai at the end of T'ang destroyed many old books on mathematics, but those which survived until the Northern Sung period were printed and can still be found today. The period between the end of Sung and the beginning of Yüan marked an epoch in Chinese mathematics, and in the north Li Chih and in the south Ching Chiu-shao, Yang Hui, Chu Hsi-chieh took an active part. A method for discovering an unknown quantity by calculating blocks led to the creation of a kind of algebra.

B. *Medical science and pharmacology*

Many revisions of and annotations of classical books on medical science were made in the Sung period and a number of important classical books therefore still survive, though not in their original forms. For example, Wang Ping annotated *Huang-ti-su-wên* during the Pao-ying era in the T'ang period. This book was later lost, but another manuscript revised by Lin I and others during the Chia-yu era (1056-1062) in Sung still exists. Lin I and others also revised and published *Shang-hang-lun* by Chang Chi. Not only were classical books published but also many new books on medical science, and in this respect, as in regard to pharmacological books, the Sung period is pre-eminent. This achievement was due to the improvement of printing technique and, at the same time, to the active efforts of successive emperors. It is important to note that of these books on medical science and pharmacology, only a few were the work of specialists and almost all the rest were produced by the Confucianists.

Among the principal books of medical science were *T'ai-pin-shêng-hui-fang*, written at the beginning of the Sung period, *San-in-chih-i-ping-chêng-fang* by Chên Yen, which explained the new pathology, and the two hundred volumes of *Shêng-chi-tsung-lu*, which were compiled during the Chêng-ho era, and formed the encyclopedia of medical science in those days. Much later, during the reign of Hui-tsung, a simple *Ho-chi-chü-fang* was compiled. This was highly esteemed as a handbook for the country doctors and was an index to practical methods of medical treatment. Books specifically dealing with pediatrics and gynecology were first written in the Sung period; *Hsi-yüan-lu*, a famous book on medical jurisprudence, was written by Sung Tz'ū of Southern Sung in the middle of the thirteenth century, and medical jurisprudence in general was advanced at that time; a description of the human anatomy was first made in the Sung period.

Neo-Confucianism developed in the Sung period and "Hsing-li-shuo" based upon the natural philosophy appeared. Four famous doctors who lived between the end of Sung and the beginning of Yüan were greatly influenced by this theory. As mentioned above, medical science in the Sui and T'ang periods was based on the experiential curative means established in the period of the Six Dynasties. But with the Sung period, the ancient medical science described in *Nei-ching* was revived, and the four doctors suggested new theories and new curative means. These men were Liu Wan-su of Chin, Chang ts'ung-chêng and Chu Chên-hêng of Southern Sung, and Li Kao of Yüan, and their work was so remarkable that entirely new schools in medical science were established.

As far as the books on pharmacology are concerned, at the beginning of the Sung period, Liu Han and others compiled

K'ai-pao-pên-tsao, revising *Hsin-hsiu-pên-tsao* of the T'ang period. During the reign of Jen-tsung, new books on pên-tsao were compiled according to *K'ai-pao-pên-tsao.* For example, Chang Yü-hsi and others wrote *Chia-yu-pên-tsao* which described in detail as many as 1,082 medical substances, revising old theories and adding many new substances. Together with this *Chia-yu-pên-tsao,* a famous astronomer, Su Sung, made illustrations of medicinal substances and although his book no longer exists, almost all the illustrations had been reproduced in a rather different form in later books, and today are of great value in identifying the Chinese medicinal substances.

As we have seen already in *Chia-yu-pên-tsao* illustrations and their explanations were given separately, but T'ang Shên-wei and Chên Ch'êng put both into a single volume. They also published *Ching-shih-chêng-lei-pei-chi-pên-tsao* and *Chung-kuang-pu-chu-shên-nung-pên tsao* and *T'u-ching* in 1092. Afterward, on the basis of these books, Ai Shêng compiled *Ta-kuan-pên-tsao* in 1102 and Ts'ao Hsia-chung *Chêng-ho-pên-tsao* in 1116. In the year when *Chêng-ho-pên-tsao* was compiled, K'ou Tzung-shih wrote *Pên-tsao-yen-i,* in which he eliminated all medicinal substances appearing in older books when their value was uncertain. All the above books were compiled and published in the Northern Sung period, but Wang Chi-hsien's *Shao-hsing-pên-tsao* published in the twenty-ninth year of Shao-hsing era (1159) in the Southern Sung period and apparently written on the basis of *Ta-kuan-pên-tsao* also merits attention.

C. *Gunpowder and magnetism*

Gunpowder was first made in China, the chief ingredients being niter, sulphur, and charcoal. Although Tseng Kung-liang first described the method of compounding gunpowder in his *Wu-ching-tsung-yao* in the middle of the eleventh century, a method of compounding something like gunpowder appears in a book written still earlier by Taoists. At all events, it may be said that from the appearance of *Wu-ching-tsung-yao,* gunpowder became militarily important.

It is said that the Chinese were the first to make practical use of the magnet. Of course, in China as elsewhere it had long been known that magnets attracted iron substances, and lodestone spoon, which points to the north-south direction, had been used for divination from some centuries before the Christian Era. The lodestone spoon evolved into the magnetic needle about the fourth or fifth century.

In *Wu-ching-tsung-yao* there is a description of Chih-nan-yü or the fish that pointed the direction. This Chih-nan-yü was a fish-shaped piece of wood to which a magnet was attached, so that it pointed north and south when it was set afloat. In ancient China, there was a device called Chih-nan-ch'ê, which has been wrongly considered as a magnetic needle, whereas it was not a magnet at all but a contrivance geared to point to the south.[3] Shên Kua's *Meng-ch'i-pi-t'an* explained how to suspend a magnetic needle with a string, and noted that it does not always point due north owing to the declination of the needle. It is likely that a magnetic needle was first used for navigation in China at the end of the eleventh or at the beginning of the twelfth century. Some scholars claim that it was brought to Europe by the Arabs.

The first volume of J. Needham, *Science and Civilization in China,* was published in 1954. His work is not yet finished, but readers who wish to know more about Chinese science are requested to consult these remarkable works.

[3] Chen-to-Wang, *Ssu-nan Chih-nan-chen yü Lo-ching-p'an* (in Chinese) Discovery and Application of Magnetic Phenomena. Chung-kuo K'ao-ku-Hsueh-pao (Journal of Chinese Archaeology), III (1937), IV (1949), V (1951).

TRANSLATIONS OF ORIENTAL
SCIENTIFIC WORKS

(To the End of the Thirteenth Century)*

J. M. Millas-Vallicrosa

I. IMPORTANCE OF THESE TRANSLATIONS IN COMPENSATION FOR THE DEFICIENCIES OF THE LATIN SCIENTIFIC TRADITION

In order to form an idea of the importance and significance in the cultural development of medieval Europe of the scientific translations derived from the Orient, we must remember that the European science of that period, as heir to the classical culture of Rome, was handicapped from the outset by a radical and irremediable deficiency. It is a universally recognized fact that imperial Rome was utterly uninterested in pure scientific speculation. Generally speaking, Rome was not even aware of the intense intellectual activity and the creative spirit in science that were manifest at Alexandria. The abstract speculations of the Neoplatonic school, the mathematical problems raised by Diophantus and Menelaus, the astronomical equations put forward by Hipparchus and Ptolemy, made no impression on the chief city of the world. All historians admit

* Journal of World History, II, 2.

this indigence in the Rome of the Caesars, which was mitigated only by the scanty scientific material to be found in the *Quaestiones naturales* of Lucius Anneus Seneca and in Pliny's *Naturalis Historia*. A. von Braunmühl, in his history of trigonometry, acknowledges the fact that the Roman mind was concerned first and foremost with practical matters, and was thus unfitted to excel in such a science as astronomy. The only branch of mathematics in which the Romans took any real interest was surveying, that being necessary in establishing the boundaries of their estates; and the *gromaticorum* records show that even here they had grasped only the rudiments. It is M. Chasles, the great authority on the history of geometry, who declares that the *gromatici* do not deserve to be known as geometricians, since they confined themselves to very elementary practical problems of geometry, and even so made frequent and glaring errors. Not a single Roman left his mark on mathematics, mechanics, or technology. And F. Lot says that medieval Christendom inherited from the ancients nothing more than a collection of prescriptions, and a very incomplete one at that. It is thus only natural to take as the starting point of the present study the fact that the Romans displayed this sterile attitude in matters of science, and that the classical Latin culture was therefore unable to link up with the world of pure speculation existing in the Alexandrian schools. Almost the only curiosity shown by pagan Rome toward Greece and the Orient was directed either to religious questions or to utilitarian matters, consonant with the attitude toward life that characterized the Roman people. We might say that the purely speculative and scientific outlook required a different atmosphere, which they were unable to provide. But it must not be forgotten that Rome fulfilled another function, as ruler of the nations—*Tu regere populos, romane, imperio memento,* in the words of the poet—and that it was that political function which, by guaranteeing durable peace, made possible the scientific atmosphere of Alexandria, at the opposite cultural pole from its political metropolis.

The fact remains that Europe in the early Middle Ages was seriously deficient in scientific culture, this being one of the more regrettable features it inherited from pagan Rome. Consequently, when a handful of Western scholars, such as Cassiodorus, St. Isidore of Seville, Rhabano Mauro, and the Venerable Bede attempted, at the dawn of the medieval period, to rescue the remnants of learning that had survived the barbaric deluge, the only scientific information they could assemble was of very poor quality, because they preferred to draw upon Latin sources and were almost completely out of touch with the genuine scientific traditions of Alexandria. Several centuries, indeed, were to elapse before that genuine tradition fertilized the virgin soil of medieval European thought, and when it did so, the contact was made through translations of Oriental and above all of Arab origin, which, after serving as a medium for the transmission of Greek, Persian, and Indian original material—to which they sometimes added a great deal—were translated in their turn into Latin or one of the Romance languages.

II. ARAB CULTURE AS THE CONTINUATOR AND INTEGRATOR OF THE SCIENTIFIC CULTURE OF ALEXANDRIA

Whereas, as we have seen, the Latin cultural tradition shows a cleavage, a failure to connect up with the great current of scientific knowledge that flowed from Alexandria, the Alexandrian culture was zealously preserved, commentated, and amplified by the same Eastern peoples who had originally helped to build it up, but who—more particularly since the seventh century—had ceased to use Greek as their learned language and now employed either Arabic, the tongue of a young political power that was carrying all before it, Syrian, or sometimes Hebrew. It is a recognized fact that between the sixth and eighth centuries the Greek tradition steadily ebbed away from the Semitic-Hamitic world of the Near and Middle East. Constantine's intention in founding Constantinople had been to create another Alexandria, which should draw the Eastern peoples into the Empire; but that intention failed. Those Oriental nations—Arameans and Syrians, Palestinians and Egyptians—had been subjected to powerful Greek influences ever since the time of Alexander; but now, under the rule of Byzantium, frequent social and spiritual friction arose between them and the metropolis, so that they gradually shook off their Greek customs and the ancient Semitic languages were revived as the media of culture. First came Syrian and afterward Arabic, into which practically all the scientific attainments of Alexandrian culture had to be translated.

This means that, at least in the scientific sphere, we find no opposition between Greek and Arab; on the contrary, one gradually replaces the other. By about the beginning of the sixth century, or perhaps even a little earlier, the School of Alexandria had been entirely converted to Christianity, and its last survivors were the principal instructors of the Syrians, the Persians, and ultimately the Moslems in scientific matters. Contact between the culture of Alexandria and the Middle Eastern peoples was established chiefly by the learned men who emigrated eastward, retreating from the religious disputes that raged in Byzantium: in the year 489 the Emperor Zeno closed the flourishing school kept at Edessa by the Nestorians, who sought refuge with the Sassanid Persians and added their numbers to the famous school of Jundisapur. In 529, Justinian closed the Neo-Platonic Academy of Athens, and the result was a further exodus of Greek scholars to Persia. The Middle East, far beyond the ancient *limes* of the Roman or Byzantine empires, was thirsting for culture; the emigrants received an eager welcome, and the scientific seed they brought with them fell on good soil. The work of translating from the Greek, which was usually undertaken by Nestorian or Monophysite Syrians, began immediately after this. At first the translations were made from Greek into Syrian. One of the principal translators during this phase was Sergios of Resaina (d. 539), a Monophysite whose translations included philosophical and medical works—Plato (?), Aristotle, Porphyry, Dionysius the Areopagite, and Galen—and who also wrote original works in Syrian, dealing with logic, the influence of the moon, and probably a study of Geoponics. Among other Syrian writers and translators during this period were Severo Sebokt and Paul the Persian. The latter was in correspondence with the great Persian Emperor Nushirwan (reigned 531-579), under whom the scientific activity of the celebrated school of Jundisapur reached its zenith, achieving a synthesis between Greek science and fresh contributions from India and Persia. Although there has been some controversy among critics as to the importance of these first Syrian translations, there can be no doubt as to their decisive influence upon subsequent Arabic translations. H. Geon has recently pointed out the great interest of these centers of Syrian activity at Edessa, Nisibis, and Jundisapur and has shown that the Syrian translators created a whole philosophic and scientific terminology that afterward helped the work of those who translated into Arabic.

The Jewish element, which had attained so much importance in Alexandria, also continued to make itself felt in the Middle East. Although as a result of the disasters by which they had been smitten—the capture of Jerusalem by Titus (A.D. 70) and the conclusion of the war waged by Bar-cochba (A.D. 135)—the Jews were uprooted from their country, it is an undoubted fact that in Galilee, and even more in Babylonia, they continued to uphold their religious and cultural traditions. So we need not be astonished at the emergence in the sixth century—not in the ninth or tenth, as was thought at one time —of Asaph the physician, who may have had some connection with the school of Jundisapur. In his book of medicine, which is certainly the most ancient to have been compiled in the Hebrew tongue, he speaks of embryology, physiology, pathology, hygiene, pharmacology, and antidotes, accompanying all this with references to the Aphorisms of Hippocrates and to the Hippocratic oath, besides giving a medical calendar with allusions to the Persian months. Dr. S. Muntner, who has made a special study of Asaph's work, maintains that parts of it are very ancient and may have been written in the second or third century A.D.—for instance, the translation of the Aphorisms of Hippocrates and the physician's oath, and the references to Greek scholars (such as Dioscorides) and to Syrian and Persian authors.

We thus see that about the sixth and seventh centuries there were in the Middle East various centers of scientific culture in which the material inherited from Greece, augmented by or amalgamated with Persian and Indian contributions, was being translated into Syrian, Hebrew, or Pahlavi. The heirs to these earliest translators were the Arabs who, first under the Ommayads and to an increasing extent under their successors, the Abbassids, succeeded in generating a magnificent atmosphere of scientific culture in Bagdad, which, during the time of the Caliphs, was a veritable *Dar al-ulum,* or House of Learning. Bagdad was the true successor to Alexandria, with the additional feature that Alexandrian science was there coupled with the Persian and Indian scientific tradition, and was splendidly enhanced over a long period—especially in the ninth and tenth centuries—by fresh scientific study and observation.

It was the second of the Abbassid Caliphs, al-Mansûr (754-775), who gave the first impetus to this brilliant scientific movement among the Arabs. Moreover, being an invalid, he sent for the Nestorian physicians from the famous clinical school at Jundisapur, and from that time onward the Ibn Bajtya-su family represented and exerted at Bagdad the scientific influence they had formerly possessed at Jundisapur. Related to it was another Christian family, that of Hunayn ben Ishaq, in whose hands the work of translating from Greek into Arab developed to the fullest extent. Another group of translators from Greek into Arabic was formed by two Syrians still under the immediate influence of Byzantium, Qusta ben Luqa, a Christian, and the learned Tabit ben Qurra. It is evident that these translators, though many of them were of Syrian origin, were translating direct from Greek into Arabic, although on points of technique and scientific terminology they had the benefit of the early Syrian translations to which we have already referred.

Greek did not, however, provide the only source of Arab translations and commentaries. At first, during the reign of the Caliph al-Mansûr, the majority of translations were taken from Hindu and Persian works; especially on the subjects of astronomy and mathematics, these latter preceded what came from the Greek. Persian writers, sometimes with the assistance of some Jewish scholar, made Arabic translations or summaries of writings on astronomy, algebra, and didactics, which were flourishing branches of study in the Indus valley; and since they traveled westward through Persia, it came about that a considerable amount of scientific writing on these subjects was translated from Pahlavi as well. It is these contributions that give Arab science its special character. Later, in the reign of Caliph Harun al-Rashid (786-809) and his successor al Mamûn (813-833), when the enthusiasm for translating scientific works from the Greek was at its highest pitch, the Oriental learning—astronomy, astrology, mathematics—was fused with the Greek, as can be seen in the works of Muhammad ben Musa al-Jwārizmī. In this way the Arabs, with all the scientific data of earlier civilizations at their disposal, could launch out on their own, correcting and excelling the Greek and Indian writers, testing Ptolemy's Tables, supplementing and improving his Geography, creating a technique and a system of observation incomparably superior to those of the Alexandrians and, in fact, raising their scientific culture to a level that places it among the most illustrious monuments of human progress. Here I cannot refrain from quoting an opinion that carries all the weight conferred upon it by the authority and objectivity of Prof. A. C. Nallino, the historian: "Some of the Arab lists of fixed stars were no mere copy of Ptolemy's list, but had an importance of their own; ultimately the Arabs proudly outdistanced their Greek predecessors by their use of trigonometric formulae, the quantity and quality of their instruments, and their technique of observation. There is the greatest contrast between Greek and Islamic astronomy, both in the number of observations made and in the continuity and accuracy of those observations." Botany, agriculture, and the knowledge of medicinal herbs were all vastly developed in the hands of the Arab writers; their passion for herbalizing drove the Arab botanists and pharmacologists across every frontier within reach, while the alchemists' experiments laid the foundations of present-day chemistry.

In an atmosphere so pervaded by scientific fervor as that of Abbassid Bagdad and other Islamic cities, translators from Greek, Hindu, or Pahlavi into Arabic must have reached a standard of the highest fidelity and accuracy. We know that one translator made special journeys in order to procure various manuscripts of the work he was to translate. And although these translations, like others made in the Middle Ages, have the defect of being so literal that they sometimes become obscure or even unintelligible, we cannot agree with Renan's unfavorable opinion of them. In our own day the great conscientiousness and accuracy of the Arabic and Jewish translators have been vindicated by the eminent authority of Prof. H. A. Wolfson. Moreover, it must be recognized that thanks to these Oriental translations we not only possess evidence of unquestioned importance to the bibliographical history of the original texts and for the preparation of critical editions of them, but that works of the classical period whose originals have been lost have been preserved for us in their Arabic or Hebrew versions.

III. ARAB AND CHRISTIAN SPAIN AS A CULTURAL MEETING
    POINT BETWEEN ORIENT AND OCCIDENT

How did Western, Christian Europe come to know of this vast body of scientific work, built up in the Arab world thanks to the generous patronage of the first Abbassid Caliphs, and in which the scientific heritage of Greece was preserved and increased, side by side with that of India and Persia? If the Roman Empire could endow the nascent Middle Ages with only a meager and defective stock of scientific knowledge, how was medieval Europe to enrich itself with the scientific culture accumulated by the Arabs, far away in the Middle East? This felicitous cultural contact, which was to fertilize the rest of Europe, could only be made through the two Mediterranean peninsulas, Spain and Italy—more especially the former—which served as cultural meeting points between the Eastern and Western worlds.

It is an undoubted fact that by the end of the classical period certain Mediterranean cities, such as Marseilles, had colonies of Eastern merchants known by the generic name of "Syrians," who were able to serve as intermediaries between East and West; it is thought, in particular, that they brought to Europe the secret of various industrial processes, such as the *Compositiones ad tingenda,* which have come down to us in the celebrated manuscript 490 *Lucensis,* and in which Berthelot discerns a probable Oriental or Byzantine influence. But this contribution, which may be regarded as anterior to the great wave of Arabic translation, was very slight and forms an exception. Neither do the few translations made from the Greek by Irish writers, such as Johannes Scotus Erigena, working for the Court of Charles the Bald, have any interest for us, since they were not only few in number but dealt more with theology and philosophy than with the natural sciences.

Spain, the westernmost of the two Mediterranean peninsulas, was at this time—from the ninth to the eleventh centuries—very largely under Moslem control, and thus inevitably became the main channel of transmission through which the first translations—representatives of the Eastern scientific world—reached Christian Europe during the early Middle Ages. And there is no doubt that the advance guard of these translations, made in Spain from Arabic and Hebrew works, arrived on the scene much earlier than was at one time supposed. E. Renan, speaking of what is known as the Toledo School of translators, which flourished in the first half of the twelfth century, declares that the appearance of the translations it produced divided the cultural history of Europe into two parts; "in the first of these, the human mind had no other food for its curiosity than the poor vestiges of the teaching of the Roman schools, assembled in the compilations made by Marciano Capello, Bede, and St. Isidore and in a few technical treatises which had been saved from oblivion by their practical utility. In the second period the science of the ancients returned to the West in a more complete form, in Arabic commentaries or in the original works themselves." The dividing line must, of course, be pushed a great deal further back— by almost a century and a half, since it was really at the end of the tenth century that the first Oriental translations made in Spain, generally from Arabic into Latin, began to fertilize Western thought. In the early period they were few in number and practical in character, dealing with mathematics and astronomy; later came philosophical treatises; and the wave of translations reached its peak with the so-called Toledo School. In any case the dividing line came before this, and the late tenth and early eleventh centuries should be regarded as the dawn of a day that reached its brilliant noontide in the twelfth century.

To appreciate this to the full, we must bear in mind the position occupied in the cultural sphere by Arab and Christian Spain during the tenth century—a period so much decried by historians as one of darkness and the sword, of terror and death in Christian Europe. Arab Spain formed a magnificent contrast to the decadence that marked Europe under the last descendants of Charlemagne, for with Abderrahman III (912-961) there began the Emirate that was to rival and surpass the declining Abbassid Caliphate. That great emir was the arbiter of the destinies of almost all Spain and the western Mediterranean; he spared no pains to further the progress of literature, science, and art in al-Andalus, and extended his protection to students of the sciences, whom he defended against the bigoted hostility of the *Alfaquïe* obscurantists. It is typical of the cultural policy initiated by this Emir of Cordova that when seeking an alliance with the Byzantine Emperor Constantine VII Porphyrogenitus (905-959) he took as the greatest proof of the latter's friendship his gift of a magnificent manuscript of the work on medicinal herbs, Περί ὕλης ἰατριχῆς, by the celebrated Dioscorides of Anazarbos, written in letters of gold and adorned with exquisite paintings of the plants described. Nicolas, a Greek monk, was entrusted with the task of translating a great part of the Greek text into Latin, while the Emir's own minister and physician, the Jewish scholar Hasday ibn Saprut, undertook to translate Nicolas's Latin version into Arabic. The ancient Arabic translation of the famous work of Dioscorides, made by Hunayn ben Ishaq, was thus perfected and supplemented in al-Andalus, the difficult task of identifying the various plants being facilitated by providing alternative lists of names for different countries.

The generous patronage of the first Emir of Cordova was continued and even augmented by his son and successor, Al-Hakam II, who arranged the palace library, which reached a total of 400,000 volumes with a catalog that filled forty-four fifty-page registers. This second Emir of Cordova had such a passion for books that he maintained agents in all the cultural centers of the Middle East—Bagdad, Damascus, Cairo, and so forth—to buy the latest works of literature for him, and sometimes paid exorbitant sums for the first copies, so that a work might become known in Spain even before it was circulated in the East. The encouragement of culture thus exemplified by the earliest emirs was imitated by the aristoc-racy and other magnates and later by the Arab rulers in many other parts of Spain, more especially Saragossa, Toledo, Valencia, and Seville. Thus it was that in Arab Spain during the second half of the tenth century and throughout the elev-enth century, a number of the local courts were the centers of an intense scientific activity, while Cordova itself, under its emirs, may justly be described as the true heir to the role hitherto played in the scientific world, with such exemplary success, by Abbassid Bagdad, which was now beginning to decline. For at Cordova during the latter half of the tenth century there arose schools of scientists, mathematicians, astronomers, physicians, and botanists who not only elucidated the writings of the Eastern Arabs but wrote commentaries on them, compared them, and added to them. In astronomy they zealously observed the movement of the stars with the help of carefully constructed astrolabes and quadrants, while in medicine, botany, and agriculture they continued to make experiments and to import plants and acclimatize them in the botanical gardens created thanks to the munificence of the rulers. Cordova, for instance, was the home of the great astronomer Abū-l-Qāsim Maslama al-Mayrītī (d. circa 1007), of whom we know that as well as becoming the foremost mathematician of his day in Spain, he was skilled in the technique of astronomical observations, corrected and adapted the Astronomic Tables of Muhammad ben Mūsa al-Jwārizmī, and founded a most distinguished school of astronomers. Nor is it surprising to find at Toledo, in the latter half of the eleventh century, a group of astronomers and observers, in-cluding Ibn Sā'id and Azarquiel, to whom we owe the cele-brated *Tablas Toledanas* and other large-scale astronomical works. And Toledo also included among its citizens at the very same time Ibn Wāfid, a physician and pharmacologist of outstanding importance, and Ibn Bassāl, the author of a noteworthy book on agriculture.

This being so, and Arab Spain, at the end of the tenth century and throughout the eleventh and twelfth centuries, being distinguished for its atmosphere of keen scientific enthusiasm, we come to the question of whether something of that atmosphere spread to the Christian region. Until recently little or nothing was known on this subject, but it has lately been shown that in the second half of the tenth century the first fruits, as it were, of Arab science did begin to make their appearance among the Christian population of the peninsula; and these earliest translations from Arabic into Latin heralded the period of Oriental translations that continued through a great part of the Middle Ages. For the sake of clarity, I propose to divide the period into centuries, indicating for each century the different groups from which translations proceeded in large or small numbers.

IV. THE TENTH CENTURY—FIRST TRANSLATIONS FROM ARABIC INTO LATIN

A. *Translations made at the Monastery of Santa Maria de Ripoll (Catalonia)*

The cultural and scientific blossoming of Moslem Spain did not leave the Christians indifferent or inattentive. It should not be imagined that the Arab and Christian communities in Spain were like two entirely separate and contrasting worlds. Within Islamic Spain lived considerable numbers of Christians, known as Mozarabs, whose culture was closely related to that of the Moslems. We know that their enthusiasm for the Arab language and poetry was such that it became a danger to the Latin tradition. We know that in the year 961, Bishop Recemundo, also known as 'Arīb ibn Sa'd, drew up a calendar in Arabic, largely based on Arab astronomy and meteorology. Even the Christians who lived outside the frontiers of the emirate managed to remain on good terms with Cordova, which the nun Hroswitha declared to be the jewel of the world. The prestige of Cordova's power, culture, and art was tremendous even in the small, independent Christian states in the north of the peninsula. At the request of the Emir al-Hakam II, a certain Bishop of Gerona, Gotmar, wrote a *Historia de los reyes francos,* which has come down to us as part of a book by al-Mas 'ūdī entitled *Las Praderas de Oro (The Golden Meadows).* During the reign of this emir, delegations sent by the independent states, from Barcelona to León, were constantly visiting Cordova to conclude peace treaties, and many of them included bishops and abbots, who must have taken a keen interest in the scientific culture so brilliantly displayed by Cordova. And it is not surprising that they should have secured Latin translations, made by bilingual Mozarabs or perhaps by Jews, of some of the treatises on geometry and arithmetic, studies so necessary to the correct reckoning of funds, or of some work on the astrolabe or the quadrant, instruments so indispensable for taking the altitude of the sun and stars, telling the time, and measuring height or depth.

At all events, the Monastery of Santa Maria de Ripoll, an illustrious house of Benedictines at the foot of the Pyrenees —patronized by the Counts of Barcelona and Gerona, equipped from the first with a valuable *scriptorium* and library—was the first Christian cultural center recorded as having produced a series of translations of scientific works from Arabic into Latin, in the middle years of the tenth century. These translations have come down to us in a manuscript, No. 225 of the collection of Ripoll manuscripts, now preserved in the Royal Archives of Aragon; to judge by the writing, it dates from the end of the tenth century. This manuscript constitutes a *corpus* of treatises on natural science, arithmetic, geometry, astronomy, and computation for the use of the scholars in the monastery itself. A considerable proportion of these miscellaneous treatises are translations from Arabic into Latin—including several treatises on mathematics, instrumental astronomy, clockwork, and similar subjects. I shall never forget the emotion I felt at my first sight of this venerable manuscript, of such importance to the history of scientific culture in Christian Europe, since it preceded by more than a century the main body of translations from Arabic into Latin. Moreover, this miscellaneous manuscript is a copy of a still older one, so that the Latin translations it contains go back to the middle of the tenth century. This explains why they are given anonymously, in fragmentary form, not even the translator's name being mentioned. Some of them show every sign of having been translated direct from the Arabic; the style itself reveals as much, and they are scattered with Arabic words, spelled phonetically according to the pronunciation of that language in Spain. Other translations, however, are written in a more careful Latin style; they are less word for word, less flavored by the original Arabic, and would appear to be revised versions of direct translations, amended to make them more intelligible to the ordinary reader. In some cases, too, there is a foreword by the translator or compiler, written in a polished style that reveals classical influence, and in marked contrast to that of the work itself.

These translations are of such importance that I shall go into some detail about them, in order to relate them to their Arabic originals and show the connection between the two. The following is a concise list of the translations from the Arabic included in the Ripoll manuscript No. 225, the different treatises being indicated by the method of notation first employed in Bubnov's time:

Demensura astrolabii (*h'*)—(Fol. Iv.-10 r). Literary introduction and revised version, written with due regard for style, of a direct translation (*h"*) from an Arabic original—probably the first part of the work by Mā-sā-Al-lāh, on the construction of the astrolabe.

De utilitatibus astrolabii (*J*)—(Fols. Ir-Iv, 10 v.—17 v., 18 r-20 r, 23 v.-24 v). The Ripoll ms. 225 includes more than half of this text, *J,* published by Pez, Migne, and Bubnov and sometimes attributed to the celebrated Gerbert. It is a well-written revision of a direct translation from the Arabic (*J'*), and probably represents the second part of the work by Mā-sā-Al-lāh, on the use of the astrolabe.

Geometria incerti auctoris—(Fol. 20 r.23 r.). Only a few chapters of this typical *Geometry* are given; they are written in an unpretentious style and present problems of the measurement of heights and distances, with the use of the astrolabe, the geometrical square, mirrors, etc., which were undoubtedly derived and extracted from a treatise of Arab origin, *De operatione vel utilitatibus astrolabii.*

De mensura astrolapsus (*h"*)—(Fol. 23 r-23 v). Short fragment of a direct translation (*h"*) from the Arabic, probably corresponding to the first part of Mā-sā-Al-lāh's work, on the construction of the astrolabe.

Astrolabii sententiae (*J'*) *A*—(Fol. 24 v.-25 v.). Foreword, in literary style, to a treatise on the use of the astrolabe; related to Chapter 1 of text *J*.

De nominibus laborum laboratorum in ipsa tabula (*J'*) *B*— (Fol. 25 v.-30 v.). Explanation and terminology of the different parts of the planispherical astrolabe; written in the very simple style characteristic of direct translations from the Arabic. Related to Chap. II of *J*, of which it may well be the source, and probably derived from Chap. I of the second part of Mā-sā-Al-lāh's work, on the use of the astrolabe.

Capitula horologii Regis Ptolomei (*J'*) *C*—(Fol. 30 v.- 35 r.). Explanation of the operations that can be carried out with the astrolabe; in this manuscript the text is abridged and written in the simple style characteristic of direct translations from the Arabic. Related to *J*, of which it may well be the source, and probably derived from the second part of the above-mentioned work by Mā-sā-Al-lāh.

De horologie secundum alkoram (*J'a*)—(Fol. 17 v.-18 r.). The Ripoll ms. contains only one chapter of this text on the spherical astrolabe; it describes some of the operations which can be effected with that instrument.

Regulae de quarta parte astrolabii (*J"*)—(Fol. 35 r.-38 r.). Explanation, written in a simple style characteristic of direct translations from the Arabic, of certain applications of the slide quadrant; this text has some relationship to a problem in the above-mentioned *Geometria incerti auctoris,* or with its Arabic source.

De astrolabii compositione (*h"'*)—(Fol. 65 v-84 v.). Written in a style that is, for the most part, diffuse and artificial, this manuscript gives a description, rather than an explanation, of the art of constructing astrolabes; it is a revised or adapted version of passages of *J' h'* and *J'* made by a compiler who had no great understanding of Arab technique. Certain chapters, such as that entitled *De astrolabio quadrato,* correspond to gaps in text *J*.

Descripcion de un aparato de relojeria—(Fol. 87 v-93 r.). Abridged text, which is perhaps not of Arab origin.

Descripción de un gnomon—(Fol. 94 r-97 r.). Corresponds to the duration of the longest day for the climate V, in Chap. XVIII of the *Liber de utilitatibus astrolabii* (*J*).

De divisione igitur climatum quae fit per almucantarath— (Fol. 98 r-102 v.). Abridged text, related to *J"*; it also describes some applications of the astrolabe and the right-angled triangle in geodesy, which have a certain relationship to problems in the *Geometria incerti auctoris.*

We thus see that most of the translations preserved in this Ripoll ms. deal either with geometry or with astronomical instruments. Although in some cases it has been possible to deduce from what original Arab work the translations and the later revisions were taken, we do not know the identity of the pioneer translator. As already pointed out, the text *J,* which is a careful revision of *J',* became very celebrated and has been printed under the name of Gerbert. But this hypothesis must be dismissed, because the Ripoll copy is slightly the earlier and comes from a different original. We believe, however, that Gerbert was in touch with the Ripoll monastery, and he may very well have made use of these Oriental translations and have made them known to scholars in France and Italy when he subsequently returned to those countries. The Oriental translations in the manuscripts of the Ripoll *scriptorium* help to explain the case of Gerbert, the *Gerbert's Frage*—to account for the prestige he enjoyed, the reputation, as something not far short of a magician, that grew up around the *Scholasticus* of Rheims and tutor to the family of the Emperor Otto I; this prestige is perhaps simply the result of the stupefaction induced in his pupils, at Rheims and in Italy, by the new learning from the East—arithmetic, geometry, and astronomy—which Gerbert had acquired during his sojourn in the *Marca Hispanica.*

We know from the biography of Gerbert by his disciple, the monk Richer, that in 967, while still a young novice in Aurillac he was put into the care of Borrell II, Count of Barcelona, to be taught the liberal arts; the count entrusted the youth to Atton, Bishop of Vich, who taught him chiefly mathematics.

It would appear from what Richer says that Gerbert remained at Vich and in the *Marca Hispanica* for about three years, making great progress in mathematics and music. At the end of the three years, Richer tells us, he was taken to Rome by Count Borrell and Bishop Atton, who presented him to the Pope; and the Pope was so much astonished by young Gerbert's learning that he recommended him to the Emperor. But though Gerbert never went back to the *Marca Hispanica,* he did not forget the friends he had made there. From Rheims, and later from the Abbey of Bobbio, he kept up a correspondence with a number of them. Among his collected letters are a number addressed to men of distinction in the cultural life of Catalonia, written in affectionate terms and sometimes asking them to send him scientific works—a point that interests us more particularly. In Letter No. 24, addressed to a certain Lupito Barchinonensi, he says *Itaque librum de astrologia translatum a te mihi petente dirige* . . . What was this work on astronomy that "Lupitus" had translated—undoubtedly from the Arabic? We cannot identify "Lupitus" himself with any certainty, for there were several people of that name in Catalonia at about this time. It is thought, however, that Gerbert was probably referring to various astronomical treatises derived from the Arabic, which we have already come across in the Ripoll manuscript 225. In letter No. 17, which is probably of a slightly earlier date and is addressed to Giraldus of Aurillac, and in letter No. 25, to Miro Bonfill, Bishop of Gerona, Gerbert is particularly eager to have sent to him at Rheims a work on the multiplication and division of numbers brought out by *Joseph hispanus: De multiplicatione et divisione numerorum libellum a Joseph ispano editum* . . . This must obviously have been taken from the classic work on arithmetic by Muhammad ben Musa al-Jwārizmī, which had by then—though, as we shall see, only recently—become known in Christian Spain, and which uses Arabic figures for its calculations. There has been considerable speculation as to the identity of this *Joseph hispanus,* who probably made the Latin translation from the original Arabic text; it is thought that he must have been either a Mozarab or a Spanish Jew.

From all this we see how Gerbert profited by the Oriental learning—first of Vich, with Bishop Atton, and doubtless in the *scriptorium* of Ripoll, which is so close to Vich; and later, at Bobbio and Rheims, when he got his friends in the *Marca Hispanica* to send him scientific works translated from Oriental sources. He thus seems to have been the first ambassador who carried this new Arab science across the Pyrenees; to it he owed his great scientific reputation; he taught it to his numerous disciples, especially at Rheims, and they introduced it to learned circles in Lorraine, which soon showed signs of having been initiated into the new techniques of mathematics and astronomy.

To make clear the full importance of these early, not to say precocious, translations from the Arabic, it should be added that at this period—during the second half of the tenth century and first half of the eleventh—everything that bore

the stamp of the great Spanish-Arabic culture was in vogue
among independent Christians on both sides of the Pyrenees.
Many of the Latin manuscripts produced at this time in the
most renowned monasteries of Spain contain miniatures that
reflect Mozarab taste; in the margins of some of them are
Arabic notes, indicating the Mozarab origin of the manuscripts themselves. It is of interest to our present subject to
note that two venerable Spanish manuscripts—the *Albelden-
se,* written in the year 976, and the analogous *Emilianense,*
written in 992—use the new Arabic figures, in the *gobari*
form, giving an explanation of their Indian origin and pointing out how admirable they are for arithmetical purposes.
This shows that Christian Spain was already being initiated
into the new, Arab arithmetic, the fullest description of which
was to be found in the classic work by Al-Jwārizmī.

B. *Other translations—the "Mathematica Alhandrei summi
    astrologi"*

Another translation of Oriental—Arabic and Hebrew—
source material is the "Mathematica Alhandrei summi as-
trologi," which appears in manuscripts at the end of the tenth
century and during the eleventh, sometimes in conjunction
with texts belonging to an earlier group, such as *J* and *J'*.
Though never printed, this work has been the subject of
several studies. Unlike its predecessors it is astrological rather
than astronomical in character, and shows Hebrew as well as
Arabic influences.

This work begins by describing the astrological qualities of
the planets and giving the Hebrew names for them and for the
twelve signs of the zodiac: *Ordo planetarum iuxta naturam et
nomina eorum secundum hebreos.* It goes on to speak of the
courses of the planets and of the various theories as to
whether each has its own sphere or whether there is only one
for all of them. It classifies the twelve signs of the zodiac according to the four climates and the four elements existing
in the world, saying that while the qualities of the signs of
the zodiac decide the fate of all human beings, those qualities
themselves are determined by the four elements and the four
cardinal points. These relationships are illustrated by a figure
*"quam supra hanc artem Alexander Macedo composuit dili-
gentissime,"* while other figures show the twenty-seven lunar

houses, the Arabic names of which are given—in a transcription from which it is clear that they were pronounced with a Spanish-Arabic accent—and their relation to the signs of the zodiac. It may be that this attempt at correlation is derived from Al-Kindi's work, *"De pluviis, imbribus et ventis,"* and that the name *Alhandreus* is a corruption of *Alchindus*. Next comes the *Epistola de Argafalaus a Alejandro*, which seems to be of Eastern origin; whereas the *Epistola de Phetosiri a Nechepso*, which follows it, derives unmistakably from a classical source and other parts of the work seem to combine both influences, classical and Oriental. This treatise had a considerable influence throughout the Middle Ages, and was handed on into the Renaissance period.

V. Eleventh Century—Diffusion of Earlier Translations in the Form of Copies and Adaptations—the Case of Hermann Contractus

It is an established fact that the translations from the Arabic we meet for the first time in the *scriptorium* of the monastery at Ripoll spread rapidly throughout Europe. This is easily accounted for by the fact that the great medieval monasteries were in constant touch with one another. It is also supposed, as already mentioned, that Gerbert contributed to this early circulation of such translations. It is thus not surprising to find in the great European libraries—particularly the Vatican Library, the Bibliothèque Nationale in Paris, and the British Museum—a number of eleventh-century manuscripts that include some of the translations we first met with at Ripoll. The new science, the method of calculation expounded by al-Jwārizmī, with its figures or ciphers, was destined to drive out, little by little, the archaic system of the abacus; the new astronomical instruments and the new tables were greeted with universal and well-deserved enthusiasm, and Christian Europe gradually advanced along the "royal road" of true science. As we have seen already, various centers of learning, such as those in Lorraine, which had reaped the cultural harvest from the seed sown by Gerbert at Rheims, revealed at an early stage—in the middle of the eleventh century—a certain familiarity with the new scientific doctrines and techniques.

On the other hand, it still seems rather extraordinary that at this period there should have appeared at the monastery of Reichenau, far away in the depths of its Carinthian valley, a crippled monk named Hermann Contractus (1013-1054), who distinguished himself by no less a feat than the writing of a treatise on the construction and use of the astrolabe. Critics were baffled for a long time by his two works, on the construction (*De mensura*) of the astrolabe and on its applications or uses (*De utilitatibus*). How could the paralytic Hermann have translated or adapted them from the Arabic? Who could have helped him in this task at the Reichenau monastery, which lay so far off the beaten track of Arab culture? Nowadays there is a satisfactory explanation to account for the case of Hermann Contractus. The text on the use of the astrolabe is the *J* text, of which Hermann is in no sense the author, since it existed almost a century earlier in the Ripoll ms. No. 225. As for the short work on the structure of the astrolabe (*De mensura astrolabii*), it is an *h* text, derived, like the *h'* and *h' "* texts at Ripoll, from *h"*, the direct translation from the Arabic. Hermann, the monk of Reichenau, having obtained a copy of the Ripoll texts, had simply made a clearer and more literary version of *h"*, which is the basic text, explaining how to construct a planispherical astrolabe.

VI. Constantino Africano and the School of Salerno

Southern Italy, too, joined at this period in the movement that centered on Oriental translations, owing its participation chiefly to a certain Constantino, known as "Africano" because he was born at Carthage. He had traveled in the East for a number of years, and then settled at Montecassino, where he died in 1087. He knew Greek as well as Arabic, so that his translations, which were usually of medical works, acted as a great stimulus to the newly founded School of Medicine at Salerno. His translations and adaptations, of which a number of editions were printed during the Renaissance, included works by Hippocrates and Galen or the pseudo-Galen, with

Commentaries, by Arab writers such as Alī ben Abbās and Ahmad ibn al-Yazzār, and by Jewish authors such as Ishaq Israelí.

VII. Translators Working in the Late Eleventh Century and the First Half of the Twelfth Century

A *Pedro Alfonso and Adelard of Bath*

During the latter part of the eleventh century and the early years of the twelfth, the flow of Oriental translations steadily increased, progressing from the phase of almost complete anonymity to one that included several translators of outstanding individuality. The originator of this new phase is believed to have been a Spanish Jew, Mosé Sefardi, of Huesca, who was converted to Christianity under the name of Pedro Alfonso. He is typical of many translators of Jewish descent who worked in the Middle Ages, all of whom made excellent intermediaries between cultures so dissimilar as those of the Orient and the Latin West. Pedro Alfonso owes his celebrity to his *Disciplina Clericalis,* which introduced the Oriental apologue and paremiologia to the West for the first time.

Quite apart from this great didactic work, however, Pedro Alfonso interests us as the translator of scientific writings from Arabic into Latin. Pedro Alfonso was a man of varied and encyclopedic learning, which ranged from theology to astronomy and medicine; it was as a physician that he visited the court of Henry I of England, about the year 1110. There he made the acquaintance of a number of scholars who were studying the new sciences of mathematics and astronomy. One of these was Walcher of Malvern, a clerk who had originally come from Lorraine, the country where Gerbert's erudition had penetrated with such effect. Walcher had first traveled in Italy and then gone to England, where he was made Prior of Malvern Abbey and developed a passion for astronomy, especially for the new instruments derived from the Arabs,

with which he successfully observed several eclipses. Somewhere about the year 1120, Walcher wrote what he described
as *Sententia Petri Ebrei, cognomento Anphus, de Dracone,
quam dominus Walcherus, prior Malvernensis eccleise, in
latinam transtulit linguam*—though rather than a translation,
Walcher's work was in the nature of an edition or adaptation
of an original work by Pedro Alfonso on the subject of
astronomy. In the Arabic astronomical terminology, which
was influenced by India and Persia, the word *Draco*
(Yawzahar) designates the ascending and declining node of
the moon. And this treatise consists principally of directions
for determining the position of the sun, the moon, and the
ascending and declining nodes, for the purpose of calculating
eclipses. The style of the work is not that of a translation from
the Arabic, but of a revision or adaptation to Walcher's own
purpose, of material taken over from his master, Pedro
Alfonso—*"magister noster Petrus Anfulsus"*; it uses the system of astronomical graduation, deriving from the Arabs,
which was taught by Pedro Alfonso; it refers to his astronomical tables, in relation to those of the celebrated Muhammad
ben Musa al-Jwārizmī—of which we shall speak later—and in
conclusion tells how Walcher put various astronomical problems before his master Pedro Alfonso, and how the latter
solved them. This new science of astronomy, with its complexities and its different chronological systems, seems to
have proved rather confusing to Walcher, and his master
took pains to help him settle his doubts.

Pedro Alfonso also wrote a book on astronomical catalogs
and tables, which he dedicated, in an introduction, to the
scholars and philosophers of France *"omnibus videlicet pery-
pateticis ac aliis philosophico lacte nutritis ubique per Fran-
ciam . . ."* in which he urges them to give up the old teachings
and embrace the new astronomical and medical doctrines
that have come from the East. This introduction is followed
by several chapters or astronomical catalogs, closely similar
to those of al-Jwārizmī. Since the translation of the latter's
book, made from Maslama of Cordova's summary, appears
in several manuscripts under the name of our Pedro Alfonso,
while in others—the majority—it is attributed to Adelard of
Bath, it has been suggested that the two writers may have
collaborated. This would solve various other difficulties, such
as the inclusion of Arabic transcriptions that indicate that
whoever wrote them had a Spanish accent in Arabic; Adelard
of Bath is not known to have visited Spain, so this point

would be most easily explained by the collaboration of Pedro Alfonso. This may have been what happened: in the first place, somewhere about the year 1115, Pedro Alfonso made a kind of adaptation of al-Jwārizmī's work on astronomy, and afterward, in 1126, Adelard of Bath translated the latter, in its abridged version, with the help or collaboration of Pedro Alfonso. This translation of al-Jwārizmī's work is of tremendous importance, for it served to teach the Latin world, once and for all, how to use astronomical tables. It stood supreme until the subsequent appearance of a translation of the famous *Tablas Toledanas.*

Adelard of Bath specialized in mathematical subjects; it is certainly to him that we owe the translation or adaptation of the *Liber Ysagogarum Alchoarismi in artem astronomicam a Magistro A (dhelardi) compositus,* a mathematical work steeped in Arabic and Jewish influences; Adelard also wrote a work on the astrolabe, in accordance with the tradition already known in Europe, and translated the *Elements* of Euclid from the Arabic. His enthusiasm for the theories of the Arab authors is reflected in his original work, *Quaestiones naturales,* which reveals his eagerness to transmit the new learning to his contemporaries. The life of Adelard of Bath shows us the development of a scholar who began as a devotee of the abacus and ended by falling in love with the new methods.

B R. *Abraham bar Hiyya, of Barcelona*

Another writer, also of Jewish descent, who played a great part as a translator at the beginning of the twelfth century was R. Abraham bar Hiyya al-Bargeloni, (i.e. "of Barcelona"). But just as Pedro Alfonso worked for the benefit of the Latin, Christian world, Abraham bar Hiyya's work took two directions. For his Jewish coreligionists of southern France, who knew no Arabic, he translated into Hebrew, in a simple, unvarnished style, the most remarkable of the Arab contributions to mathematics, astronomy, and philosophy; for the Latin world he collaborated with Plato Tiburtinus to produce a great abundance of scientific translations, one from Hebrew and nearly all the rest from Arabic. R. Abraham bar Hiyya thus played a fine, creative role in the young Europe of the early twelfth century and restored

Hebrew to the status of a scientific language, a natural medium of culture, which it had almost entirely surrendered in the centuries when it was overshadowed by the incomparable prestige of Arabic. Abraham bar Hiyya thus exerted a great influence in the Hebrew and Latin cultural fields alike.

Little is known about his life; he seems to have been a native of Barcelona and went by the Arab title of *Sabasorda* and the Hebrew equivalent of *Nasi,* meaning noble, eminent; he also lived in the south of France, in the region of Toulouse and Béziers; and his works were produced in the first half of the twelfth century. In Hebrew he compiled a considerable number of treatises on mathematics, cosmography, and astronomy, and a few of a philosophical and messianic character. The most interesting of all these—most of which are derived entirely from Arab sources—is the *Hibbur ha-měšiha wě-hatišbóret,* or "Treatise upon Geometry and Measurement," not only because it was later translated, in abridged form, into Latin, as we shall see in due course, but because Book III is derived, by way of the Arabic, from a lost work of Euclid, Περί διαιρέσεων βιβλίου. Another interesting item is a kind of cosmographical and astronomical series comprising the works entitled *Sūrat há-ares* (Shape of the World), *Hěshón mahlekot ha-kokabim* (Calculation of the Movements of the Stars), and *Luhot* (Tables), all of which are largely derived from Arabic classics by Al-Fargānī and Al-Bāttānī.

Turning to the Latin translations he helped to produce, we find that nearly all of them are described as being made by Plato Tiburtinus with the collaboration of Bar Hiyya. We have little information about this Plato of Tivoli; his translations appeared for the most part at Barcelona between 1134 and 1145. They have the merit of being some of the earliest Latin translations. A number of them deal with works on astrology, including *De horarum electionibus,* the original of which was by 'Alī ben Ahmad al-Imrāmī, an Oriental writer who flourished in the first half of the tenth century. This translation appears to have been made in the year 1133. *De iudiciis nativitatum,* the translation of a treatise by Abū'Alī al-Jayyāt, a celebrated Oriental astrologer living in the first half of the ninth century, is dated 1136. A few years later a new translation was made by the celebrated Johannes Hispanus. A translation of the *Almansoris Iudicia seu propositiones,* also called *Capitulà stellarum oblata regi magno Sarranorum Alchadam* (*ab*) *Almansore astrologo filio Abrahae iudei,* was made in the same year. The Al-Mansūr in question is probably the famous Yahyà ibn Abī Mansur. This translation was much read, for it went through several editions in the fifteenth, sixteenth, and seventeenth centuries. Works on mathematics included a translation of his Hebrew geometry, entitled *Liber embadorum,* made in 1145; this was one of the principal sources from which Europe drew its knowledge of geometry and trigonometry, and considerably influenced Leonardo Pisano's *Practica Geometrie.* In astronomy he translated Al-Bāttāni's *De motu stellarum;* this had an enormous influence and was printed a number of times. He also translated a treatise on the astrolabe by the Spanish Arab writer Ibn al Saffār (first half of the eleventh century).

C R. *Abraham ibn 'Ezra, of Tudela*

A third name deserves inclusion in this small group of writers who devoted themselves in the first half of the twelfth century to the task of making Arab scientific knowledge available in Hebrew and Latin—and who shared the particular characteristic of working both in Spain and abroad, perhaps to a greater extent abroad, where the need of translations was greater. This third writer was born at Tudela in 1092, and grew up in the brilliant cultural world of Arab and Jewish Spain. Before very long, however, he began to make extensive journeys, becoming a real "wandering Jew"; between 1140 and 1148, at any rate, he visited a number of towns in Italy, then traveled in France, from Béziers and Narbonne to Angers, and went on to England, visiting London and Winchester. He appears to have died in Spain, at Calahorra, in 1167. He was a distinguished and versatile writer who had absorbed all the knowledge available in his day, and a man of great critical judgment; the course of his travels was marked by a considerable output of works in Hebrew on a wide variety of subjects, the general effect of which was to convey a knowledge of the new sciences— mathematics, astronomy, philology—to the Jewish communities of Europe. Here his influence followed that of Abraham bar Hiyya, but went much further.

The scientific influence of R. Abraham ibn 'Ezra was not confined to the Jewish population, however, but extended to the Christian community as well. In other words he wrote in Latin as well as in Hebrew. He was obliged, of course, to know

Latin for the purposes of his European travels, and in that language—writing in the straightforward style appropriate to his scientific themes—he produced several works on astronomy for Christian readers, among whom they had a notable influence. The most important of these Latin works is the *Fundamenta tabularum,* or "Book of the Fundamentals of Astronomic Tables," written somewhere about 1154, when Ibn 'Ezra was living near Dreux, in northern France. This is a considerably amplified version of the *Tabulae Pisanae,* the astronomical tables drawn up by the same writer at Pisa some years previously, about the year 1145; the new work is imbued with a keen critical sense and takes great pains to compare the various astronomical systems and seek to account for their differences and discrepancies. Based entirely on Arab sources, it had a considerable influence in Europe. Another work in Latin that was unquestionably written by Abraham ibn 'Ezra is a treatise on the astrolabe, produced in England about the year 1160. Ibn 'Ezra is known to have written a similar work in Hebrew, and there are certain points of resemblance between the Hebrew and Latin versions. It is highly probable, too, that he wrote a short treatise on the almanac in Latin, following the Spanish-Arab tradition.

Ibn 'Ezra's influence in Christian circles was strengthened by the fact that several of his Hebrew works, such as his astrological treatise *Resit hokma,* were translated from Hebrew into French. The French translation of *Resit hokma* was made in 1273 by a Jew named Hagin, at Malines, in the house of Henri de Bates, several Latin versions being subsequently based on it. During the next century the Hebrew text was translated into Catalan and partly retranslated into Latin by Luis de Angulo about the year 1448.

VIII. Latin Translators Who Worked Mainly in the Pyrenees or the Ebro Valley

Almost at the same time as the two last-mentioned Spanish Jewish translators, we find a number of other translators at work who, though not Spaniards, had come to live in the Spanish Pyrenees or the Ebro Valley with the ambition of making translations from Arabic into Latin. They probably secured the help of Spanish interpreters, and they worked as a team or group, keeping in touch with one another and with the Toledo group of which we shall speak later on. Among them was Hermann the Dalmatian, who had studied at Chartres. From 1138 onward he had been living in northern Spain and in Languedoc (1143). As a translator he specialized in astronomy and astrology, his most important work of this kind being a Latin translation of Ptolemy's *Planisphere,* made from the Arabic translation, with commentary, by Maslama of Cordova. Hermann was still in contact with the School of Chartres, however, and kept up a considerable activity as philosopher and apologist; in 1142, while living in León, he wrote two treatises against Islam, and in 1143, at Béziers, he produced his philosophical work *De essentiis.*

One of Hermann's correspondents was Robert Ketenensis, mistakenly called Retinensis; an Englishman, he followed in the footsteps of Adelard of Bath. In 1141 he was living in northern Spain, where he became Archdeacon of Pampeluna; from 1147 onward he lived in London. At the request of Pedro the Venerable, and apparently in collaboration with Hermann the Dalmatian, he translated the Koran (1143); but most of his translations deal with algebra, astronomy, or alchemy. He translated the Algebra of al-Jwārizmī (Segovia, 1145). He also wrote a treatise on the astrolabe, following the traditional lines, and adapted to the meridian of London the Tables of al-Jwārizmī already translated by Adelard of Bath, together with other Tables by al-Battānī and Azarquiel. Considerable influence was likewise exerted by his translations of works on alchemy, such as the *Liber de compositione alchemiae,* attributed to the false Morienus Romanus.

Hermann the Dalmatian had a pupil, Rodolfo de Brujas, who worked chiefly in northeast Spain and Languedoc, and was in correspondence with Johannes Hispanus. He probably helped his master to translate the Arabic version of Ptolemy's *Planisphere* (Toulouse, 1143); for his own part he translated from the Arabic a treatise on the astrolabe attributed to Maslama, which he dedicated to Johannes Hispanus.

A final name linked with this group is that of Hugo Sanctallensis, a Spaniard who made translations from Arabic into Latin under the patronage of Bishop Miguel of Tarazona (1119-1151). Hugo's translations dealt chiefly with astronomy, astrology, geomancy, spatulamancy, and alchemy, and his version of the celebrated *Emerald Table* had a great influence; he translated 'Abd-al-Karīm ibn al-Mutannà's commentary on the same astronomic Tables of al-Jwārizmī—which is of great interest because the Arabic originals have been lost.

IX. THE TOLEDO GROUP OF TRANSLATORS

This group marks the zenith of the period of translation from Eastern sources into Latin. Since the days of A. Jourdain and V. Rose this group has been known as the Toledo School of translators. Strictly speaking, however, the word "School" should not be used in the sense of a college or corporate body, for these Toledan translators were simply a group or team, like the others we have mentioned, though perhaps in their case the group was more compact and its output more continuous.

To appreciate the full importance of the Toledan translations from the Arabic, we must bear in mind what Toledo was like in the first half, or rather the second third, of the twelfth century. The strong Mozarabic atmosphere prevailing at the time of the Reconquest had been succeeded by the powerful influence of the Romanizing, Cluniac, Francophile element. This is evidenced by the attitude of the first Bishops of Toledo and the substitution of the Roman for the Mozarab liturgy. The Mozarab element remained strong, however, supported as it was by relations with southern Spain. Even well into the thirteenth century the Christians and Jews of Toledo were using Arabic for a good deal of their private writing, and it was probably due to this combination of interests between the Mozarabs and Jews of the city, who were bilingual and familiar with the secrets of Arab science, and the prelates who, for all their foreign influence, were eager to master that new science, that Toledo became such a flourishing center of translations. The cultural movement thus established had the support of the bishops of Toledo—and not merely of the celebrated Don Raimundo (1126-1151).

Taking these Toledan translators in chronological order, we come first to *Johannes Hispanus,* or *Hispanensis,* or *Hispalensis,* or *Lunensis,* known since the time of A. Jourdain as *Johannes Avendaud* and believed to be a converted Jew. In the last few years, however, a considerable controversy has developed around the personality of this translator. Father M. Alonso, S. J., divides him into two writers; one, whom he calls Juan Sevillano, concerned chiefly with astronomy and astrology, and another, whom he calls Juan Hispano, who was Avendaud the convert and specialized in philosophy, collaborated with Archdeacon Gundisalvo, and was the author of the *Liber de causis,* the *Liber de causis primis et secundis,* and a *Tractatus de anima;* this convert, according to Father Alonso, was Bishop Juan of Segovia from 1149 to 1152, and Archbishop of Toledo from 1152 to 1166. This view is contrasted with another, upheld chiefly by Mlle M. T. d'Alverny, according to which, and having regard to the fact, already pointed out by L. Thorndike, that the names *Johannes Hispanus* and *Avendaud* never occur together in any manuscript, the *Avendaud* or *Avendehut* who appears in the foreword to Avicenna's *De anima* is to be regarded as entirely unconnected with the *Johanni*—not *Johannes*—to whom the work is dedicated, that is to say, Archbishop Juan of Toledo. As for *Avendehut,* Mlle d'Alverny is inclined to follow earlier suggestions by identifying him with the well-known Jewish philosopher and historian of Toledo, Abraham ben David or Daud (d. about 1180), who was neither a convert nor to be identified with any collaborator of Gundisalvo named Johannes.

Recognizing that this is a difficult problem to solve definitively, but that further light in constantly being shed on the subject, we will now list the works attributed to this group or team of translators, whether in the form of original compositions, translations, or adaptations. Under the name of Johannes Hispanus come a number of translations, some of them abridged, of Arab works on astronomy: the "Book on the Movement of the Stars," by al-Farganī; the treatise on the astrolabe, by Maslama, and also, apparently, the treatise on the astrolabe by Masā-Al-lāh. Furthermore, we have already seen that Johannes Hispanus was the author of various original or adapted works on astronomy, such as the *Practica astrolabii,* of astronomic tables and of a clarification of certain doubts concerning the movement of the stars. Some translations of astrological themes have also come down to us, including works by Masā-Al-lāh, Abū Mas'ar, al-Qabīsī, Tābit ibn Qurra, etc. On the subject of arithmetic there is a version of al-Jwārizmī's arithmetic. Translations of works on philosophy sometimes show signs of collaboration with Archdeacon Gundisalvo; this is the case with the translation of the celebrated *Fons Vitae* of Selomo ibn Gebirol, and also, according to some manuscripts, with Algazel's *Maqāsid*. The philosophical translations on which Johannes Hispanus collaborated with Gundisalvo are apparently more faithful and accurate than those that appear under the name of Gundisalvo alone. Another very important translation was that of the *Epistola Aristotelis ad Alexandrum de conservatione corporis humani*, for this work, falsely attributed to Aristotle, marks the introduction of the *Secretum Secretorum* to the West.

As for the literary style of these translations, it must be admitted that the Latin language as employed in certain original works and adaptations by Johannes Hispanus is rather sluggish and ponderous.

Of Domingo Gundisalvo we know that he was Archdeacon of Segovia and was still alive in the year 1190. He wrote several philosophical works in the Neo-Platonic tradition, derived from earlier translations, including *De processione mundi, De unitate, De immortalitate animae*, and *De divisione philosophiae*—the last, based largely on al-Fārābī's *Kitāb ihsà al-ulūm,* had a great influence in the Middle Ages.

As for Avendaut or Ibn Daud—assuming that he and Johannes Hispanus were indeed two different people—he is thought to have contributed to the translation of parts of Avicenna's *Kitāb al-Sifa*, in some of which he may have collaborated with Gundisalvo. We should not leave him without mentioning that Plato Tiburtinus, the collaborator of Abraham bar Hiyya, dedicated his translation of Ibn al-Saffār's Treatise on the astrolabe *"ad amicum suum Johannem David"* and that Rodolfo de Brujas dedicated his translation of Maslama's treatise on the astrolabe to *"dilectissimo suo Johanni David"*; both these translators were working in the first half of the twelfth century, and their friendly relations with Johannes David and the dedication of their two translations seem to corroborate the fact that he, too, as we have seen, devoted himself by preference to astronomical subjects and to that of the astrolabe. There thus seems to be no doubt of the existence, in the first half of the twelfth century, of a Spaniard named Johannes David, or Ibn Daud, who concerned himself with Arab scientific and astronomical works.

The greatest translator in the Toledo group, however, was Gerardo of Cremona (1114-1187). A man possessed of great moral qualities and an insatiable curiosity in matters of science, he was particularly eager to acquaint himself with Ptolemy's *Almagest*. He came to Toledo, then the leading city of the scientific world, and remained there for the rest of his life. There he learned Arabic, and with the help of collaborators, one of whom we know to have been Gālib, made an enormous number of translations from that language; over eighty translations are definitely due to him; they cover the entire field of Arab and Greco-Arab learning, from mathematicians such as Banū-Mūsā, Euclid, and Apollonius (retranslated from al-Jwārizmī's Arabic), astronomers such as Ptolemy and Azarquiel, the great medical theorists from Galen to Avicenna's impressive *Canon,* the philosophical works of al-Kindī, al-Fārābī, and so forth. It is staggering to think that he could have completed this vast body of work, even with the help of assistants and assuming that in some cases he simply gave his approval to translations made by others. The tremendous, and in most cases very careful output of the translator Gerardo of Cremona marks the highest point reached by the Toledan group and by the activity of translators from the Arabic in general, which by the late twelfth and early thirteenth centuries had made available to Europe, with its young universities, the finest fruits of Greco-Oriental science, which were to nourish European thought from then onward.

We cannot leave this Toledo group without mentioning another of its translators, who leads us right into the thirteenth century—Canon Marco of Toledo, concerning whom Mlle M. T. d'Alverny and G. Vajda recently published an extremely informative article. We know from various sources that at the close of the twelfth century and the beginning of the thirteenth he was Canon of Toledo, and that in 1213 he was promoted to the episcopal Chair of Burgos. His work as a translator and apologist seems to have been partly due to the encouragement of the celebrated Archbishop of Toledo, Don Rodrigo Ximénez de Rada, who realized the importance of being able to face Islam with the weapons of practical learning as well as with those of the spirit. He probably sponsored some of the translations made by Canon Marco, which reveal a considerable knowledge of Arabic and a great determination to be accurate, which led him to invent several neologisms. He translated Galen's *De tactu pulsus* from the Arabic translation by Hunayn b. Ishāq. As a basis for controversy he translated the Koran and the *'Aqīda* of Ibn Tumart with the two *Muršida,* and Laudes.

Mention should also be made here of another translator from Arabic into Latin—a certain Alfred of Sareshel, who was working in Spain at this period—end of the twelfth century or beginning of the thirteenth—as we can see from certain Spanish expressions that occur in his work, and as Roger Bacon's testimony also shows. He translated and wrote a commentary on Aristotle's *De plantis,* dedicating it to Roger of Hereford; and he also translated the alchemical section of Avicenna's *Kitāb al-sifā.* Somewhere about the year 1210 he composed a treatise, *De motu cordis,* based on Oriental sources, in which he maintained that the heart was the seat of the soul. He also wrote a commentary on the meteorology and the *Parva naturalia* of Aristotle.

X. Translators from Arabic to Hebrew. The Qimhi and Ibn Tibbon Families

After the Almohad invasion of Spain it became impossible for Jews and Christians to live side by side in the Moslem regions, with the result that there was a Jewish exodus from Andalusia to the Christian states of the peninsula. The families of Qimhi and Ibn Tibbon settled in Languedoc and Provence, which at that time maintained very close relations with Catalonia. These two families distinguished themselves more especially by their translations of scientific works from Arabic to Hebrew, in which they followed in the footsteps of Abraham bar Hiyya and Abraham ibn 'Ezra. The Qimhi family took more interest in questions of grammar and exegesis than in natural science; thanks to them, all the Hebrew grammatical and philosophical learning that had been expressed in Arabic by Spanish Jewish writers such as Ibn Yanāh found its way into Hebrew and thence into Latin. Josef Qimhi (d. circa 1170) translated Ibn Paquda's *Kitāb al-hidāya* from Arabic into Hebrew and made a Hebrew verse translation from the Arabic of Ibn Gabirol's "Choice of Pearls."

The Ibn Tibbon family were much more prolific in their output of translations from Oriental sources. Their oldest member was Juda ben Saul ibn Tibbon (d. after 1190), known as "the father of Jewish translators." His translations from Arabic into Hebrew included philosophical works such as *el Kitāb al-amānāt wal-'i tiqādāt* of Gaon Saadia, Ibn Gabirol's treatise on *Corrección de los caracteres del alma,* the work by Ibn Paquda to which we have already referred, the *Cuzari* of Yehudá ha-Levi, and various grammatical works by Ibn Yanăh.

His son Samuel (d. 1232), who traveled in Spain and the East, was one of the most prolific Hebrew translators. From Arabic into Hebrew he translated works of philosophy including the celebrated "Guide to the Perplexed," by Maimónides and several lesser works by the same author; he also translated three opuscules by Averroes, and Aristotle's *Meteorology*. He was eclipsed in activity, however, by his son Mosé ibn Tibbon, who translated about thirty different works into Hebrew, most of them dealing with theology and philosophy, such as Averroes' less important commentaries on Aristotle, al-Fārābī, Maimónides, Temistio, and al-Batalyusi; he also translated works of writers on mathematics and astronomy, including Teodosio, Euclid, Yābir ibn Aflah, the celebrated al-Bitrugi who was known to Latin scholars as Alpetragius, and works on medicine such as Avicenna's "Smaller Canon." As we shall see later, the Ibn Tibbon family continued its activities throughout the thirteenth century.

XI. Other Translators from Arabic to Hebrew

In Spain, too, we naturally find some Jewish translators who worked from Arabic into Hebrew. In Barcelona there was Abraham ben Sěmuel ibn Hasday (d. 1240), who made translations of the pseudo-Aristotelian *Séfer ha-tappuah*—later retranslated into Latin—of Ishāq Israilī's Book of the Elements, the Arabic original of which has vanished, and Algazel's work on ethics, *Kitāb mizān al-'amal*. He also made new Hebrew adaptations of Barlaam and Josafat.

Another meritorious translator from Arabic into Hebrew was Juda ben Sélemo al-Harizi, a Spaniard who lived for a long time in the South of France, traveled in the Middle East, and later returned to Spain, where he died about 1235. He translated Maimónides's "Guide to the Perplexed" and part of his commentary on the Misná, and 'Ali ibn Ridwān's Epistle on Education, and won great fame with his translation of el-Harirī's *Maqāmas* and his imitative work, *Tahkemoni*.

During the same period there were a number of other

translators from Arabic into Hebrew who, though of Spanish extraction, worked in other countries. These included Selomo ben Yosef ibn Ayyub, of Granada, who made his translations at Béziers—among them were Averroes' *Comentario medio* to Aristotle's *De coelo,* Avicenna's *Aryūza,* the *Libro de los preceptos* of Maimónides, and a few short treatises by Ibn Yanah. Sem Tob ben Ishaq, of Tortosa, lived at various periods at Barcelona, Montpellier, and Marseilles. He was still alive in 1267. He translated Averroes' *Comentario medio* to Aristotle's *De anima,* and two celebrated works on medicine, the *Kitāb al-Tasrīf* of Abul-al-Qāsim al-Zahrāwi and the *Kitāb al-Mansūrī* of al-Razī. He also translated the *Aphorisms* of Hippocrates.

Yet another translator from Arabic into Hebrew was Zĕrahia ben Ishaq ben Saltiel Gracián or Hen, a member of a famous Jewish family of Barcelona. He concentrated on philosophy, translating several of the works of Aristotle— *Physics, Metaphysics, Of Heaven and Earth, Of the Soul*— al-Fārābī's *On the Essence of the Soul,* and a number of the *Comentarios medios* of Averroes. The medical works he translated included Galen's *Treatise on Symptoms,* two of the five books of Avicenna's *Canon,* and Maimonides' *Aphorisms* and *Treatise on Coition.*

The fact that most of these Jewish translators settled in Provence or Languedoc shows that southern France had become a tremendous center for translations, many of which were intended either for Italy or for the University of Montpellier.

XII. THE GROUP OF TRANSLATORS AT THE COURT OF ALFONSO THE WISE

While in the twelfth century translations were made at Toledo from Arabic into Latin, with a certain amount of patronage from the archbishops, now, halfway through the thirteenth century, works were being translated from Arabic into the young language of Castilian Spanish, under the patronage of the kings of Castile. San Fernando, who conquered Cordova and Seville, had encouraged the translation from Arabic into Castilian of certain didactic treatises, such

nd a *Lapidario*, entitled "*De la propriedad de*
which deals with the properties of 360 different
ne. But the most famous of all the works pro-
lfonso's academy of translators was the *Tablas*
rawn up at the King's order by Don Zag and
Mose to take the place of the ancient *Tabulae*
orked out at Toledo by Azarquiel and his group.
se las Alfonsies are thought to have appeared in 1272
to le been in the Castilian language, but only their
dings ave survived. Their influence in Europe was
ined be tremendous, and they were translated into
in and various other languages.

Before concluding this rapid review of the translations
oduced at the court of Alfonso the Wise, I should mention
at they covered other subjects besides those to which I have
ferred. It was very possibly in his time, or thereabouts,
hat two Arab works on agriculture—one by Ibn Wāfid of
Toledo (eleventh century) and one by his contemporary and
ellow-townsman Ibn Bassāl—were translated into Castilian;
both were to have a marked influence on Spanish agriculture,
and anonymous and incomplete Castilian translations of
both have survived to this day. Religious books were likewise translated from the Arabic at the court of Alfonso X—
including the legend of Mahomet's journey or ascension to
heaven (*mi'rāy*), which was subsequently retranslated from
Spanish into Latin under the title of *Libro de la Scala*.

An active translator from Arabic to Latin was the Francis-
can Pedro Gallego, the confessor of Alfonso the Wise, who
later became Bishop of Cartagena (1250-67); his translations
included *De animalibus historia*, drawn from an abridged ver-
ion of the Arabic work, and a treatise on economics, probably
e one by the pseudo-Galen. At the same time, or slightly
lier (1233), Esteban of Zaragoza, or of Lérida, translated
al-Yazzār's work on herbal medicine.

ER THIRTEENTH-CENTURY GROUPS OF TRANSLA-

ut the thirteenth century we find in Spain other
om Arabic into Latin or Spanish, some of whom

as *Flores de filosofía* and the *Libro*
son, the future King Alfonso X, t
young prince, encouraged the translat
including *Kalila y dimna* and the *Porid*
the *Secretum secretorum*) and later,
to the throne, sponsored a tremendous e
the scientific culture of the East into t
tilian civilization. He surrounded himself
Jewish, and Arab scholars who formed a
academy over which the King himself presid
revised the translations or adaptations thus p
introductions to them, and, in short, carried the
of an editor.

The translators and collaborators in various fie
a certain Don Bernardo the Arab—who may h
Mozarab—and several Jews, among them Ishaq ben
Rabí Zag, Juda ben Mose ha-Kohen, Don Abrah
Semuel ha-Levi. Most of the great body of trai
produced at the court of Alfonso the Wise dealt w
tronomical and astrological subjects. The great work
tronomy by al-Bāttāni was translated into Castilian by
ben Sid, Ibn al-Haytam's *Cosmografia* by Don Abraham, an
the astrological work of 'Ali abi-l-Rihal by Juda ben Mose;
Ptolemy's *Tetrabiblon* was retranslated from Castilian into
Latin by Aegidio de Tebaldis; and Azarquiel's almanac wa
also translated. In addition to these individual translatio
there was a great collective work, known as the *Libros*
saber de astronnomía (1276-77), a kind of encyclopedi
astronomy comprising direct translations from the Arabi
adaptations. It consists of four books on the stars, c
by Juda ben Mose and Guillen d'Aspa from the tent
work by 'Abd al-Rahmān al-Sufi; one book o
globe, based on Qosta ben Lūqā; two books on th
(armella), derived from Azarquiel, and two
spherical astrolabe, all four compiled by Ra
on the flat astrolabe, two more on the uni
from 'Alī ben Jalaf (11th century);
Azafea, derived from Azarquiel; tw
one book on quadrants, compiled b
on different types of clockwork,
Semuel ha-Levi.

In addition to this huge bo
were a number of translatio
as the *Libro de la cruces*, the

may be regarded as forming groups. At Burgos, in the time of Archbishop Gonzalo Garcia Gudiel (1274-80), there was a team of translators, certainly Jewish, consisting of Juan González and Salomón, which serves as a further example of the well-established custom by which translators worked in pairs.

We know practically nothing about these two, except that they were in touch with Don Gonzalo Garcia Gudiel, Archbishop of Burgos, and that Juan González was a citizen of Burgos. We know them to have made the following translations: part of Avicenna's *Sufficientia physicorum;* the same author's *De generatione et corruptione;* his *De actionibus et passionibus* and his *De meteorologicis.* The last three of these are attributed to our two translators solely on the strength of internal evidence. It should be mentioned that when he later became Archbishop of Toledo, Don Gonzalo Garcia Gudiel kept up his contacts with learned men and with translators and commentators of Arab works, such as Alvaro de Oviedo, who wrote a commentary on the *De substantia orbis* of Averroes.

At Barcelona, too, there were several Jews who made translations into Hebrew, while one of their number, a certain Yaffuda (= Yehuda) ben Astruc Bonsenior (last thirty years of the thirteenth century and beginning of the fourteenth) was employed in the chancellery of the kings of Aragon, Alfonso III and Jaime II, chiefly as an annotator of Arab maps. On the instructions of Jaime II he translated into Catalan (before 1298) a collection of maxims and proverbs known as the *Llibre de paraules e dits de savis e filosots,* most of which are Oriental in origin and similar to those in the *Mujtār al-yawāhir* of Selomo ibn Gabirol. This type of instructive compilation derived from Oriental sources had of course been exemplified earlier in the *Llibre de la saviesa* which appeared under the name of Jaime I (the Conqueror). It should be added that at the beginning of the fourteenth century Yaffuda made a translation from Arabic to Catalan of part, if not the whole, of *Tasrīf,* the celebrated work by Abū-l-Qāsim al-Zah-rāwī. It should also be mentioned that the famous Ramón Lull, who wrote some of his own works in Arabic, made a versified translation into Catalan of Algazel's work on Logic, and that the no less famous physician Arnaldo de Vilanova (d. 1311) included in his output several translations of medical works from Arabic into Latin, including *De medicinarum compositarum gradibus* by al-Kindi, *De viribus cordis* by Avicenna, *De medicinibus simplicibus* by Abu-Salt Umaya, and several other translations, some of which, however, are of doubtful attribution.

In Italy, too, there were groups of translators working from the Arabic, particularly at the court of Frederick II of Sicily, and subsequently at that of Robert of Anjou, at Naples. Frederick II was a monarch who, like Alfonso the Wise of Castile, loved philosophy and science and, also like Alfonso, assembled a circle of intellectuals—Christians, Arabs, and Jews—whom he encouraged to translate and compile works of Oriental origin. He also put questions in philosophy to contemporary writers, such as the philosopher Ibn Sab'in of Murcia. The most famous of the translators at his court was Michael Scot, who had previously worked in the same capacity at Toledo (1217). According to Roger Bacon, Michael Scot was helped with his translations by a Jewish interpreter —no doubt a convert to Christianity—named Andrés; it is possible that the name should really be Anatoli, whom we also meet at the Court of Frederick II. Because he translated several works on astrology and alchemy, and because he was for a time court astrologer, Scot went down to posterity as a wizard—Dante puts him in hell. While in Spain he translated the *Astronomia* of al-Bitruyi, Aristotle's *Historia animalium,* and his *De coelo et mundo,* with the commentary by Averroes. At the Sicilian court he translated a compendium by Avicenna, *De animalibus,* compiled several treatises on astrology, and wrote his famous *Liber physiognomiae.* As we see, Scot devoted much attention to zoology and natural history—a fact which may be explained by the great interest taken in those subjects by Frederick II, who himself, drawing upon classical and Oriental sources, composed a book on falconry, *De arte venandi cum avibus.* It should be noted that an Oriental translator in the service of Frederick II—a certain Theodore of Antioch—translated an Arab work on falconry for his master under the title of *De sciencia venandi per aves.* Also working for the Emperor was Ya'aqob ben Anatoli, who made a Hebrew translation of Averroes's *Comentarios medios* on the *Categorias, Interpretación, Analíticos primeros y segundos;* he also translated Averroes's *Comentarios medios* on Porphyry's *Isagogus,* and several astronomical works, including the book by al-Farganī, taking the Latin version as his basis.

Other translators working in Italy during this period included Salio of Padua, who, in collaboration with a certain

David, translated a *Liber de nativitatibus,* attributed to Abū Bakr, and Guillermo de Lunis, who translated Averroes's Commentary on Aristotle's Logic and on the explanation given of it by Porphyry. Filippo of Tripoli (Fenicia) translated the pseudo-Aristotelian *Sirr al-asrār* = *Secretum secretorum,* and his translation had a wide circulation, or considerable influence, in Europe.

At the court of Manfred, son of Frederick II, we find Hermann the German, who had previously lived in Spain and became Bishop of Astorga (d. 1272). He translated the *Comentario medio* of Averroes on Aristotle's Ethics, Rhetoric (?), and *Poetics,* with Al-Fārābī's Commentary on the Rhetoric. When the house of Hohenstaufen was cut off, its successor in Sicily, Charles of Anjou, also proved to be a patron of translators, and at his court a Panormitan Jew named Mose translated a treatise on veterinary medicine, falsely attributed to Hippocrates. A much larger body of translations was produced by a Sicilian Jew named Faray or Faragut, who translated for Charles of Anjou the impressive medical work by Al-Razī, *Continens,* a treatise on surgery by Mesues III, and the *De medicinis expertis,* falsely attributed to Galen, which he made from the Arabic version, the Greek original being lost.

Finally, coming almost to the end of the thirteenth century, we find several translators living in Provence and Languedoc, and maintaining close connections with Catalonia, the land where so many Oriental translations originated. These include Armengaud Blasi of Montpellier, physician to King Jaime II of Aragon, who made a number of translations from Arabic and Hebrew, such as the treatise on economics falsely attributed to Galen, the *Aryūza (Cantica)* of Avicenna with the *Commentary* by Averroes, the *De sanitate* and *De venenis* of Maimónides, and the *Tratado sobre el Cuadrante* by Don Profeit Tibbon. This same Don Profeit Tibbon, whose Hebrew name was Ya'aqob ben Mahir and who was a grandson of the celebrated translator Juda ibn Tibbon, was one of the most enlightened men of science to have lived during the thirteenth and fourteenth centuries; he not only made translations, but composed original works of genuine merit. He spent most of his life at Montpellier, and composed in Hebrew, for the longitude of that city and with the date March 1, 1900, his celebrated Perpetual Almanach, which, translated into Latin, enjoyed considerable popularity. Great fame was also earned by his *Cundrante de Israel,* or *Quadrans novus* (1290), from the Hebrew text of which a number of Latin versions and adaptations were made. Don Profeit Tibbon also made Hebrew translations of numerous Arab works, chiefly dealing with mathematics and astronomy, such as the fifteen books of Euclid's *Elements,* the same author's *Data;* the *Esfericas* of Menelaus; Qosta ben Lūqā's work on the celestial sphere; that of Ibn al-Haytam on the configuration of the world, and that of Ibn al-Saffār on the use of the astrolabe. In collaboration with Giovanni of Brescia he made a Latin translation of his own Hebrew translation of Azarquiel's work on the *Azafea.*

TRANSLATED FROM THE SPANISH
BY DAPHNE WOODWARD

SELECTED BIBLIOGRAPHY

M. Alonso. See the following articles in *Al-Andalus* (Roman numerals refer to volume numbers, arabic to the page on which the article begins).

"Notas sobre los traductores toledanos Domingo Gundisalvo y Juan Hispano," VIII, 155.

"El Liber de Causis," IX, 43.

"El Liber de Causis primis et secundis et de fluxu qui consequitur eas," IX, 419.

"Las fuentes literarias del 'Liber de Causis,'" X, 345.

"Las fuentes literarias de Domingo Gundisalvo," XI, 159.

"Las traducciones del arcediano Domingo Gundisalvo," XII, 295.

"Hunayn traducido al latin por Ibn Dawud y Domingo Gundisalvo," XVI, 37.

"Traducciones del arabe al latin por Juan Hispano (Ibn Dawud)," XVII, 129.

"Juan Sevillano, sus obras proprias y sus traducciones," XVIII, 17.

F. Bubnov, *Gerbeti opera mathematica.* Berlin: 1899.

M. T. D'Alverny, "Notes sur les traductions médiévales des oeuvres philosophiques d'Avicenne," Archives d'histoire doctrinale et litteraire du Moyen Age, XIX (1952), pp. 337-358.

M. T. D'Alverny, "Avendauth?" *Miscellanea ofrecida en homenaje al Prof. J. M. Millas-Vallicrosa*, I (1954).

H. Geon, *Les Categories d'Aristote dans les versions syro-arabes*. Beirut: 1948.

C. H. Haskins, *Studies in the History of Medieval Science*. Cambridge: Harvard University Press, 1924.

R. Levy and F. Cantera (eds.), *The Beginning of Wisdom:* An Astrological Treatise by Abraham ibn'Ezra. Baltimore: Johns Hopkins University Press; London: Oxford University Press, 1939.

F. Lot, *La fin du monde antique et le début du Moyen Age*. Paris: Bibliotheque de Synthese Historique, 1927.

J. M. Millas-Vallicrosa, *Assaig d'historia de les ideas fisiques y matematiques a la Catalunya medieval*. Barcelona: 1931.

————, *Estudios sobre Azarquiel*. Madrid-Granada: 1943-1950.

————, *Estudios sobre historia de la ciencia espanola*. Barcelona: 1949.

S. Muntner, "The Antiquity of Asaph the Physician and His Editorship of the Earliest Book of Medicine," *Bulletin of the History of Medicine*, XXIV, 2 (1951).

A. C. Nallino, "Astronomia," *Encyclopedie de l'Islam*, Vol. I.

A. G. Palencia, *Los mozarabes de Toledo en los siglos XII y XIII*. Madrid: 1926-1930.

E. Renan, *Averroès et L'Averroisme*. Paris: 1866.

J. Ribera, "Bibliotecas y bibliofilos en la Españ musulmana," *Disertaciones y Opusculos*, Vol. I. Madrid: 1928.

G. Sarton, *The History of Science and the New Humanism*. New York: Henry Holt, 1931.

————, *Introduction to the History of Science*. Baltimore: Williams & Wilkins, 1927.

M. Steinschneider, *Die europaischen Uebersetzungen aus dem Arabischen bis Mitte des 17. Jahrhunderts*, I. Vienna: 1904.

J. W. Thompson, "The Introduction of Arabic Science into Lorraine in the Tenth Century," *Isis*, No. 38 (1929), p. 186.

L. Thorndike, *History of Magic and Experimental Science*. 2 vols. New York: Macmillan, 1923.

H. A. Wolfson, *Cresca's Critique of Aristotle*. Cambridge: Harvard University Press, 1929.

TECHNOLOGICAL DEVELOPMENTS
IN EUROPE: 1100 TO 1400*

Bertrand Gille

The history of medieval technology is a formidable subject. The incredible diversity of the techniques involved, which ranged from medicine to metallurgy and from glass-making to agriculture, constitutes a major obstacle to any comprehensive picture. Attempts to present one have indeed been made, but without adequate preparation, and often in terms so general as to exclude certain indispensable particulars. One is even forced to the conclusion that historical dictionaries might in some cases be more useful than premature studies of this kind.

The difficulties encountered by the historian of technology are due in part to the very nature of the sources at our disposal. The successive phases of technical progress were not indicated at the time, because the fact of such progress was not even realized, as a general concept—so that it is often difficult to trace the development of a technical process, let alone work back to the origin of an invention. Thus the only alternatives are to study a great number of documents—a task that can only be completed by collective effort—or to examine the available illustrations. Even then, many disappointments lie in wait for those who undertake such research. The descriptions given in documents are often vague. Illumi-

* *Journal of World History*, III, 1.

nated manuscripts, frescoes, and stained-glass windows are equally imprecise, and to make matters worse, the artist's unfamiliarity with the object he had to depict was a frequent cause of inaccuracy; there was as yet nothing resembling the notebooks of the fifteenth-century technicians or the Flemish paintings of the sixteenth century, with their invaluable precision of detail (see Figs. 1, 2, and 3).

Fig. 1.   The wheelbarrow (late thirteenth century) (*Bibliothèque nationale, Paris, lat. 6769*). The wheelbarrow presents problems that are by no means solved as yet. Illustrations are difficult to interpret, since it is frequently impossible to make out whether there is one wheel or two; though here it seems clear that there is only one. The word itself presents a semantic feature that is not unique, inasmuch as it is not in accord with the facts.

Thus it is that research still needs to be organized, documents to be sought out, and illustrations to be assembled. Both categories exist in such abundance that a comparative study of them would be bound to result in more detailed knowledge of the development of technology.

In other words, the present article must be kept within

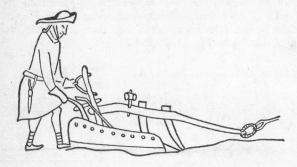

Fig. 2.　Heavy plow (circa 1340) (*British Museum, London, Add. MS. 42130*). Illustrations in manuscripts are practically the only source for the study of plowing instruments. Even so, one must beware of artist's license, stereotypes, and imitations.

Fig. 3.　A wagon (seal of Francesco of Carrara), 1396. This is a perfect example of the medieval system of representation, by which each part of a machine was shown from the angle from which it could be most clearly seen (Villard de Honnecourt's drawings follow the same principle).

narrow and prudent limits. Its only value will be to point out the gaps in our information and indicate the problems involved.

I. THE TECHNOLOGICAL FACTS

We should surely begin by considering the question in its purely technical aspect. But how is it to be approached? To describe the differences between medieval and ancient techniques, or rather the progress by which the former were differentiated from the latter, would require a knowledge of ancient techniques we can hardly be said to possess. We are thus obliged to fall back upon considerations that, while not devoid of interest, are more general in character.

It is less easy to assess developments in civilizations other than those of Greece and Rome. In this field, technical changes were undoubtedly in some cases contributory causes of a general evolution, while in other cases they were among its effects. Did Gothic art proceed from the invention of the ogival vault—or was that invention the outcome of a search for new forms? The dilemma will probably never be solved. The same is true in another field: for a long time technical problems were the inspiration of scientists, for a long time "engineers" were the only scientists. Technological empiricism would thus appear to be among the sources of scientific rationalism. One problem, indefinitely repeated, leads to a perception of its various elements and to the search for a practical solution. The improvement of man's intellectual equipment has thus also exerted an influence.

The center of active life had moved northward by the Middle Ages—a fact that is important chiefly from the material and therefore from the technological standpoint. The movement inevitably led to appreciable changes. The materials employed were no longer the same. Wood is in much greater supply, and of better quality, in the north than on the shores of the Mediterranean: the oak yields larger and stronger beams than the olive or the pine. The civilization of the Middle Ages was undoubtedly characterized by a far greater use of wood than the civilizations of classical antiquity—its towns and bridges, even at one period its castles, were built of wood. As we shall see, the extensive use of this new material was to lead to appreciable changes, particularly in architecture. But wood may be said to be merely the result of a difference of climate. Non-Mediterranean western Europe has a damper climate than southern Europe. The consequence is that its streams are much more regular in their flow, different crops are grown, the nature of the soil is different; this explains the prevalence of water mills, the unsuitability of Roman agricultural implements and methods for use on the richer, heavier, denser soil, and the conversion of transport to make use of waterways—a method almost unknown in ancient times.

Metal was used merely as an adjunct, and on a very small scale; components were never assembled by metal nails or metal screws; everything was held together by tenons, mortises, and pegs. A wooden tool was usually protected by iron (the edge of a spade or plowshare being plated with iron, for instance). The purpose of subsequent technical revolutions was, specifically, to popularize the use of metal. Blast furnaces, rolling mills, smelting, and wire-drawing were not introduced until the fifteenth century. Leonardo da Vinci's interest was attracted by all types of metal-processing machinery (such as equipment for drawing metal, for cutting screws or files, etc.).

Small hand tools showed remarkably little change. Such implements, whether used in agriculture or in handicrafts, were no doubt developed rapidly and perfected in all the diversity of their forms; the different types of ax, the different styles of blacksmiths' pliers and tongs, remained unchanged from ancient times until the eighteenth century. The equipment of the blacksmith whose tomb was found at Ostia, near the Porta Romana, includes a complete set of the tools his successors were to use until the introduction of modern machinery.[1] It would be interesting to make lists of craftsmen's tools based on the study of old miniatures and catalogs.

Thanks to some of the themes they illustrate, the miniatures in manuscripts are a valuable potential source of information. Builders' implements are shown in the many pictures of the construction of cathedrals, or of the Tower of Babel, ship's carpenters' tools with Noah's ark, and joiners' tools in St. Joseph's workshop.

[1] An inventory of the contents of a forge in 1442 differs little from one of the nineteenth century.

Tools changed their shapes only as a result of the use of new materials, and even then the old forms were often simply modified to suit the new requirements.

There should, however, be no mistake as to the difficulties of compiling such a list. The miniatures do not show small objects in precise detail. They often perpetuate old styles, instead of reflecting changes that have occurred. The documents, too, are sometimes difficult to interpret; the name of an old tool is sometimes applied to a new one, or the name may be altered although the tool has not changed.[2] There are some instruments about which our knowledge is very scanty—the brace, for instance, and others about which mistaken ideas persisted until a late date, long after documents and illustrations had been published. This latter category includes the plane, which has often been said to have originated at a late period. Yet Jean de Garlande mentions it in the thirteenth century; it is shown on two twelfth-century capitals in Catalonia;[3] better still, it is frequently represented in Christian paintings in the catacombs—which, incidentally, offer splendid source material for a study of tools. The plane was undoubtedly invented in the earliest centuries of our era.

It was certainly in the sphere of mechanization, however primitive, that the inventive spirit of the Middle Ages found an outlet. The water mill offers the most striking example of this. Its history was first retraced, with admirable thoroughness, by Marc Bloch, and its adaptation to a multitude of industries has since been studied.

The water mill dates from about the beginning of the Christian era. It was invented in the Mediterranean region, but did not really come into its own until medieval times. There are few mentions of it in writing until the sixth century, but by the seventh century it was already attracting the attention of the legislators of the Alamani, the Bavarians, the Salian Franks, and the Visigoths. During the eleventh and twelfth centuries it spread to central and northern Europe, not merely in isolated examples but in large numbers: the Domesday Book lists 5,624 water mills in England in the latter part of the eleventh century.

It has been supposed that the wheels of the earliest mills

---

[2] This occurs with the brace, mentioned by Jean de Garlande in the thirteenth century, but not shown in illustrations until the fifteenth century.

[3] These capitals are in the cloisters of Gerona Cathedral and of the Monastery of San Cugat, near Barcelona.

were placed horizontally. But paradoxical though the fact may seem, it cannot be denied that Vitruvius's mill had vertical wheels, as did all the mills shown in medieval illustrations; the interior mechanism changed hardly at all (see Fig. 4).

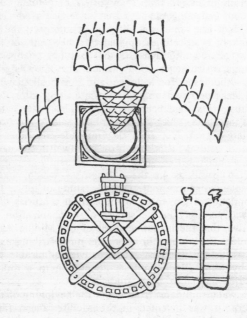

Fig. 4.   Corn mill (Church of San Isidro, Madrid, twelfth century). The few drawings of the internal mechanism of a water mill that have come down to us are all alike, showing identical cogwheels and windows (cf. the manuscript of Herrade of Landsberg).

These mills were first introduced in industries that made use of horse gear—instruments with a continuous rotary movement, such as the corn mills and oil presses devised by ancient Rome. Corn mills originated at an early period, while oil and beer presses are mentioned in the eleventh and twelfth centuries. Later came the wood mill (fourteenth century) and the mill for turning a lathe.

The ancient Romans, who used the noria (known, significantly, by its Arab name), do not seem to have employed the large hoisting wheel, directly propelled by the current of the stream. This appears to have been in use in Syria in the eighth or ninth century. There is a mention of one at Toledo in 1043, and in the twelfth century they were apparently to be found in many parts of Spain. Incidentally we should not infer from this, as has often been done, that the irrigation network in southern Spain was created by the Arabs; they merely took over the Roman system, though they did extend and improve it.

The Middle Ages found a further ingenious use for the water mill. It proved possible, by placing cams in a certain fashion on the driving shaft, to move the handle of a tool which was then brought back to its original position, either by its own weight or by the action of a spring. Mallets, hammers, or saws could thus be adapted for propulsion by waterpower. The earliest mention of a fulling mill is thought to be in Dauphiné in the middle of the eleventh century. In any case there was one in the Forez region by 1066, and in the twelfth century this form of equipment was being used extensively.

The tilt-hammer came somewhat later. An 1116 mention of it, at Issoudun, is apparently spurious. A Catalan text of 1138 seems to allude to the tilt-hammer, but it is mentioned with greater certainty in the second half of the twelfth century.

The water mill was quickly adapted to the manufacture of paper, too; in 1238 and 1273 at Xativa, Spain, in 1268 at Fabriano, Italy, in 1338 at Troyes, France, and during the fourteenth century in all parts of Europe.

It proved harder to solve the problem of the saw. Ship's carpenters used a vertical saw, fastened either to a bow or to a pole that acted as a spring. The pole was also used with the hydraulic saw, a detailed drawing of which has survived in Villard de Honnecourt's sketchbook. In this case the saw was brought down, not by a pedal but by the action of cams arranged on a driving shaft connected with a paddle wheel.

The water mill thus proved to be extremely adaptable. If a map were drawn up to show all the mills used for these various purposes, we should certainly find that the different types of apparatus were very densely distributed.

Much less study has been devoted to the windmill than to the water mill, so legend is still persistent. Despite a rather vague passage in Hero of Alexandria, it seems unlikely that the ancients were acquainted with the windmill. It has been alleged that an Arabic text mentions it as existing in the high plateaus of Iran, whence, we are told, it was brought to the Arabs in the seventh century. These first windmills seem to have been built with a vertical axle, which simplified the difficult problem of shifting the wings around when the wind changed its direction.

It is thought that there were windmills in Tarragona as early as the tenth century. A decree issued by Pope Celestin III (1143-1144) contains a reference to windmills. The Statutes of Arles between 1162 and 1180 provide the first positive documentary evidence of the existence of windmills in Western Europe. Delisle mentions one in Normandy at the same date; in the thirteenth century they were known in most parts of France.

There is proof of their existence in England and in Flanders at the end of the twelfth century. In Poland they are mentioned in the first half of the fourteenth century.

Owing to the lack of exhaustive research, the history of the windmill is thus still rather shadowy. The earliest illustrations in which it is shown belong to the thirteenth century. All the windmills depicted are of the same type. They are still built entirely of wood and perched on an enormous wooden tripod, on which they can revolve with the help of a handle (see Fig. 5). The fixed windmill with revolving roof must have been a fifteenth-century invention: in any case it involved a very awkward problem of interior mechanism.

Fig. 5.   Windmill (seal of the millers of Bruges, 1408). Illustrations of windmills (which are, it is true, not numerous for this period—some ten in all) are all alike; they show only one type of mill. As to its mention in documents there is less certainty; research in Spain and Italy might be rewarding.

Military machines were also entirely revolutionized. The artillery of ancient times operated solely by means of the recoil produced by twisting cables made from entwined sinews, with a windlass. The ballista and the catapult were the best applications of this ballistic principle. Byzantium made no innovations in this respect.

Charlemagne's armies, in the ninth century, were already equipped with armaments of high quality, particularly machines for conducting sieges. From the twelfth century onward, portable equipment also included a weapon that constituted an exceptional advance in power when compared with any of its predecessors. There has been considerable controversy as to the origin of this new mechanical weapon—the crossbow. Evidence that has recently come to light proves that it cannot have existed prior to the Carolingian period.

The crossbow is a bow of improved pattern, inasmuch as the spring is no longer of wood but of metal, consisting of a band of steel, and later, of several bands, superimposed. A separate instrument then became necessary to stretch the bowstring, and a hook, connected with a trigger, to release it. The weapon thus had a much longer range and a better aim. By the twelfth century its use had become sufficiently widespread for the Lateran Council, in 1139, to prohibit its use as too lethal.[4] To the head of the crossbow was fitted a stirrup in which the archer placed his foot, thus holding the weapon to the ground. He then caught the bowstring in a hook suspended from his belt and straightened himself up, at the same time fitting the string into the notch that held it. In the thirteenth century the spring had been made so powerful that it became necessary to use the *pied de biche*—an ordinary lever, fixed to the shaft of the crossbow in the manner of a fulcrum; all that was necessary was to pull down the lever toward the shaft. This increased the power of the weapon but made it slower. Halfway through the thirteenth century, Jean de Garlande refers to the crossbow *à tour;* the *tour* was a small windlass, fastened to one end of the shaft by pulleys that acted as a gearing-down device and fitted with two hooks that pulled the bowstring. The lever-fitted crossbow is probably not older than the fifteenth century. We thus see that the weapon was gradually brought to considerable per-

---

[4] A late tenth-century manuscript shows several crossbows. The Castril Museum at Granada possesses a fourteenth-century crossbow, found in the Alpujarra. Others of this period are to be seen in the Zürich Museum.

fection. One may well feel surprised that these very simple mechanical principles were not applied at an earlier period. But the improvements probably depended upon other technical advances, such as the production of a finer quality of steel for the plates. Technical processes are nearly always interacting.

The first positive mention in Western annals of the trebuchet, the most distinctive example of the new artillery, dates from the siege of Paris by the Normans in 886. The new machine was used by the defenders of the city. As early as 873, Charles the Bald had made use of "new and refined machines" in the capture of Angers, where the Normans of the Loire Valley had entrenched themselves. Trebuchets were still in use during the siege of Rennes, in 1370.

This type of artillery used the ballistic properties of the sling, with suitable mechanism by which they were tremendously enhanced. The enormous sling was fastened to a

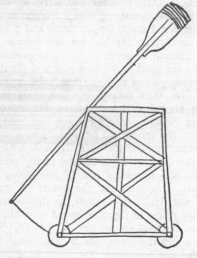

Fig. 6.   A trebuchet (*Cantigas* of Alfonso the Wise, Escurial Library). There are many illustrations of trebuchets; this one is a very simple form. Some manuscripts even show the construction of these instruments, of which Villard de Honnecourt gives interesting details.

shaft with a counterpoise at its lower end. The counterpoise was pulled up the shaft by windlass and springs, and hooked to the top. When released it returned to its point of balance, so that the shaft sprang upright and the huge sling was whirled around in a curve, at one point of which the cannon-ball shot out of it. Villard de Honnecourt, writing in the thirteenth century, is already able to give some particulars of the construction of these machines. By the beginning of the fifteenth century they had almost ceased to be mentioned in the notebooks of military engineers that have come down to us. These instruments gave rise to certain definite and rela-tively complex problems, with which I shall deal further on (see Fig. 6).

Artillery of this type was naturally supplanted by firearms. There is great divergence of views as to when firearms first made their appearance in western Europe, and much has been written on the subject. Reliable particulars are very scarce. F. Lot and G. Sarton give dates that do not entirely agree. Sarton considers that the use of gunpowder was known by the final years of the thirteenth century and that firearms were introduced almost immediately afterward, in the first two decades of the fourteenth century. The first positive evidence is afforded by an entry in a Florentine register for February, 1326, and a miniature dated 1327. After 1350, references become fairly frequent.[5]

There may possibly be some connection between the use of gunpowder and the development of the various types of "Greek fire." This generally had a basis of naphtha, and cer-tain of its forms were known already in early Roman times. It became the monopoly of the Byzantines, who used it suc-cessfully against the Arabs as early as 678. Their last his-torian remarks that Greek fire must take the credit for the halt of Saracen expansion, amounting almost to a withdrawal, which began in the latter half of the seventh century. In the tenth century it became a state secret.

The Arabs were bound to begin using Greek fire sooner or later. By 806 the Moslems were employing mangonels to fire cannonballs wrapped in tow that had been soaked in naphtha. They were still using them in 1123, at the siege of Edessa. Although the writings of Ibn al Baitar (d. 1248) pro-

---

[5] The oldest known cannon is in the Rijksmuseum, Amsterdam, and dates from 1377. The Musée de l'Armee in Paris also has a fourteenth-century example; these cannon are made of iron bars soldered together, reinforced, and held in place with iron bands.

vide the only evidence that the Arabs were acquainted with saltpeter, it is safe to say that at the siege of Fustat, in 1168, they used grenades loaded with a mixture of saltpeter, sulphur, and coal dust, which was practically equivalent to gunpowder. It seems clear from the manuscripts of Marcus Graecus (eleventh or twelfth century) that in his day powders suitable for priming were already being mixed with the liquid crude oils used to make Greek fire. The routing of St. Louis' army at the walls of Mansûra has been attributed to these inventions.

The vogue for machines certainly began in the Middle Ages. This is amply demonstrated by the flow of manuscripts displaying, from the earliest years of the fifteenth century, an enthusiasm for the mechanization of even the simplest activities, and a fascination with technology, which were destined to spread to the whole of mankind. This new spirit cannot have suddenly sprung into existence; it developed gradually, fostered by the success of the machines themselves. It is often difficult to reconstruct an ancient instrument with the sole guidance of some vague literary or administrative description, but one can sense the admiration of the writer who set it down. The Greeks may perhaps have had the same attitude toward Archimedes!

Villard de Honnecourt is one of the first to give drawings of some of the machines he saw in use, particularly the screw jack. Hoisting apparatus, as we learn from these same early fifteenth-century manuscripts, was always a subject for investigation. The monk Gervais refers to this in his chronicle. Samuel Ha-Levi Abulafia, a Jewish engineer employed by Alfonso the Wise, perfected a number of hoisting devices and wrote a treatise about them that was translated into Italian no later than 1341. Turning to presses, we find that Villard de Honnecourt, in a passage that has unfortunately been mutilated, describes how to work out the pitch of a screw. He also gives a sketch of the saw used for leveling piles. The life of a certain saint, written at the close of the eleventh century, records the existence of a machine that could straighten and re-erect a wooden structure that had become warped and been knocked down. Orderic Vital, writing about the siege of Alençon (1118), mentions a machine for severing the water conduits of a besieged town. In the thirteenth century the municipality of Marseilles possessed machinery for launching ships.

By contrast, the deepest mystery still surrounds certain

instruments that, though most ingenious, must have been in such common use that they were doubtless regarded as unworthy to illustrate a chronicle. Among these was the jack, essential for raising heavy weights; we see it in use in the fifteenth century without knowing when it originated.

The same uncertainty prevails with regard to the most ordinary types of lathe. The lathe was probably known in ancient times, though no visual record of it has survived. The Middle Ages were acquainted with three types of lathe, but they were all worked by reciprocating movement, for ignorance of the principle of the connecting rod and crank method prevented the construction of continuous-motion lathes. The lathe was turned in one direction by means of a pedal and a cord and brought back in the opposite direction either by another pedal—as shown in one of the windows of Chartres Cathedral—or a spring, a pole—as seen in a manuscript now in Paris—or a bow (see Fig. 7).

Only the "spinning lathe," as the spinning wheel used to be called, has left more definite traces; why, we shall see later. But here again there is a mystery; the spinning wheel in its primitive form—moved by hand and consisting simply of a spindle mounted without flyers—is mentioned in 1280 at Speyer and in 1288 at Abbeville. It spread very slowly.[6]

Mechanical inventiveness found its culmination in the automat. The ancients, exemplified by Archytes as far back as the third century and by Hero of Alexandria nearer to our own day, had devoted themselves with impassioned energy to the fabrication of such ingenious devices—which, though useless in themselves, brought into play certain mechanical principles that could easily be applied to daily work. It is thought that Leo, the Byzantine philosopher, also wrote a treatise on the subject, about the year 835. The Arabs were not merely the pupils of the School of Alexandria; the Banu Musa brothers wrote a treatise in or about 850, and al-Jazari, in 1206, was one of the leaders of the school, another being Reidwan of Damascus (1203). Literary works have preserved for us the memory of many of these toys, which astonished and mystified the common people—and caused some slight uneasiness to the Church: a good example of them, still to be met with occasionally on some Paris sidewalks, will be found in the *Hortus deliciarum* of Herrade of Landsberg.

---

[6] It is often confused with the shuttle-filling apparatus.

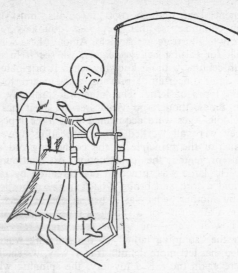

Fig. 7.   A turner (thirteenth century) (*Bibliothèque na-
          tionale, Paris, lat. 11.560*). Several types of lathe
          were used in the Middle Ages. The present type,
          comprising driving rod and crank, was not yet
          known—the first illustrations of it date from the
          beginning of the fifteenth century. The lathe was
          operated by a cable wound around the spindle and
          fastened at one end to a pedal and at the other to
          a rod that acted as a spring. There was thus a re-
          ciprocating movement.

From automats to clocks is only a step. We see that it has
been taken when we come to Villard de Honnecourt's angel,
whose finger always points toward the sun (see Fig. 8).
For here there is a problem that could not have been solved
without a clockwork mechanism of some kind, and Villard
shows us the first, clumsy example of an escapement system.
As early as 1271, Robert the Englishman, in his commentary
on John of Hollywood, describes a clockwork mechanism
using weights. The mechanical clock was certainly known by
the late thirteenth century; in Germany the first attested examples were constructed in the fourteenth century; in France
and England, and in Italy, they date from the first quarter

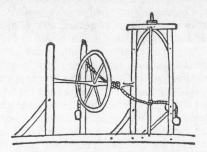

Fig. 8   Mechanism of Villard de Honnecourt's angel (thirteenth century). This was an early and as yet
unskillful experiment with the escapement system
that has been so often described. It serves to show
the distance that must be traveled between an
idea and its practical application. The idea is theoretical and raises mechanical problems of detail that
in many cases can be solved only by a succession
of inventions, each going part of the way.

of that century.[7] A link with the automata is constituted by
the clock-striking figures, the oldest of which would appear
to be the one at Orvieto, which dates from 1351, that at
Courtrai having been transferred to Dijon in 1382. But in
1340 the clock at Cluny already had a cock that flapped its
wings.

A good deal of all this, of course, was intended solely for
amusement; but nevertheless it involved mechanical inventions, and their subsequent developments were limitless. If
we study the successive technical processes introduced into
any one of the medieval industries, we shall be forcibly reminded that the Middle Ages differed from antiquity only in
their greater degree of mechanization and in their development
of certain chemical processes. Knowledge of chemistry, despite the erroneous concepts on which it was originally based,
progressed considerably between 1100 and 1400. In the
textile industry, for instance, there was no change in the
method of shearing, or in any of the preliminary processes,
except that the use of fats that had come to be recognized
as harmful—such as cod-liver oil and whale oil—was for-

[7] The oldest is that of Dover, now in the Science Museum, London.

bidden in the processing of oiled woolen cloth. Combs were slightly improved; carding, however, was a medieval "invention" that does not overstep the threshold of the fourteenth century. Carding, incidentally, was among the operations that were mechanized at a very early stage (late fifteenth century). Mention has already been made of the first appearance of the spinning wheel—an important innovation, for it led to the abandonment of methods dating from prehistoric times. Weaving looms, too, were greatly improved, perhaps under the influence of silk looms. Four-heddle looms are seen in fourteenth-century illustrations. Looms for complicated work, used chiefly for silk, seem to have made their entry right at the end of the fourteenth century. It was at the same period, or perhaps rather earlier, that the first mechanically operated mill for reeling silk came into use in Italy—at Bologna, according to legend—some writers even mention a definite year, 1273.

Fulling had been mechanized in the eleventh century. The process steadily gained in popularity, although fulling by trampling with the feet remained fairly widespread, since it was reputed to be less drastic. This latter method was, indeed, revived in some places at a very late period—at Blois in 1292, at Nogent in 1403, at Chartres in 1444. The various finishing operations remained unchanged throughout the period with which we are dealing.

With regard to dyeing, we must admit to a great dearth of information. The ancients were familiar with most of the coloring matters used in the Middle Ages, and with the principal mordants, particularly alum. It would therefore seem that in this respect the Middle Ages invented nothing new. Further evidence of this may be seen in the very fact that the dyeing industry shifted from Florence, where it was most at home, to Flanders. Perhaps the Flemish dyers were more skillful in mixing colors than their predecessors had been.

Advances in the chemical industry seem to have been in some measure the result of an improvement in the technique of distillation. The heart-shaped Alexandrian condenser, inefficiently cooled by wet rags, was abandoned in favor of the modern-style alembic, equipped with a tubular overflow-shoot that was corkscrew shaped, serpentine, or in the form of a spring, and standing in a vat through which a flow of water was maintained.

The Arabs had already endowed chemistry with several new products (sal ammoniac, borax, soda, potassium), but the

Middle Ages, with the help of this new distilling apparatus, carried their discoveries further. This resulted in a knowledge of the mineral acids, which the ancients had isolated only in the form of gases. Alcohol made its first appearance at Salerno about the year 1100, and the process of manufacturing it was improved by the adoption of dehydrating agents such as potassium carbonate (it appears in two forms—as *aqua ardens,* of approximately 60°, and as *aqua vitae,* at 90°). By 1160 a method had been discovered—by distilling a mixture of saltpeter, alum, and vitriol—of producing the nitric acid that was used in separating gold and silver, and sulphuric acid was later obtained by the distillation of alum (thirteenth century). Saltpeter seems to have been known in Italy by the year 1150. Another practical step was the substitution of tallow candles for wax tapers.

As we saw in the case of the textile industry, technical progress was almost entirely confined to machines. Ancient times had never conceived the notion of general mechanization. It seems likely that this novel attitude toward technology really originated in medieval times. Our information is in many respects too sparse to form the basis of an exhaustive history of the subject, but the evidence already assembled makes it clear enough that priority was given to technical developments. It was during the fifteenth century that machines really came into their own. Villard de Honnecourt had already accustomed us to some degree of curiosity about mechanical problems; and the year 1405 marks the beginning of a succession of what may really be called descriptive catalogs of machines, which followed and improved upon one another right through the century, culminating in those of Leonardo da Vinci and the various subsequent "compendia" of mechanical inventions, which were the far-off ancestors of Diderot and d'Alembert's Encyclopedia.

There is one branch of technology on which great stress has been laid, to the extent not merely of attributing to it a somewhat exaggerated importance, but of adopting it as a symbol of technical progress in the Middle Ages—which is, to say the least of it, excessive. While it is true that technical methods of transport are far from unimportant, and that they altered considerably between the tenth and fourteenth centuries, the changes that took place should not be regarded as primordial. Let us try to arrive at an exact definition of those changes and determine their real significance.

The harness and equipment used for horses in modern

times (the nailed horseshoes, the stiff collar, and the tandem team) are to be seen in Chinese bas-reliefs of the Han period, in the second century of our era. They seem to have made their appearance in eastern Europe between the sixth and ninth centuries, and suddenly spread through western Europe in the twelfth century. Those are the bare facts of a historical development with which we are today acquainted in all its details.

There is certainly no justification for considering that this invention was the cause, not only of a technical revolution, but of a general social revolution as well. I have already pointed out the rashness of this theory. Indeed, there is still some doubt as to whether horses were not already being shod in late Roman times. Some important queries have also been raised by a geographer: May not the restrictions prescribed for loads in the Theodosian Code have been a precaution to protect the road surfaces from undue wear and tear (the modern French Highway Code includes comparable provisions)? Were not the draft animals specially trained for the ancient system of harnessing? Does not Pliny refer to the tandem? The Mediterranean climate did not tend to produce good pasturage and was consequently not propitious to the breeding of large cattle. But on the other hand—and this applies in some measure to the Middle Ages as well—was there any very great circulation of goods? The essential transport of the period did not employ carts—which, even with good harness, would have been difficult to use on the hilly roads of the Mediterranean countries—but pack animals. Harnessing methods were thus not a major problem in classical times. The problem did arise very naturally, however, in the northern countries, where stockbreeding developed on a larger scale owing to the availability of grazing grounds, and where distances were greater and roads not so steep. Shoeing could be customary only in countries where metals were used on a large scale—in other words, which possessed a much greater abundance of timber and mines than had been known in the ancient world.[8]

Something of all this still applied in the Middle Ages. Bales of wool, which formed one of the staple items of medieval transport (though anyone who takes the trouble to

[8] J. Sion shows most convincingly that the problem should be considered from a wider angle. He also notes the manner in which transport costs were divided up—as a result of which it was feasible for wines to be carried northward from the Mediterranean.

collect statistics will see that that transport was still on a small scale, both in volume and in weight), were carried by pack animals and not in carts. The heavy wagons that conveyed the building materials for cathedrals were drawn by oxen. In the north, four-wheeled carts were used to transport heavy goods, but only from one river to another, for the greater part of the traffic was by water.

Moreover, the conveyance of heavy goods by wagon did not become really practical and generalized until the invention of the articulated forepart. The dray of the ancients was perfected in medieval times. Haulage was steadied by the invention of the swingle-bar in the thirteenth century. The articulated forepart seems to have been introduced in the concluding years of the fourteenth century. The seal of Francesco da Carrara, dated 1396, shows what definitely appears to be an articulated forepart.[9] This invention also led to considerable advances in heavy artillery—cannon being permanent, whereas trebuchets were constructed at the actual moment of a siege and, being of wood, were discarded when it was over.

The history of transport thus calls for a fresh review, with the help not only of existing documents, but of the lavish supply of illustrations available to us. This would shed light on a considerable number of related problems that have hitherto been neglected. Geographical necessities and the development of other techniques, such as that of stockbreeding, should be studied concurrently with the types of harness and vehicles used.

Another celebrated invention influenced maritime traffic. At the beginning of the thirteenth century the old lateral rudder used since ancient times was replaced by the sternpost rudder, which was much easier to handle. Here again, however, there are many gaps in our information. If it is admitted that the Ipswich seal may be a forgery, the Elbing seal, of 1242, and the miniature illustrating the commentary on the Apocalypse that is preserved in the Breslau library, would then become the oldest known portrayals of this type of rudder. Reproductions have also been published of a piece of sculpture in Winchester Cathedral, believed to be a Flemish work of about 1180. But this is still very uncertain.

What appears certain is that the invention originated in the

---

[9] This seal is in the collection of the Archives Nat., Paris (see Fig. 3). A fifteenth-century manuscript is reproduced by Lefebvre des Noettes.

Baltic region. Seals dating from the middle of the thirteenth century show how it traveled westward by way of Kiel, Stralsund, and Stubbekjöbing, reaching Damme by 1309. It is extremely difficult to account for the appearance of a sternpost rudder in a Persian miniature attributed to Wasiti and dated 1327 (see Figs. 9, 10, and 11).

Fig. 9. A ship of the Scandinavian type (seal of La Rochelle, 1229). This is a very distorted view of the traditional Viking ship, its bow and stern almost identically shaped and turning up sharply.

Fig. 10. Ship with a rudder of the modern type (seal of Wismar, 1250). This vessel is completely different in appearance from the one shown on the La Rochelle seal.

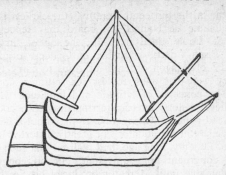

Fig. 11. Ship from the Persian Gulf (*Ms. Scheffer, Biblio-thèque nationale, Paris*). This is a typically puz-zling document: it shows a version of a ship that is highly fantastic in many of its details, yet has a sternpost rudder, the hinges of which are clearly visible, so that the miniaturist cannot have imagined the whole thing. Moreover, this particu-lar artist is well known, in general, for the ac-curacy of his drawings.

On the subject of shipbuilding itself, very few good studies exist. This is virgin soil, for though work is being done on the subject, nothing has as yet appeared in print. The medieval ship was descended from the old circular vessels of antiquity, which were slow and clumsy: the type of craft used in the Mediterranean during the thirteenth century is thought to have developed under the influence of a ship originating in Spain or the Basque country; this latter had a sternpost rudder, and square sails on the mainmast and foremast, while the aftermast retained the lateen sail.

Some authorities date the introduction and popularity of this type of vessel from the earliest years of the fourteenth century, while others maintain that it developed from the Scandinavian longship. The question of the distribution of the "Basque vessel" is one that deserves study. Thus the medieval ship gradually changed its shape and its rig, though we do not know exactly by what steps. It was still not easy to handle, however; medieval vessels could not sail close to the wind and were therefore often becalmed.

The course was set chiefly by rule of thumb. Charts began

to appear in the thirteenth century (the earliest is mentioned by Guillaume de Nangis, on board the Genoese vessel in which St. Louis sailed in 1270; the oldest surviving chart is the "Pisan Chart," probably of Genoese origin; in 1354 Pedro IV of Aragon ordered his ships to carry two charts), but they were flat ones, useless for setting a course by the stars. The concepts of latitude and longitude were familiar to medieval sailors; by transferring these two coordinates to cross-ruled paper it was possible to make out a flat chart that was excellent at the equator but greatly distorted in any other position. Ptolemy, long ago, had realized that such charts were neither congruent nor equivalent; but no congruent chart was obtainable until Mercator produced his, in the sixteenth century. These medieval charts gave the distances to be covered, and the rhumb. It should be noted that the log, too, dates only from the sixteenth century (1577). Ramon Lull, at the end of the thirteenth century, advised navigators to make use of geometry and arithmetic. Tables, first issued, no doubt, at the end of the thirteenth century, made it possible to correct a course.

The astrolabe was described by Philiponus of Alexandria in the sixth century. The oldest dated astrolabe that has come down to us is a tenth-century Persian instrument. But the astrolabe was certainly used far more by astrologers than by mariners. The magnetic compass was known in China toward the end of the eleventh century (1089-1093). Its presence in Europe is attested toward 1190, though it was probably not adopted in navigation until slightly later. In China it had been in use for that purpose since the beginning of the twelfth century, as is proved by a document of 1112. During the twelfth and thirteenth centuries it came into general use on the high seas of eastern and southern Asia. The Arabs possessed it in 1242, and the European countries at about the same date. The declination appears to have been known as early as 1086-1093, though it was certainly not possible to mark the angles on a chart, so that the compass was an instrument of very restricted use and no more than an approximate course could be steered with its help. It could be employed for plotting the galleries in mines. In any case, navigation by the stars was not introduced until the second half of the fifteenth century, despite the fact that, according to Idrisi, expeditions were setting out as early as 1124 to seek for the western boundaries of the world, and that other expeditions, in the direction of the Canaries, followed one another at intervals from 1341 onward.

Progress in maritime matters would thus appear to have been somewhat limited. Problems identical with those confronting land transport provide a fair analogy here—sea trading was on a comparatively small scale; links with the East were few; and until the fifteenth century there was little commerce with northern seaports. The sea route had one advantage, which might be regarded as appreciable—it avoided the numerous tolls and dues exacted from users of roads and inland waterways. But against this must be set the danger of shipwreck. Improvements in the design of ships made it possible now and then to introduce unexpected and far-reaching changes in certain industries; at the end of the fourteenth century, for example, the curing and barreling of herrings began to be effected while the ships were still at sea, and this made a fundamental difference to the way of life of the population in certain coastal areas of Flanders and England.

In order to maintain its seagoing trade, Bruges was forced into constant maintenance work to prevent its harbor from silting up; breakwaters had to be built on the Reie in the last quarter of the twelfth century; at its point of junction with the Zwin a dam was constructed, with a lock and lock gates to raise the level of the water; this was a considerable advance on the system of inclined planes that had been used until then, for above six feet of load draft and seven feet of air draft it became necessary to break bulk.

A larger and more widely distributed volume of traffic than had existed in ancient times called for different technical methods. This applied to commercial bookkeeping, an intellectual technique the development of which may well have been of decisive importance.

This foreshadows another form of progress, a kind of "chain reaction." We have seen that within a particular industry—the textile industry, for example—progress at one stage of manufacture may lead to progress at related stages. But it may also happen that a technical improvement introduced in one sphere results in a parallel advance in a completely different sphere. A machine or a tool devised for one technical purpose in many cases may be adapted for another without any great change being involved.

It should be emphasized that in many technical processes the methods and equipment of the Roman epoch continued to be employed—especially those of the first few centuries of our own era, when substantial improvements had already been made. Even where machinery is concerned, we still find the treadmill cranes shown in Roman reliefs,[10] while the hunting and fishing equipment so vividly depicted in the Queen Mary and Luttrel psalters[11] have scarcely changed since Roman times.

These brief observations will be enough to show in what considerable respects our information is still inadequate. All I have attempted to do, in the field of pure technology, is to indicate some landmarks, offer some examples, and try to discover possible methods of work. The ideal would be to make a separate study of each branch of technology, investigating all the implements or processes employed, in an attempt to arrive at conclusive results. In the absence of detailed monographs of this type, it seems practically impossible to achieve worthwhile results.

II. PROBLEMS OF THE ORIGIN AND TRANSMISSION OF TECHNIQUES

It would no doubt be rash to attempt to answer the general questions raised by medieval technology by making inferences from the scanty information we possess on the subject. So here again I shall confine myself to advancing a few hypotheses accompanied here and there by particulars that to some extent justify them. These tentative hypotheses may at any rate provide historians with a starting point for future research.

The question of invention is certainly one of the most misleading of all imaginable problems, especially during the period with which we are concerned. Invention, in the modern sense, presupposes a definite line of reasoning that starts from established premises and leads to some practical achievement that has been its specific aim. Examples of this are the principal discoveries marking technical progress in the sphere

[10] Cf. the treadmill hoisting apparatus shown in a Roman bas-relief now in the Lateran Museum.
[11] Both date from the beginning of the fourteenth century.

of electricity. But to think of medieval technicians in this way would be to credit them not merely with an amount of scientific knowledge but with a logical training, which they were far from possessing. As we shall see, it seems more likely that during our period—between the tenth and fifteenth centuries—the contrary was the case—that it was the endless recurrence of particular technical problems that compelled scientists to seek to define each one in general terms. In other words, experiment was born of technical experience, for technical experience is a perpetual experiment.

Medieval technology was essentially empirical. This means that reasoning played a very minor part in it, that it was no more than an assemblage of material, or a fumbling approach to chemistry. The advance was imperceptible—hence the lack of any sense of progress.

We must therefore resign ourselves to employing the terms "technical development" or "technical advances," rather than "invention." But here again a number of problems arise. How did those advances come about, and whence did they arrive? Was there a purely Western trend of development? Did the Oriental civilizations, whose achievements were quite equally brilliant, make no contribution to these gradual changes of technique? This is a particularly interesting question, for the affirmative and the negative reply have both been put forward with considerable emphasis. Study of the technological data has not yet been carried far enough for any firm position to be established.

There are, for instance, points that have been the subject of affirmations unsupported by any written document or illustration. Such is the case with the spinning wheel; some writers claim that it was invented by the Hindus, or somewhere in the Far East, and others assert that it originated in the West, in or about the thirteenth century. I have already given what information so far exists as concerns the West; but we must not confuse the Jules Verne type of visionary anticipation with actual technological facts.

On the other hand, there are documents that suggest that certain techniques developed independently, side by side with one another, in East and West. The mill came into use in the eastern Mediterranean at the end of the first century B.C.; its existence in China is attested in the first century of our era—in the year A.D. 31, to be precise. It is quite possible that this parallel development may have occurred in other branches of technology.

We must also pay close attention to the terms used to designate various technical activities, for these are apt to cause misunderstanding. For example, the fact that cast iron was known in China as far back as the first century B.C. does not necessarily mean that blast furnaces were also known there. The iron used may have been twice-smelted.[12]

Even allowing for these reservations, it remains evident that a number of technical processes did reach us from the Far East. The modern system of harnessing horses seems definitely to be of Chinese origin, and may very possibly have been brought to western Europe across the vast north European plains that are so well fitted for stockbreeding. Paper existed in China in the year A.D. 105, in central Asia in the fourth century, and at Samarkand in 750; it was brought to the West by the Arabs in the thirteenth century. Printing probably originated in Japan at the end of the eighth century; the oldest known example of it is a Buddhist *sutra* discovered in the subterranean temple of Tunhuang, dating from the year A.D. 888. The classics of Confucianism were all in print by 930. Printing had spread to central Asia by the thirteenth century, after which it passed to Egypt. Interchangeable type is believed to have been invented by Pi Sheng in 1045, and metal type in Korea in 1390. Daud al Banakati, writing in Persia about the year 1300, praises printing as a method of spreading identical and flawless copies of a document. The successive phases through which printing passed in Europe are still very imperfectly known. Separate letters for outlining initials in manuscripts are said to have been used at Engelberg in 1147, blocks of type at Ravenna in 1289, and separate metal letters at Limoges in 1381, at Antwerp in 1417, and at Avignon in 1444.

Other inventions, too, still give rise to question. The dates at which they appear suggest that they were imported from the Far East, but there is a total absence of documentary evidence to confirm such impressions. The wheelbarrow existed in China about the year A.D. 230. But was it the same wheelbarrow that is depicted in our own thirteenth-century miniatures? The magnetic compass was in use in China a hundred years before it seems to have been known

[12] During the symposium on "Iron through the Ages," held at Nancy in October, 1955, Joseph Needham showed that hydraulic bellows and triphammers must have been known in China in the first century A.D. In any case we have illustrations of them dating from the earliest years of the fourteenth century.

to the West; but we have no knowledge of any intermediate stages. Even in the case of typography there is a considerable hiatus between the Orient and the banks of the Rhine. In the earliest years of the Christian era the Chinese were already acquainted with various explosive mixtures, sulphur and saltpeter, and later (seventh to tenth centuries) they invented true gunpowder. They had the idea of grenades (1231) and of cannon (1259-1272). But some authors deny that gunpowder based on saltpeter was a Chinese invention, and believe it to have been discovered in the West in the late thirteenth or early fourteenth century. These are fields of inquiry that really call for investigation.

The routes by which inventions were transmitted are equally uncertain. The Arab route having attracted closer study than most, there is a tendency to declare that it was the only possible one. But what about the Byzantine route? And the Venetian route? Marco Polo, Plano Carpini, and Guillaume de Robrouk were not the only travelers to visit the Oriental lands. And what about the route through Mongolia and Russia? The gaps in our knowledge are obviously considerable. Were the travelers even disposed to carry home whatever new technical processes might have been revealed to them? Were they capable of discerning the novel features of a particular instrument or method, when compared with Western techniques? Such things are liable to escape the nonprofessional eye. Marco Polo's reports show a preference for the subject of shipping—the Grand Khan's vessels, with their four masts and twelve sails, the ships of the Persian Gulf, which have only one mast, one sail and a rudder (which must therefore have been of the sternpost type), arranged in a particular manner. He does, indeed, remark on the use of pit-coal in China, but that had been in use in western Europe for more than a century. The tales told by all Arab and Christian travelers should be studied from the technological angle to discover what information they managed to convey.

Prisoners of war had their influence, too. It was thanks to them that the breeding of silkworms was carried to Sicily and thence all over Italy. Craftsmen seldom wrote accounts of their travels. Yet skilled labor was amazingly mobile at that period: Guillaume de Robrouk had the surprise of meeting a Paris goldsmith, Guillaume Boucher, at the court of the Grand Khan in 1253-1254, and at Peking in 1292 Giovanni da Montecorvino made the acquaintance of a surgeon from Lombardy.

Insufficient attention has been paid, no doubt, to possible technical developments in the intermediate countries. We have already seen that large hoisting wheels were first employed by the Arabs, in the Middle East, and that the windmill originated, in all probability, on the tablelands of central Asia. We have noted that, by a strange anomaly, the sternpost rudder appears on a vessel in the Persian Gulf in 1237, a date at which no example of it is known to have existed in Western Europe (Fig. 11). It has also been suggested that the diagonal groined arch came to us from the Middle East. Here again, however, the problem is somewhat complex, for archaeologists are by no means agreed as to the respective influences of the Roman arch, of Persian and Arab architecture, of Moslem and northern strains, and of the bearer ogives of Armenia. To all these influences—though there is perhaps a tendency for influences to be overrated—we must indubitably add the technical and practical experience of the architects of that period.

"Until the first half of the twelfth century—when master masons, guided by their professional traditions, their thorough knowledge of techniques, their awareness of possibilities and their desire to ensure the conditions most favorable to the construction of light arches at a great height above very well-lit naves—any builder who was planning a vaulted ceiling, divided into compartments and reinforced with fillets, would select one of the two types of vaulting that were universally popular in the latter half of the twelfth century and in the thirteenth century—that based on the ogival arch, which originated in the Île de France and played a determining role in the development of Gothic art, and that based on the Angevin filleted arch, which was to spread far and wide, not only in western France but in many other European countries." Such builders must all have been influenced, in varying degrees, by these different trends.[13] The problem is still much discussed, and its solution would contribute information of outstanding importance to the history of technology in general.

It was at Mansûra, in 1249, that the Crusaders, Joinville among them, first encountered Greek fire, the exact nature of which the Western nations never succeeded in discovering. The Byzantines, Arabs, and Turks made constant use of it. Naphtha (or its by-products) was used to make it, either alone

[13] M. Aubert and J. Verrier, *L'architecture française à l'époque gothique*, Paris, 1943, pp. 8-10.

or, more frequently, with other ingredients. The Byzantines were obliged to renounce this weapon in course of time, for they gradually lost their sources of naphtha supplies. They made up this loss by adopting gunpowder.

The study of the Arab agronomists affords another example of the value of Near Eastern research to those concerned with the history of technology. The beginnings of Arab geoponic knowledge can certainly be traced in the writings of classical authors like Columella and Varro, whose work was taken up by Anatole of Berito (fourth century, translated by Costa Ben Luka at the end of the ninth century). That science began to expand in Spain during the period of the Caliphate (tenth century), largely thanks to the newly developed interest in botany and pharmacology. Cordova became the site of botanical gardens or fields for the experimental planting of seeds, many of which were imported from the Middle East with the intention of improving existing varieties, and for use in medicine. This tradition was carried on, through the Agricultura Nabatea (early tenth century), by the works of the more exclusively Arab writers, the Persians, Chaldeans, and Syrians. Cordova then produced agronomists who worked in its gardens. Albucasis (d. 1013) and Ibn Wafid wrote manuals that were destined to influence Spanish agriculture and, through Spain, the whole of the West. Toledo produced Ibn Bassal, whose treatise shows evidence of his considerable experience. Seville and Granada each had their experts. All these works were translated—abridged or in full—into Spanish and played an important part in the development of Mediterranean agriculture.

There are thus many points remaining to be elucidated in connection with the far-flung origins of technical processes. Little has as yet been done to extract information from possible sources. A technical process seldom makes its way from a distant country without leaving a geographical trail behind it. Did the ogive come from the East? What traces did it leave in Italy—whither the northern Cistercians are said to have brought it after its appearance between the Seine and the Rhine, and in Spain, mentioned by no one? Did the magnetic compass originate in China? By what route did it travel after that? There is no existing study of the physical conveyance of these techniques, or of the men who were responsible for it. The Crusaders? They have been credited with bringing home windmills—which did not exist in Syria; in other documents the Crusaders are said to have introduced the windmill to the Near East.[14] The diagonal arch is found almost simultaneously in several countries by the end of the eleventh century, and though appreciable differences of technique are to be noted, the intention is always the same—to simplify the construction of the groined vault.

Even if we confine ourselves to studying the spread of technical knowledge within a more restricted geographical area, that of western Europe, we are brought up against a number of difficult problems. What is needed is to list, and mark on the map, all the information that can be assembled regarding one particular instrument or technical process and thus trace the path by which it may have traveled. To take an actual example, let us consider the tilt-hammer, a fairly simple piece of apparatus, easy to construct, and which need be sought for only in districts where iron ore is to be found. The first document which mentions it, an Issoudun charter, is undoubtedly a fake. Most of the late twelfth-century examples were in Catalonia; the forges we find mentioned in Champagne during the twelfth century all appear to have been manual forges, situated in forests and not on watercourses. But another point deserves mention; of thirty-two deeds relating to the iron industry which have come to light in France, twenty-five were drawn up by Cistercians. So the Cistercians were evidently skilled technicians—a fact we shall presently find corroborated. The progress of the tilt-hammer seems to keep pace with that of their order: the earliest tilt-hammers known to have existed in Germany, England, and Denmark were constructed by Cistercians. The Cistercians are associated with other technical problems as well—the problem of the ogival vault, to mention only one. In 1134 the novice-master, Achard, a gifted architect, inspected all the new abbeys and noted their identical planning. Many of the bishops who went in for building were Cistercians. In Italy the Romanesque style of architecture persisted until the Cistercians brought to that country the true ogival vaulting and the Gothic building methods. Might not the Cistercian techniques and their expansion provide a very rewarding subject of study?

As monks whose days were given to labor, the Cistercians tried in their monasteries to make themselves proficient in

[14] The first windmill in Syria is said to have been built by German Crusaders. For this reference I have to thank the kindness of my fellow historian, J. Richard.

all the practical activities that this involved. They probably had their own agricultural methods, also deserving of study. But they certainly had their own industrial processes. These monks even ended by grouping their various mills—the tanning mill, the fulling mill, the ore crusher and the corn mill—in a single building, erected either beside or across a river. Two magnificent examples of this have been preserved in France—at the Abbey of Fontenay, in Burgundy, and the Abbey of Royaumont, near Paris.

This constitutes a kind of collective progress in technical methods. M. Bloch endeavored to suggest through what hands the water mill might have passed in the course of its dissemination. The main lines of its advance from East to West, along the invasion routes, and its movement in concentric circles around the Mediterranean, now seem to be more or less established. These new technical inventions were carried along by emigrants who brought their equipment with them —slaves such as the Bavarian who, a captive in Thuringia about the year 770, constructed a mill for his master in that region; colonists, like the Franks who, before 775, built the village of Mülhausen on the Unsrut; or religious, like those who settled in the Odenwald about 732. Collective migrations of technical methods were, indeed, the most profitable, as Colbert realized when he tried to introduce into France all kinds of technical processes not previously known there.

These collective migrations undoubtedly occurred in the case of the basic instruments—in what we may call the great technological discoveries. But what about the countless modest technical improvements—the novel process in dyeing, the architectural "brain-wave"? Here there can be no question of collective migration. This brings us onto shifting ground, with no fixed landmarks. We should no doubt bear in mind two main divisions—ideas and applications.

There have, of course, been many studies of the medieval working classes; but these rarely touch upon the subject with which we are concerned except in some of its legal aspects. The regulations governing apprenticeship do not teach us anything much. They pay far more attention to moral and social requirements than to technical matters. And it seems improbable that the somewhat stringent rules laid down in these contracts, or the length of the period of apprenticeship itself, can be assumed to indicate that a really thorough vocational training was given to apprentices.

Even the rules of the various guilds—which, except in the

case of the cloth industry, have not been very closely studied from this point of view—shed very little light on technical matters. Those of the cloth industry—perhaps because we know them better—do, indeed, seem more definite; but they are confined to limited and very specific prohibitions. With the exception of those that deal with certain processes, such as spinning with the spinning wheel, or carding, the chief purpose of these prohibitions is to prevent the use of harmful substances in the processing and dyeing of the wool. They remained in force throughout the period we are considering, but the clauses forbidding the use of wool that had been subjected to certain mechanical processes were withdrawn—for the good reason that in point of fact those processes constituted technical improvements. The ban on spinning wheels was gradually lifted; so was that on carding. The latter was still forbidden at Brussels, for instance, in 1374 and at Troyes in 1351, but was authorized there in 1385 and 1377. All corporate regulations show a distinct tendency to create loopholes for the admission of cheaper technical methods.

Moreover, these technical provisions were by no means confined to guild regulations. There is one field—that of mining legislation—where many documents exist, though the study of them does not appear to have been carried very far as yet. Between the period of antiquity and the Middle Ages, this legislation changed its character; from relating chiefly to fiscal matters, it became technical. Numerous instances of this are to be found in Italy, from the twelfth century onwards. In France we find such regulations issued in Champagne in the thirteenth century, at Vicdessos (Ariège) in 1355, and at Allevard (Dauphiné) in 1395. But these, again, were aimed solely at the prevention of certain accidents; they give us incidental information about precautions connected with lighting, the timbering of galleries, etc.

Various technical prescriptions were thus handed on thanks to the collective organization found in many branches of medieval activity. But as always happens with regulations, these technical prescriptions tended to become ossified, to ignore signs of progress. They give the first evidence of the establishment of technical traditions, with its unquestionable dangers, which we shall be able to estimate in due course—traditional methods of apprenticeship or discipline (which is really the same thing), traditions that in most cases took the form of prohibitions and were liable in the long run to slow down technological development.

There is another problem that has received scant attention—that of the migration of workers, which often led to the transmission of techniques. It would no doubt be highly instructive to investigate the registers and documents that mention the presence of foreign workers in a particular district or occupation. They are so numerous that some interesting hypotheses might perhaps be deduced from them; but in the absence of such studies I shall be obliged to confine myself to a few examples selected at random from my own reading.

The Germans were always regarded as masters of the arts of mining and metallurgy. Throughout the first half of the fourteenth century we find a great number of German miners working in the English silver, lead, and tin mines. In the late fourteenth and early fifteenth centuries the forges of Berry and the Nivernais were manned by German blacksmiths (though they may really have been from Lorraine) and by others from Liège. In Dauphiné, by the end of the thirteenth century, the forges were recruiting many of their workers in Savoy and Piedmont, which were reputed to produce skilled blacksmiths. In the thirteenth century all the mining terms used in Sweden were German, which can only have been due to the immigration of German workers into the Scandinavian countries.

In the absence of positive documentary evidence, semantics can, indeed, furnish useful clues as to the origin of various implements. But extreme caution is needed here, for while a foreign name is rarely given to a home-produced tool, an imported tool may very well be renamed in the language of its new country. It thus seems likely that tools that bear foreign names may be attributed, almost without question, to the regions where the relevant languages were originally spoken—or at least that this may provide one link in the long chain by which certain techniques were transmitted. Experience shows, however, that great circumspection is required even in this matter. To take an actual example, the etymological dictionaries attribute to the names of many tools used for working in wood a Flemish origin, which the facts do not seem to confirm in any respect, such as the plane, the bit-brace, and the jointer, the first two of which are mentioned in the fourteenth century and the third in the fifteenth.

It would also be very instructive to investigate cases where loans for technical equipment were refused; but we do not yet possess the necessary elements for such a study. The reasons for refusal are numerous—the old hand mills were sometimes preserved to avoid fresh taxation; some geographical areas—such as the Massif Central in France and Apulia in Italy—were difficult to penetrate. But there were also cases where the people were attached to their traditional equipment—even today some villages in Tuscany still use agricultural implements differing little from those of Neolithic times. One of these technically conservative regions covers the whole of eastern Europe, from Saxony to Russia. But the survival of certain agricultural or political boundaries may also contribute to the preservation of antiquated techniques.

There is undoubtedly a collective aspect of the transmission of techniques or, conversely, the barriers erected to keep them out. It seems that there has been a lack of studies of the subject rather than a dearth of documentary evidence. Research appears, in any case, to be less difficult here than in other problems of technological history.

The secret of many "inventions" and technical changes no doubt lies buried with the nameless hosts of craftsmen and peasants. But another category of workers was unquestionably involved, though its limits are not easy to define. Nowadays we should call it the category of technicians, "engineers." In this field, at least, we now differentiate much more strictly than was done in earlier times. This is because technical education, first thought of in the sixteenth and seventeenth centuries and introduced in practice in the eighteenth, has raised technical knowledge to the same status as other branches of scholarship. This was not so, of course, in the period with which we are concerned. Technical methods are, in fact, handed on not only through space, but through time.

Only one profession—architecture—has been studied, and that in a manner not yet systematic enough. Technical knowledge was no doubt first acquired "on the job." The building of a cathedral took long enough, in some cases, to provide training for several generations of architects. A foreman would jot down in his notebook particulars of any process or machine that was new to him. It is interesting to observe the similarity of style and form between the notes made by Villard de Honnecourt in the thirteenth century and Leonardo da Vinci in the fifteenth: ". . . by this means one can measure the width of a piece of water without crossing it . . . . And should you desire to have a good span-roof of timber, pay attention here . . ."

The same thing happened with architects as with workmen. It would be a great mistake to imagine that people did not travel about in the Middle Ages; technicians, in fact, went about more freely than any other class of persons. Architects, in particular, frequently traveled from one building site to another, improving their technical abilities and adding to their knowledge. A recent book on Gothic art is prefaced by a very instructive map showing the journeys made by architects from the twelfth to the fifteenth centuries. In a recent address on Leonardo da Vinci, M. Febvre showed that the men of the Middle Ages and their sixteenth-century successors knew how to use their ears. The technicians of that period, at any rate, knew how to use their eyes as well. Technical processes were not taught in schools, they were learned by practice. This is evidenced by the notebooks that became more and more numerous from the thirteenth to the fifteenth centuries; for what we find in them are not written descriptions, but sketches. Each drawing is accompanied by a very brief note explaining that "such and such a thing is done thus."

Architects, military men, and sailors no doubt brought back from their travels a far richer store of technical information than did the churchmen and merchants who journeyed to the Far East; for these, like the majority of Arab and Western travelers, were better at using their ears than their eyes, from which they got little benefit.

Moreover, the great ones of the earth were always ready to summon to their courts any engineer whose reputation had made its way there. Alfonso the Wise, in the thirteenth century, felt considerable respect for all the engineers in his service, many of whom he had called from foreign countries, and has left us much information about them. Many similar examples could be given.

Some building projects went on so slowly that the builders' yards became permanencies, lasting for decades or even for centuries. They were veritable schools, where technical methods were passed on from one generation to the next, and which saw the inception of the advances that burst upon the world in the first half of the fifteenth century. These no doubt gave the first impulse for the creation of "lodges" among the foremen working on the cathedrals and on the canal schemes in northern Italy.

Engineers (mainly military, for they operated the "engines") appear as well. At the siege of Tyr, in 1124, the Latins called in an Armenian engineer, Havedic, who was reputed to possess great skill in directing the fire of stone-throwing machines. In 1216 the Albigenses employed an "able engineer of trusty and antique heart." St. Louis, before calling up his army, took pains to assemble "such as were able to build engines for hurling stones, and mangonels." According to their latest historian, technicians were probably united as early as the thirteenth century in an organization in which a certain order of rank was observed. Joinville names Jocelin de Cornaut as the chief *mestre ingingneur* employed by St. Louis at Mansûra. Such men also took a hand in the work of fortification, which was directed by two corporations, the carpenters and masons. Under Philippe III, in 1257, Master Hubert, who *fesait engins,* was a carpenter. A carpenter named Thomas was the *magister ingeniorum* of Philippe le Bel.

Just as Villard de Honnecourt's inquiring mind led him to make sketches of machines in his notebook, so we find sketchbooks and treatises by certain military engineers that show that their interest was not confined to engines of war. The earliest of these was compiled in 1335 by Guy de Vigevano for Philippe VI (Valois) when he was about to set forth on a Crusade; and it already depicts ships fitted with crank-operated screws. At the close of the fourteenth century, Conrad Kyeser, of Franconia, composed his treatise, which included not only military devices but hoisting machines, mills, hydraulic plant, and machinery of all kinds. This treatise must have had a wide circulation, for quite a number of copies have survived to the present day. The late fourteenth century also witnessed a great increase in what were known to the Germans as *Feuerwerksbücher,* similar to Kyeser's treatise, and some of them showed the first diving equipment; a vast number of such works have been preserved in manuscript. This brings us to another method of transmission: treatises and sketchbooks were copied and circulated far and wide; and when printing was introduced, in the fifteenth century, it seized on them as useful material.

Between the technicians and the workmen there is an intermediate class that already existed during this period; its members too were addicted to travel, often with a view to discovering novel processes. We have a striking example of this at a slightly later date—that of a foreman in a salt-works who was following his occupation at Salins in 1448 after studying the manufacture of salt in many different countries, visiting Burgundy, Lorraine, Germany, Spain, Provence, Poitou, and Italy for that purpose. Similarly, a

Portuguese city sent for an Italian shipwright to rebuild its fleet, and Charles V asked for a German clockmaker to repair the big clock on his palace. During the second half of the fourteenth century, craftsmen from the Flemish provinces, from Brabant, and from northern France went to teach their crafts to Italians.

There was thus an undeniable cosmopolitan spirit among technicians. The military disturbances consequent upon the Hundred Years' War interrupted travel and with it the transfer of technical processes from country to country. When the troubles died down, in the latter half of the fifteenth century, the European economic systems recovered their vitality, but were subjected to far more centralized and powerful political authorities. The migration of workers and techniques gradually came under the control of national governments. This led imperceptibly to the system of industrial trading. Next came manufacturing secrets, followed by what has been called "industrial espionage." But that attitude, too, existed even in the Middle Ages; it was a long time before the Bolognese would divulge their mechanical process for winding off silkworm cocoons.

Europe was, in fact, about to witness the inception of the idea of technical progress, in which the Middle Ages had been singularly deficient. People would admire a new machine; the authors of certain chronicles are full of praise for various "engines" used in sieges. But no document ever gives us reason to suppose that there was any anticipation of steady improvement in technological matters in general. Less interest was taken in improving tools and machines than in increasing manual dexterity or devising clever mixtures for use in dyeing. Progress still lay with man, not yet with the tools and machines that were his inanimate assistants. Even the fifteenth century was more interested in training good pilots than good shipwrights. Gunpowder and printing did not seem as sensational to their contemporaries as nuclear energy, for instance, does to ourselves. Medieval man was not as obsessed with technology as modern man has gradually become.

III. The Civilization of the Technical Age

Lacking as we do any complete and precise knowledge of the development of techniques, it may seem rash to attempt to study its influence in the wider sphere of civilization. But here there has been a greater awareness of facts, and closer attention on the part of historians. Even so we should not rejoice too soon, for many gaps still remain.

There are, of course, some techniques where influences are not easily determined. Taking the example of agriculture, where technical processes differed appreciably in the Middle Ages from what they had been in the period of classical antiquity—at least to judge by the writings of the great Roman agronomists—we find that almost all the improvements originated in the earliest centuries of the Christian era; soil improvement was known, if not widely undertaken, marling seems to make a reappearance in the reign of Charlemagne, ashes and manure were to play a prominent part, rendered necessary by climatic conditions that called for the clearance of extensive areas of woodland and enabled stockbreeding to be immensely increased. As to the rotation of crops there is a dearth of information. Was this a Cistercian technique? Does it date from Charlemagne's reign? The plow, complete with coulter and moldboard, was known even in Virgil's day. Was it spread through the channel of different agricultural systems? The Mediterranean method of treading out corn was exchanged for the flail in or about the fourth century. In all these important changes the influence of agricultural methods and climatic conditions and the development of other branches of technique are so inextricably interwoven that it is hard to disentangle them.

Moreover, there are many different traditions. We have seen how the Roman agricultural tradition, enriched by the experience of the Moslems in Spain, made its way to all parts of the Arab world. There was also a tradition directly derived from the Roman authors themselves, which was amplified as time went on by the writings of agronomists accustomed to a non-Mediterranean type of agriculture. In the background of sudden discoveries, such as the inspiration that prompted the Portuguese, in 1325, to stabilize the sand dunes of Leiria by planting pine forests on them, men such as Walter d'Henley (1250), Pietro Crescenti (1306), and Thierry d'Hirson (1328) were contributing to unperceived transitions. Their influence must have been far from negligible; Pietro Crescenti was translated into French by 1374, and his manuscripts had a wide circulation.

It is interesting to follow up certain clearly defined technical processes, the dissemination of which should not be difficult to trace. Among them are the techniques of shipbuilding. The Scandinavian vessel was gradually improved (we know by what stages it developed) until it culminated in the Viking ship—long, comparatively narrow, clinker-built, and, it would seem, not fitted with mast and sail until a fairly late period. This type had been carried to the British Isles by the seventh century, if not before. About the ships used by the other European countries on the Atlantic seaboard we know absolutely nothing. They were not shown in illustrations until the thirteenth century, and by that time the Viking type of vessel had been adopted along the whole western coast of the Continent, from the North Cape to Portugal (Fig. 9).

After this an important change took place in ships—"castles" were built above the gunwales. At first these were makeshift wooden structures, but their sides were soon incorporated in the hull. The Mediterranean basin did not find out about this type of vessel until the late fourteenth century. Yet contact between the two fleets had existed for a long time and had been intensified as a result of the Crusades and of the manner in which trade had developed since the thirteenth century. Why did the Italians and Catalans abandon their traditional types and adopt the Atlantic form? A Florentine chronicler remarks upon the abruptness of this enthusiasm and specifies that it began in 1304. Was it due to political influences? Or to economic repercussions (this was the beginning of the Florentine bankers' big drive northward)? The question deserves study.

Technical changes raise many such problems of civilization. For convenience in describing these we may divide them into two groups—intellectual problems and social problems, those facing the technician as a thinker and those confronting him as a member of a political, religious, or social community.

The problems in the former group are the most difficult. What part was played by reasoning in the development of this or that technique? We have already asked this question.

Was the medieval technician a scientist? Is it correct to speak of medieval rationalism, as some authors have done—with reference to the ogival vault, to be precise?

To ask ourselves what was the extent of the knowledge possessed by the medieval technician or architect would of course be placing the problem in a false light. For it would mean assuming that his knowledge was organized and arranged systematically, in a way that it certainly was not. But it would be at least equally incorrect to regard his activity as entirely empirical. Men who are deeply versed in certain professions must inevitably have observed certain constants, discovered certain proportions and harmonies that, expressed in mathematical formulas—elementary though these undoubtedly were—could be handed down in workshop or family circle from one generation to another. This is precisely the method employed in all engineers' notebooks, from Villard de Honnecourt to Leonardo da Vinci.

Let us take another actual example. Architecture lends itself with particular ease to this kind of exercise and offers many specific illustrations. A study has recently been made of the problems of buttressing and subsidence in Gothic edifices. At Vézelay and Chartres the buttresses are placed too low, at Amiens they are too high. It was discovered that the thrust was distributed over a certain distance, and corrections were made that were useful to later architects. For it would be surprising if the catastrophes that sometimes occurred in the course of building had been completely forgotten. On the other hand, the subsidence of stones—for soft limestone was frequently used—was very seldom suspected, though at Meaux in 1268 and at Beauvais in 1284, after the chancel collapsed, a change was made in the building materials.

It is interesting, in itself, to note that in the event of danger or uncertainty a great architect would be called in, for this shows that a fund of knowledge was being built up. In 1316 alarm was caused by the list developed by the pillars of Chartres Cathedral, and Pierre de Chelles, foreman of works at Notre-Dame de Paris, was sent for: it was no doubt on his orders that the extra buttress was placed above the springer of the vault.

Thus we see that as time went on architectural experience began to be systematically organized. We have no early-thirteenth-century plans, but a few have survived from the latter part of that century—for instance, those of Rheims (1250) and Strasbourg (1275). Villard de Honnecourt kept a notebook during his building projects, and several models are sketched on the few pages of it that have been preserved. Beginning in the fourteenth century, such plans become numerous. This indicates a considerable intensification of the preliminary "brainwork" carried out before the actual building began. One of the most difficult problems was the stonecutting. This was done in special workshops where wooden panels were cut out with the saw and the stones trimmed to this pattern, as is done occasionally even nowadays. Both in the case of the stones, for which these panels could be used, and in that of the building as a whole, there had to be a transference from a plane surface to a three-dimensional volume; yet even in plans, cotations are an exception: they begin to appear in Italy in the fourteenth century (in the plan of Siena Cathedral by Lando di Pietro, dated 1339). There were no true geometrical plans. The elevation had therefore to be made on the basis of a plan that was not strictly accurate. The different methods of doing this were jealously guarded secrets, which first began to be divulged at the end of the fifteenth century. In 1391, when the architects employed on Milan Cathedral realized that the task was too much for them, other architects were summoned, and so—an illuminating fact—was a mathematician. The document in which this event is recorded indicates that there were several methods, one of which was called "by the square" and another "by the triangle." There seem, indeed, to have been some fairly simple formulas for triangulation, various examples of which are given by Villard de Honnecourt. The most experienced architects had evidently managed to lay down building formulas that show that they reflected about the problems they encountered and had succeeded in recognizing certain constant factors sufficiently definite to form the basis of reliable precepts.

The plans for Milan Cathedral, drawn up by the architect Stornacolo right at the end of the fourteenth century, led to an argument between the last representatives of the lodges —the advocates of professional secrecy—and the moderns, including Brunelleschi. The argument was concerned chiefly with the way in which geometry should be interpreted and applied to the building operations. Medieval builders made elevations from their plans by the same method they used for stone-cutting—by moving geometrical figures over a flat surface so as to calculate volumes by purely manual methods, estimating the surface relationships between the geometrical figures. Does this, however, necessarily mean that their methods entailed "no identification of geometrical figures with numbers, no trace of the system for establishing a relationship or ratio between their lines and the abstract constructions of the intellect, which was to be the great discovery of the Renaissance"? Brunelleschi's discovery may not have come to him all by itself, or in one burst. The jottings seen on plans in the last sixty years or so of the fourteenth century are no doubt meant only as references, but the use of figures is symptomatic of a new and previously unknown spirit.

The construction and use of the trebuchet would have been impossible without a definite theory of ballistics. Here, too, long experience with that instrument may have led military "engineers" to express certain observations in the form of figures. At all events, the change from an almost parabolic trajectory to a flat one testifies to an effort of reflection going well beyond the purely empirical outlook so frequently attributed to the technicians of this period.

Considerable progress had, moreover, been made in mathematical knowledge, largely through the indirect channel of another technique—bookkeeping. As early as the year 1202, Leonardo Fibonacci, a Pisan, was championing the Indo-Arabic system of numeration in his *Liber abaci* and laying down the rules of arithmetic in their application to accountancy problems.

In the thirteenth and fourteenth centuries, the development of accountancy helped this technique to advance from its primitive stage to its most modern forms. The oldest ledgers that have come down to us are no more than memoranda intended to refresh the memories of merchants. The ledger kept by the Holzschuler family of Nuremberg (1304-1307) shows only credit entries accompanied by the names of witnesses of the various transactions, as a precaution in the eventuality of legal proceedings. The earliest Italian ledgers were kept in exactly the same way, though in a slightly improved form: a debtor acknowledged what he owed by putting his commitments in writing with his own hand (this was done, for instance, in the daybook kept by Ugo Teralh, a draper at Forcalquier, in 1320-1332).

Bookkeeping was one obligation, and the launching of companies created others, since it became necessary to show the capital and the joint accounts. The money order was the last new factor to introduce changes in bookkeeping.

In the earliest Italian ledgers (1211 and others of the

thirteenth century), the old method is still followed—chronological order, blank spaces left for the winding up of each transaction, names of witnesses recorded. The account books kept by the Ugolini from 1249 to 1263, to register their dealings at fairs, separate the debit and credit entries, and leave blanks between the accounts of the different customers —this is the forerunner of the current account. Subsidiary books came into use as transactions increased in number and spread over a wider area. At the end of the thirteenth century the Bon Signori—Sienese bankers—had cashbooks and books for current accounts, salesbooks and registers for associates. Lists were also employed and were in common use during the fourteenth century. The growing number of subsidiary ledgers (such as those kept about the year 1322 by the Florentine manufacturing company of Francesco del Bene) shows that other means of ensuring accuracy were available in addition to frequent auditing of accounts.

The Peruzzi, whose firm had many branches, kept all their books in two parts, debit and credit. The private accounts are larger and no longer make it necessary to be constantly carrying sums forward. The current account came into being when it first occurred to bookkeepers to enter debits and credits face to face. It seems to have been the Venetians who first thought of this. The rest of Europe took a long time to copy the new idea. Ledgers were used by two Frenchmen, Bonis of Montauban (1345-1369) and Jacme Olivier of Narbonne (1381-1391).

The double-entry system owes its name, not to outward forms such as credit and debit entries, and not to accounts opened for customers or goods, but to the fact that each entry appeared twice in the ledger—on the credit side of one account and on the debit side of the other. The ledger thus necessarily contained a complete set of personal and impersonal accounts. It comprised five categories of accounts —individual, assets, outgoings, results (profit and loss), and capital. The earliest example of this is found in the accounts of the city of Genoa, in 1340. The earlier books being lost, we do not know the exact date of this "revolution." The change can be observed in the books kept by Francesco Datini, of Prato, who settled at Avignon about 1350. His earliest books are kept like those of the Peruzzi, but certain impersonal accounts are already shown. Then, about 1383, the debit and credit columns begin to be entered in the

Venetian manner. At the close of the fourteenth century, double-entry has become a matter of course.

These gymnastics in bookkeeping demanded a sound knowledge of arithmetic. The development of the teaching of mathematics is striking in this connection, for until the seventeenth century mathematics was regarded as useless except in mechanics, the construction of fortifications, and "police," as Mersenne still called it. It was a branch of study that gained only grudging admittance to the universities; in Paris in 1215 it was allowed only on holidays, to facilitate the study of music and the computation of the calendar, and in 1378 for astrology as well. While it is hardly necessary to point out that Bacon, at Oxford, lumped together mathematics, perspective, the experimental sciences, and alchemy as forming that section of the "mechanical arts" that might give birth to a new science. But once it was realized that arithmetic was useful in trade, schools were opened to teach it as a specific subject—at Genoa as early as 1310, at Florence in 1338, at Lucca in 1345. Textbooks appeared in increasing numbers, and pure arithmetic gradually evolved out of the examples provided by bookkeeping.

In any case fourteenth-century science, especially in Paris, was marked by a trend of the utmost importance. As early as the thirteenth century, Roger Bacon had advocated the experimental method—at Oxford, where mathematics was still taught. In the fourteenth century, Paris began to adopt the new critical empiricism that had been in vogue at Oxford. It has been pointed out that this revolution kept pace with new economic expansion and with the emergence of the great Italian banks, which awakened an interest in realism and utilitarianism among the middle classes. Aristotelian logic, coupled with the experimental method, was to shape that wonderful instrument, modern science.

There is undoubtedly a connection between this scientific development and the evolution of technical processes, of which we have just considered various examples. The mathematical discoveries of the fourteenth century certainly encouraged the rationalization of a number of techniques. Changes in arithmetical techniques (facilitated by the now universal adoption of Arabic figures) were themselves influenced by the bookkeeping methods of the Italian merchants. There would thus appear to have been reciprocal influence between science and technology. Geometry did not advance beyond the Euclidian phase, and was still applied solely to practical problems. Trigonometry and perspective progressed only in practical application, as certain techniques succeeded in deducing some simple elements from their problems, as was the case with architecture. Arab trigonometry, fathered by Ptolemy and the Hindu Arybhata, reached western Europe in the fourteenth century and was to provide an essential foundation for certain techniques.

It is possible that physics was guided toward its accepted form by the technicians, once they had thus laid down a number of simple general problems. It is symptomatic that Buridan took examples from the trebuchet to prove his theory of impetus. Modern physics required a factual basis, and in the absence of organized logical experience, technical problems alone could supply precise data for it.

The fourteenth century was a period when speculation was much to the fore, and technology had its place among the subjects of speculation. The situation was rather similar to the one in which Greece was placed by Pythagoras and his disciples—remarkable technicians who tried to lay down a practical foundation for Greek science. A reaction followed, in exactly the same way, in the form of a return to books— and what is more, in the case of the Renaissance, to the books of the ancients—just when a promising path seemed to be opening up. Except by a few pioneers—all of whom, incidentally, were engineers—such as Leonardo da Vinci and Galileo, experiment was not really resumed in full force until the seventeenth century.

But the repercussions of technical developments were not exclusively intellectual. There were social consequences as well. Neither group, however, appears to have played a really dominant part in the history of civilization during the period with which we are concerned. New techniques did not transform life as they have done in our own day; manual work still predominated. We therefore find none of the social revolutions that generally follow a sudden extension of mechanization. Moreover, it is rare to find in contemporary authors any trace of the misgiving caused by technical development. That development was going on imperceptibly— proceeding down a gentle slope, as it were. The few writings that dealt with technology—foremost among them may be placed, despite its distinctive character, the work of the monk Theophilus, which is fairly well documented, for he mentions technical methods used by Greek artists as well as processes in current use in France, Germany, and Italy—are no more than collections of recipes. Theophilus's work undoubtedly had its hour of fame, for in the late nineteenth century copies of it came to light in many libraries. The original manuscript is agreed to date from the thirteenth century and to be of Italian or German authorship. Theophilus merely lists the different techniques in use in his day, of which he has selected the most satisfactory; he does not assume that continuous progress is being made, nor is he moved to boundless astonishment by the methods he describes. Villard de Honnecourt, halfway through the century, perhaps goes a step further by seeking out techniques and machines that are to some extent labor-saving. In any case, with the exception of a few who deplore the destructive power of certain military machines, no writers show the slightest awareness that the world is falling into the clutches of technology.

Yet it becomes apparent from an attentive study of medieval technological civilization that the machine was already influencing certain forms of social life, certain aspects of the human universe.

The mechanization of industry, and in particular the widespread use of waterpower, led to considerable movements of population. Villages moved downhill, to the banks of streams. Certain industries were stabilized—among them the iron industry, which had previously been itinerant in its search for ore and fuel, but of which one section—the forge —henceforth occupied permanent sites, in river valleys.

The towns, too, were affected by these changes. The introduction of hydraulic power often led to fundamental alterations in their structure, especially as in some cases it was urgently needed as a means of feeding the increased population and for purposes of industrialization. To take a few examples—in the tenth century, Troyes had only two rivers at its disposal, the Seine and the Meldançon; a great number of channels were opened out of these between the eleventh and the thirteenth century, to provide the necessary driving power; in the twelfth century the town already possessed eleven mills, built between 1157 and 1191, and by the fifteenth century forty-one mill wheels were turning there. Rouen had eight mills at the end of the tenth century; on the Robec, a little stream that flows into the Seine, there were two mills in the tenth century, five in the twelfth, ten in the thirteenth, and fourteen at the beginning of the fourteenth century actually within the town walls. Liège had twenty-six mills in the thirteenth century, on the many channels into which its streams had been directed. The medieval towns were like miniature versions of Venice.

It can even be said that to a certain extent this mechanization contributed to the foundation and growth of a number of cities, though it is curious to note that the towns where trade was busiest—and especially those where fairs were held, with the exception of a few, such as Troyes—did not become great industrial cities.

Division of labor is a phenomenon peculiar to industries at a certain stage of their technical development. It is little practiced in the primitive phase or in highly mechanized industries. Division of labor was therefore widespread in the industries of the Middle Ages. The best possible evidence of this is provided by the salt industry in fourteenth-century France. The salt water was run into the cauldron by the *desserre*. Boiling and concentration of the brine were carried out by three workmen (the *have*, the *vaite*, and the *garde*) under the supervision of the *moutier*. Two teams of women were responsible for stoking the fires. After this the *mettaris* took the salt to the *fassaris*, who kneaded it, and on to the *sécharis*, who put it to dry; finally the salt was put into barrels by another team of workmen—and the coopers themselves were a separate, though associated body.

It was the same with the textile industry. Here the differentiation of the various crafts and enterprises was particularly well marked. In ironworks, too, there were a number of quite separate activities, the work done in the forge being divided into hammering, shingling, drawing, and platinizing.

Medieval machines, however rudimentary, contributed to the building up of special legislation. They formed a nucleus for certain institutions that proved to be among the most enduring and characteristic of the whole feudal system. Despite the material from which they were constructed—almost invariably wood, which was neither scarce nor very expensive —these machines required a comparatively large capital outlay; and—still more important—they affected proprietory rights, such as the ownership of rivers, which already had their recognized place in the legal and political system. Owing to the existence of these subsidiary rights, as they may be called, and in order to assert control over equipment that, if not indispensable, was at any rate far more efficient than anything that existed previously, monopolies were gradually established, covering the whole of a given country. Later centuries were to adopt methods similar to monopolies by granting privileges to royal manufactories, and these are even reflected in the patents taken out in modern industry.

I will not revert here to a legal problem that has been the subject of numerous studies—none of which, however, seems to be exhaustive. But it should be noted that local monopolies were by no means restricted to the two instruments they are usually acknowledged to have affected—the press and the mill. In addition to the well-known communal rights applying to boars, which may have arisen from technical methods of improving breeds, we find such monopolies operating in respect of nearly all equipment that made use of waterpower —the forge, the fulling mill, the tanning mill, the whetting-mill, the malt press, and the beer press. Did such local monopolies result from mechanization, or from the overlord's assertion of his right to control a stream?

The attempts to boycott mills on the part of the peasants thus compelled to use them have already been mentioned. In some cases this refractory spirit was appeased by the establishment of communal rights on agreed terms. In other instances reluctance to use the communal (taxed) equipment caused the country people to cling obstinately to their old-fashioned implements. In some areas hand mills survived till a very late period.

The local monopoly is not the only example of a system of rights centering on some piece of mechanism. Certain very costly machines also encouraged the formation of groups. In the Dauphiné, many rural communities were born or grew up around a corn mill or a hemp mill. In Italy, too, a village would have its communal tanning or fulling mill. Some communities formed for economic reasons likewise included machines among their capital equipment. At Chartres the tanning mill belonged to the tanners' guild. The municipality of Marseilles owned several machines for launching galleys; private individuals hired these when necessary, and had to pay a tax if they preferred to use some other equipment (so that here again there were the beginnings of a monopoly).

Furthermore, complicated machinery created, or rendered necessary, a right of association: some of the earliest medieval industrial companies that have come to our knowledge were formed to operate a tilt-hammer or a paper mill.

The technical provisions included in the rules of the cloth-makers' guild and of certain other corporations are known to most people and have been carefully studied. But it is seldom realized that regulations of this kind, including many articles dealing with technical matters, already existed in the Middle Ages. Among the best examples are the little local sets of regulations for mines, many of which were issued in Italy and France from the twelfth century onward. Among them are some drawn up for Champagne in the thirteenth century, some for Vicdessos (Ariège), and some issued at Allevard (Dauphiné) in 1395. Technical provisions are prominent in all of them—instructions for sinking shafts, for pumping equipment, for hoisting tackle, timbering, and ventilation, often accompanied by the most detailed specifications.

In cases where the technical methods of the ancients were preserved unaltered, the regulations of ancient times invariably remained in force. An example of this is to be found in the supply of water to towns, for which systems similar to those of the Romans were employed. In many places, indeed, they were inferior to those of antiquity. Beginning in the fourteenth century, Liège obtained its water supply through the channels (*areines*) draining the mines that had been worked in the surrounding hills ever since the twelfth century. The Richefontaine *areine,* which drained the water from more than 150 mine shafts sunk in the hill on which the citadel stood, was harnessed by the city authorities in the fourteenth century to provide the population with water; a reservoir was dug out in the shale and the water was brought through a lead pipe to another reservoir, whence it was piped to the hospitals and public fountains. Private houses were not supplied with water until the sixteenth century.

In Spain—as throughout North Africa and more especially in Tunisia—the Romans had created a vast irrigation system. The Arabs merely brought this network back into operation, after it had been considerably damaged in successive invasions. They made improvements in some of the water catchments and extended the canals. It was found necessary to draw up regulations covering both technical and administrative matters. Similar instances are to be found in parts of France—in Roussillon and in the vicinity of Aix and Arles.

A further contribution to the creation of special legislation, carefully adapted to the techniques employed, resulted from the ambitious hydraulic undertakings of the Middle Ages—which, in addition to those already mentioned, included the leats on the Ticino, begun as early as the twelfth century, and those of the Adda—begun in the thirteenth century and extended in the fourteenth century as far as Milan. It

would be interesting to make a closer study of the latter
scheme, for as it was pursued for several hundred years it
gave opportunity for the gradual improvement of technical
methods and led up to the great Renaissance engineers and
to Leonardo da Vinci himself.

While these various machines and technical processes had
their influence on men's lives, they themselves were in turn
influenced by men. Medieval machines were very unstable,
their construction changing its character to meet the prevailing economic situation. This was because there was no
mechanism that could not be modified easily and at no great
cost. Water mills frequently changed their purpose in the
course of centuries, and the changes sometimes followed one
another in rapid succession: the St. Paul mill, built in 1211,
was used successively as a corn mill, a whetting mill, a powder
mill, an oil press, and then again a whetting mill. This sort
of thing went so far that the grant of water rights was
sometimes accompanied by the proviso that the mill must
keep to one purpose.

The conclusion of this study finds us in a better position
to appreciate the extent of the gaps that still remain in our
knowledge. How many technical processes are still quite unknown to us? Even among those that have been most successfully investigated—I am thinking here of the textile industry—uncertainty still persists in many respects: as to the
origin and history of the spinning wheel, the techniques of
dyeing, wool combing, and numerous other matters. The
technical level varied from one industry to another. Some
practices remained unchanged since Roman times (water
supply, and such hoisting tackle as the treadmill crane),
while others were completely transformed. The reasons for
technical progress are difficult to determine because we are
so ignorant of the details of technical development. There
were no medieval "inventions," if by "invention" we mean the
outcome of a logical train of reasoning. The fumblings of the
Gothic architects, of dyers, and of agronomists all go to
prove this; it is more correct to say that they resulted in
sporadic successes among a host of errors than to speak of
inventions.

In other words, our attempt to define the Middle Ages as a
civilization of techniques was foredoomed to partial failure.
Even in a sphere as closely studied as that of agriculture it
has not yet been possible to determine the influence of tech-

niques on the community. Sensational changes must have resulted, for instance, when the system of laying land fallow was introduced, and when the use of horses for plowing became general. As our knowledge of technological developments increases it will no doubt become necessary to reconsider a great number of problems. The structure of a community is largely conditioned by its technical level, which in turn depends upon natural conditions. There are many possible types of interference here.

Specialists in medieval history still have plenty of work awaiting them, and this has now outgrown the capacity of the individual student. Collective research must and can be organized, particularly in a field as well defined as the history of technology. One of the few merits of the foregoing study may well be that of inciting others to take up such research, and to encourage the formation of teams.

TRANSLATED FROM THE FRENCH
BY DAPHNE WOODWARD

NATURE AND MAN

AT THE SCHOOL OF CHARTRES

IN THE TWELFTH CENTURY *

M. D. Chenu, O. P.

I

To the very degree that it has dominated our history of
Western civilization, the classification "Renaissance" stands
in need of a rigorous re-examination, unburdened of dogmatic
judgments and oversimplified abstractions. It was created, it is
true, in support of absolute considerations on the development
of culture in the Western world, and had its origins in a
sharply defined notion of the role of antiquity, which in turn
made it necessary to create the classification "Middle Ages"
to fill the gap. But ever since Burckhardt and Voigt set down
their definitions it has been the subject of unmitigated criticism, particularly where our increased knowledge of the
medieval era has brought to light its serious ambiguities. The
very facts that it had to be folded over, as it were, to cover
the major episodes of the Middle Ages, that the first term
"Carolingian Renaissance," then "Twelfth-Century Renais-

* *Journal of World History*, II, 2.

sance" had to be coined, and that finally the events of these Middle Ages had to be included in the pattern of a "Renaissance of Antiquity" divided into three stages with the Italian Quattrocento as its culmination, has brought us today beyond these classifications of expediency to a deeper understanding of the features common to all these different stages that are still loosely grouped under the single heading of Renaissance.[1]

The "Renaissance" as a phenomenon of history cannot be summed up merely as the blind imitation of the masterpieces of Greco-Roman Antiquity in literature, the arts, science, and philosophy, such as might be made under certain extreme circumstances in an archaeological reconstruction. With due allowance for differences in time, place, and persons, it meant literally a re-naissance, that is, a rebirth, a new dawning and new creation that cannot be reduced to its ancient sources by the very fact that it was a new dawning of the human mind. Imitation, where it existed, was used to help the creative spirit and to feed it. The impelling forces that fashioned this new awakening must be seen outside the pale of the geographic, economic, social, political, or religious contexts of antiquity (and the historian must not fail to realize this), for these contexts did not merely form the outer wrapping for a restoration—in the heavy political sense history books at-

[1] The terms *Antiquity* and *Middle Ages* stem from a common idea of Europocentrism that prematurely idealizes the prevailing conditions and removes from our perspective of civilization whole segments of human endeavor. Did not Ibn Khaldun, the Arab historian (fourteenth century), already show better judgment when he observed that the geo-historical cycle of "antiquity," in Egypt, Chaldea, as well as the Mediterranean basin, had as their basis the nomad shepherd sedentary farmer relationship?

As for the term "Middle Ages" and its grammatically neutral form, it too is a common name that did not originally mean the *translatio studii* whereby the Western intellectuals of the twelfth-thirteenth centuries, in imitation of the *translatio imperii*, described the origin of their culture, thus excluding both Byzantium and Islam even from the Mediterranean world. The term "Renaissance" is no more than the expression, within the framework of an "antique" perspective, of the capacity for permanent renewal that characterizes Western Christianity.

On the historical concept of "Renaissance," cf. W. K. Ferguson, *The Renaissance in Historical Thought: Five Centuries of Interpretation* (Boston; Houghton Mifflin, 1948). For its application to the twelfth century, and the latest state of the controversy, in the articles by E. M. Sanford, "The Twelfth Century: Renaissance or Proto-Renaissance," and V. T. Holmes, Jr., "The Idea of a Twelfth Century Renaissance," in *Speculum*, XXVI (1951), 635-642, 643-651.

tach to the word—but were the inner pledge of a new discovery undreamed of before then.

The School of Chartres, during the twelfth-century "Renaissance," offers us a most illuminating case in point. For we
must not overlook the fact that if the men of Chartres undertook the reading of Euclid and the translation of the *Almagest,*
they did so not with the idle curiosity of bookmen in search
of souvenirs of the past but as a result of their sudden awakening to the discovery that the universe was governed by scientific laws. Nor should we forget that if they read Ovid's *Ars
amandi* it was as no more than a breviary for the new attitude
toward the power of passion expressed by the courtly love of
their time. And finally we must bear in mind that if they wrote
their commentaries of the *Timaeus,* these were the product of
an urge to learn about the origins of man and the universe,
and no mere quest for scholarly exegesis. Thus the literary
curiosity of the Chartrains, with all that this implied, was
put to direct use to further their new discovery concerning
nature and man. Historical humanism, it is true, has always
been enriched by a return to the ancients, and with the help
of philology has helped to create a warmth and sympathy with
the past that do not preclude a certain aristocratic refinement. But antiquity can appear in a temper other than its own
and, even at the price of historical truth, can give birth to a
new creation through a subtle assimilation in which none of
the essence of the ancient inspirations is actually lost. Yet one
can hardly call the simple updating of the themes of the
ancients the primary cause or the true sign of such a cultural
renewal; it is only the first step of the inquisitive spirit: the
real creation occurs within man's mind; the newly discovered
ancient sources may well have been accessible to everyone
for ages but remained infertile and unproductive until the
creative spark gave them new direction.

Certainly, little more should be necessary to explode the
hollow notion that the twelfth and subsequent centuries merely
copied the works of antiquity than to remind ourselves of
Chartres itself, the pinnacle of that age, where we find the
cathedral rising in an apotheosis of creative fervor and its walls
being decorated with astonishingly realistic scenes from contemporary life, at the very moment that Gilbert de la
Porrée was setting down his glosses of Boethius. Or we could
equally well study John of Salisbury, then Bishop of Chartres
(+ 1180) to discover the quintessence of his strangely modern
political thinking in *Polycraticus,* notwithstanding the fact that

this highly erudite work owed so much to the sources of Antiquity. But let us begin more modestly at the point where medieval man first began to find himself as his eyes opened to the world of nature. This was the period that witnessed an extraordinary surge of mechanical development, and by following its path we shall certainly not be neglecting some of the noblest manifestations of the human spirit.

In his history of technics, L. Mumford shows us how we have underestimated humanity's achievements before the dawn of the modern era, and he underlines the importance of the advances made during the Middle Ages. In the opening chapter of his narrative he describes how both artist and artisan played a common role in the awakening of interest in nature:

"In the fresh naturalistic sculpture of the thirteenth-century churches one can watch the first uneasy stir of the sleeper, as the light of morning strikes the eyes. At first, the craftsman's interest in nature was a confused one: side by side with the fine carvings of oak leaves and hawthorn sprays, faithfully copied, tenderly arranged, the sculptor still created strange monsters, gargoyles, chimeras, legendary beasts. But the interest in nature steadily broadened and became more consuming."

We unhesitatingly subscribe to Mumford's thesis, which moreover has been fully endorsed by the art historians. We believe that the development of technics was both the expression of, and the introduction to, a true, positive discovery of nature, for at the same time as he achieved mastery over nature man revealed himself to himself, as it were. At first this revelation was only subconscious, but it was soon to manifest itself in open curiosity about the external world when the artisan's struggle with the materials of his craft opened the way to a new type of thinking in sober contrast with the intoxicating dialectics and the subjective fantasies of the time.

In the history of the Middle Ages the twelfth century was marked by a transformation that shook the whole material foundations of existence and constituted "one of the most profound [cleavages] ever to have occurred in the development of European society" (M. Bloch). With the breaking up of the feudal system and its large land holdings, with the economic and political emancipation of urban craftsmen organized into corporations, and with the rise of a market economy accompanied by a growing circulation of goods and people, the introduction and expansion of new techniques had the effect of revolutionizing the material conditions of life as well as the manner of perceiving, apprehending, and portraying the world.

Water mills and hydraulic wheels which utilized the power of water and produced circular motion, lifting machinery which reduced physical effort, a new type of harness which transformed transport and travel and gave greater freedom to man, the construction of bridges, the creation of war industries which put an end to ancient chivalry (the Council of Lateran of 1139 banned the new crossbow as an abhorrent weapon), magnetic compasses and fixed rudders which made possible navigation on the high seas, mechanical clocks which synchronized the actions of men and standardized time—all these examples of efficiency, though still few in number, already existed everywhere and profoundly modified not only the various trades but the whole environment and fabric of existence; life was no longer ordered by the tempo of man but by mechanical time. Chartres was one of the intellectual centers that quickly recognized and became interested in these extraordinary changes. At Saint-Victor, it is true, Hugo also included the mechanical arts in his cultural directory, "lanificium, armaturam, navigationem, agriculturam, venationem, medicinam, theatricam." But in effect this reflected Hugo's bookish knowledge of the ancients, although it does reveal his open mind. John of Salisbury, who was a better sociologist, made a study of the new place occupied in the cities by the trade corporations, including the rural associations and the mechanical trades. The theologian observed that the growing specialization of these corporations clearly benefited the community as a whole but that it had already become well-nigh impossible to formulate legislation delineating precisely the innumerable functions of each of them. The study of man's proper place in the world of forces at work was indeed one of the classical themes of the philosophy of the Chartrains but in no way impaired their religious instinct. God was the Creator of all things and from the very beginning His causality transcended man's every act and movement as well as all physical phenomena; nature was the principle of all fertility and every generation obeyed a series of determined laws henceforth clearly recognizable; as for man, he put nature to his own use by imitating it. Here, too, the works of the ancients furnished the Chartrains, through their reading of Chalcidius, himself inspired by the *Timaeus,* with an early pattern on which they constructed their thoughts; but if, as we see, these scholars did draw upon one another, by doing so they enriched the traditional texts with their own experience. William of Conches has given us several examples of this, and Master Gilbert incorporated into his writings what we would today call the food and shoe industries.

In this mechanical universe man emerged bewildered from empiricism; he depersonalized his actions and became aware of the objective profundity and articulation of things in the world ruled by natural law. Order ceased to be the mere product of esthetic imagination or religious conviction; a method now existed whereby order could be verified and upheld, since nature was penetrable and predictable. To fathom these immutable laws of nature became one of the goals of science. The *quadrivium*, the science of *res*, had an educational value equal to that of the *trivium*, the science of the *verba*, which was turning out so many rhetoricians and dialecticians. Indeed, were not the artisans of Chartres Cathedral of a stature equal to that of Abélard? Of all the schools then in existence it was precisely Chartres that specialized in the study of the *quadrivium* embracing the scientific disciplines of the seven arts. Admittedly, Bernard of Chartres (Chancellor from 1119 to 1126), one of the teachers venerated by the new generations, was Master of Speculative Grammar, and Gilbert de la Porrée (Chancellor from 1126 to 1138) was Master of Logic; but whereas emphasis was directed toward the literary disciplines at Orleans, "the capital of Poetry in France" (E. Faral) and toward theological "questions" at Laon, everyone at Chartres evinced a taste for the study of mathematics and the physical sciences. A good example of the particular balance sought after at Chartres can be found in the *Heptateuchon* produced by Thierry of Chartres (+ 1175), which was a manual of the whole Chartrain program encompassing the Seven Liberal Arts. Even theology speculated on numbers and unity, and assumed a mathematical form that was to be preserved for several generations as an integral part of Platonistic teaching, which always favored this approach.

Thus amongst the *auctores* who constituted the basic texts of Chartres we find Boethius' arithmetic, Ptolemy's *Canons*, and the medical treatises of Galen and Constantine the African side by side with Donat, Priscian, Virgil, Cicero, and Quintilian, who were studied everywhere else. The poet Hildebert of Lavardin (+ 1130) maintained frequent contact with Chartres; but Adelard of Bath, that indefatigable traveler in quest of Greek and Arabic works of science, received his education and training at Chartres. Translator of Euclid and publicizer of the chemical treatise, *Mappae clavicula,* he lived to see his *Quaestiones naturales* transcribed after those of Seneca. His contemporary and rival in translation, Hermann of Carinthia, produced a Latin version of the *Planisphere* (1143) and dedicated it to his master, Thierry of Chartres. It was this translation that re-established the fame of Ptolemy. The decline of Chartres in the second half of the century, which was probably due to the competition of Paris, in no way diminishes the efficacy of the reading of the ancients, any more than it prejudices the value of the intellectual spirit that reigned there. The *Porretani,* who took their name from their master, Gilbert de la Porrée, and whose importance can be gauged by the animosity displayed by their adversaries, were to enrich the heritage of the first generations of Chartres at least in certain domains and particularly that of natural philosophy.

II

Two eminent figures, Adelard of Bath and William of Conches, enable us to measure the highly original contribution to the philosophy of nature made by the reading and compiling of the *auctores antiqui,* such as Seneca's *Quaestiones naturales* and especially the *Timaeus,* the work both scholars cherished most. With these men the concept of nature witnessed a true rebirth, particularly when viewed within the human and religious framework of their own century.

In examining the three themes—Creation, miracles, and the works of nature—that the Chartrains dealt with in a manner characteristically their own, it is important to note the sharp distinction they made between the first two, which they held to be truly divine, and the third, which, though also divine in supreme essence, they regarded as operating according to autonomous laws. In those days, the diffuse faith of Christians was prescribed by the image of the universe put forward by St. Augustine, in which the omnipotence of God was declared to manifest itself equally in the flowers of spring and the budding of Aaron's rod, in the wine harvested from the vineyard and the miracle of Cana, in the infants born every day and the resurrection of a dead person. This religious confusion that devaluated the second causes obtained even in a symbolic view of the world, so that we find the explanation of phenomena by their immediate causes disappearing in favor of interpretations that, quite legitimately of course, could be given these phenomena in sacral or poetic terms within an overall reference to their supreme destiny. The many schools of neoplatonism then in vogue conferred on these interpretations a high degree of philosophical profundity notwithstanding the elements of naïveté they may have contained. It should be added that a literal reading of the Bible—the material and historical contents of which were governed by its religious intent, and moreover reflected Semitic ideas and modes of expression—had the effect actually of discouraging interest in the natural and historical origins of the earth.

We may well imagine, therefore, with what alarm religious persons greeted the sudden assertion of the existence of natural phenomena and the challenge to the symbolic interpretations. To comment on Genesis through the medium of the *Timaeus,* as was regularly done at Chartres, was no scholastic exercise of eccentricity; it was the enunciation of the laws of nature that the mystery of transcendental revelation in no way invalidated; and it was made not without some risk to those of simple-minded faith, nor indeed without a certain amount of concordism. This in fact was the first episode in the modern dialogue between reason and faith, and it occurred at the very moment when Abélard, in Paris, was embarking on the same course in dialectics.

When the cry of blasphemy was heard William of Conches, the most spirited theoretician of the group, rose in anger against those who held that the discovery of reasoned explanations for the workings of nature was a denial of God, since, he said, God was the true Creator of both nature and reason and so doubly glorified in this discovery. "But," protested one good Christian, "is not the birth of a human being a work of the Creator?" To which William retorted: "I take nothing away from God: He is the Author of all things, evil excepted; but 'nature,' with which He endowed His creatures, accomplishes a whole scheme of operations, and these too turn to His glory since it is He who created this very nature." To those who confronted him with the images of the biblical story on the origin of man, he replied: "To seek the 'reason' of things and the laws of their genesis is the great mission of the believer which we must carry out by the fraternal association of our inquiring minds. Thus, it is not the Bible's role to teach you the nature of things; that is the domain of philosophy."

Meanwhile, the same arguments were being put forward in virtually the same terms by Adelard of Bath, an impassioned student of Arabic science and philosophy. In his *Quaestiones naturales* he too proclaimed aloud his faith in reason as a means of discovering the inner law of things and his opposition to those who supported authoritarianism of thought. It is through reason, he said, that we are men. For if we turned our backs on the amazing rational beauty of the universe we live in we should indeed deserve to be driven therefrom, like a guest unappreciative of the house he is received into.

The logic of this position led these same theologians to adopt an interpretation of *Genesis* completely opposed to the commonly accepted one: namely, primordial chaos had not existed. William rejected the almost universally held view of those who, under pretext of glorifying the wisdom and powers of the Lord in introducing order at will into the universe, dismissed the ordinary sequence of the laws of nature, which in themselves sufficed to account for such order. The historical setting was nothing more than a kind of anthropomorphism, just as in the *Timaeus* (30 a: ". . . Taking the visible mass in the state he found it, resembling chaos shaking and heaving in wild convulsions [the Demiurge] transformed it from disorder into order") the historical setting was based on a myth Chalcidius erroneously took at face value. In a famous letter to Saint Bernard, William of Saint-Thierry violently attacked the "new philosophy" of Conches who, speaking of the creation of Woman, had dared write: "*irridet* historiam *divinae auctoritatis* . . . . physico *illud sensa interpretans, arroganter vertitati historiae suum praefert inventum, parvipendens magnum sacramentum.*" Thus stood physicism at loggerheads with symbolism.

III

On the basis of this naturalism the Chartrains began to reorganize their minds and redirect the focus of their intellectual curiosity, even in matters religious. No longer were they interested in extraordinary events, like the *mirabilia* that had so fascinated their elders that the more fantastic they were the more they saw in them signs of true providence; instead, they charted the course of their attention toward the orderly, determined sequence, especially in the phenomena of life. To them nature was above all the principle of generation. *"Opus naturae,"* we have already seen, *"est quod similia nascantur ex similibus, ex semine vel ex germino, quia est natura vis rebus insita similia de similibus operans."*

Biological experimentation played no role in the development of this new attitude of mind: we are dealing here with a philosophical approach, derived from a syncretism combining the reading of the *Timaeus* with ideas taken from Boethius, the common inspiration of the Neoplatonists as well as a source of their ambiguities. Far surpassing the masters of Chartres, the *Porretani* were now to take this theme of nature and expand and stylize it. Let us therefore write Nature with a capital letter; for we now find it personified, like some goddess in the literature of the time, but here expressing a truly profound philosophical concept:

> *O Dei proles genetrixque rerum . . .*

Thus begins the ode of Alain of Lille, not unlike a religious hymn. Even before him, though Bernard Sylvestre, in his *De mundi universitate,* had allegorically depicted Nature associated with Nous bringing order out of chaos. Alain exploited the allegory in the pedantic metaphors of his *De planctu Naturae,* and its impact was to survive not only the crisis of Aristotelianism but the great flowering of poetry of the ensuing centuries. For even though the literary conceits he used soon became outmoded the profound message they cloaked lived on, i.e., the wonderment of men who, enthralled by the marvels of the *Bestiaries* and the *Lapidaries*, and the bondage of intellectual and social immaturity, emerged to discover the harmonious force of life, its instincts, its laws and freedom, the rhythm of the seasons, and the cycle of living organisms:

> *O Dei proles genitrixque rerum,*
> *Vinculum mundi, stabilisque nexus,*
> *Gemma terrenis, speculum caducis,*
> > *Lucifer orbis.*
> *Pax, amor, virtus, regimen, potestas,*
> *Ordo, lex, finis, via, dux, origo,*
> *Vita, lux, splendor, species, figura,*
> > *Regula mundi.*

Beneath this moral with its pagan overtones lies a feeling that is manifestly religious: Alain addresses Nature as a goddess who then recounts how she comports herself in this world as in her own noble demesne, and how man has introduced disorder into this harmonious world precisely where the laws of nature should reign in triumph. Because man too is part and parcel of nature, the code of his conduct is to be found within himself, in the determinism of his own being, as it were, and by the grace of his own freedom; nature is the principle of a moral life, and to adhere to it is the rule of righteousness and at the same time the guarantee of happiness. If Nature complains (*De planctu*), it is decidely because in his freedom man repeatedly contravenes the laws of his own nature. Here Alain takes us further than the Chartrains, who did not extend their concept of nature to encompass the moral order; but he remains at one with their inspiration.

It would seem that we have now reached a point that is the exact antithesis of the great Christian theme of submission to divine law, of obedience as the rule of conduct, and humility as the doctrine of our condition, since it is within himself, by his own will and not by mandate received from without, that man really finds the truth and goodness of his life. But this is not so; for the autonomy of Nature is not absolute—its truth and force derive directly from the Lord and serve as his vicar and handmaiden. Nature is master of the universe but only by delegation from the Almighty. Despite his most daring pronouncements, Alain of Lille, like William of Conches, remained deeply and fundamentally religious, though he stood on a frontier of Christianity quite different from that of St. Bernard.

It must be admitted that it was a very delicate matter to negotiate the above fine distinction between autonomy and dependence, or to put it slightly differently, between these profane values and their sacred origins. It meant that the religious mind had to bring its sharpest edge of reasoning into play at exactly the right place to avoid being corrupted or compromised. One can well understand, therefore, that the acceptance of this new attitude did not come about without a certain upheaval: the attacks of William of Saint Thierry show that the opposition was as sincere as it was clumsy. But more important, the validity of this new attitude was not recognized until a real crisis occurred and the rumblings of a doctrinal anticlericalism began to be heard. The crisis developed because of a resentment of sorts against the abuses of the power of ecclesiastics who had condemned the secular view of the universe. This crisis was soon to take on more serious proportions with the introduction of Aristotle's metaphysics of nature and rational epistemology. But even then Alain's allegory of Nature proved the force of its impact and was to sweep far beyond the intellectual circles of the schools. The moral and doctrinal principles he had expounded were soon to explode into the heart of the thirteenth century, when John de Meun produced the second *Romance of the Rose* in the vernacular. The barb this time was far more pointed and there was more than a hint of raillery against the religious meaning given to the mysteries of nature in his secularized interpretation of how the forces of the cosmos operate. The condemnation of 1277, as clumsy as it was (we know that St. Thomas Aquinas was seriously implicated in the affair), was no empty gesture.[2]

For every "philosophy of the world"[3] is an attempt, and a legitimate one, to explain the world in its entirety. It would be both wrong and incongruous to expect a zone of mystery, a holy refuge, to be set aside for the supposed benefit of religion to the detriment of any such philosophy. All nature is the domain of secular science, just as all nature comprehends sacred values: what changes is the angle of vision, and science and religion should both recognize this. But it cannot

---

[2] It must not be concluded from this that John of Meun was anti-Christian nor that he made nature a divinity.

[3] *Philosophia mundi:* this is the very significant title of one of the works of William of Conches.

be denied that the enthronement of Nature marked the end of a certain Christian view of the universe, just as the ideological and political struggle against the Holy Roman Empire signified the end of another view of Christianity. The years 1200 were to see this unique dual assault carried out on a common front with John of Salisbury opening the breach despite his passionate support of Thomas à Becket. Scientism and laicism may have managed to create a degree of commotion and fever, but in the last analysis the operation was a sign of normal growing pains. At the portals of Chartres, Christ continued to be the Saviour of creation.

Consequently, theology made the most of the situation by undertaking the rational promotion of the new ideas within the faith. Once again Alain of Lille, the master of natural philosophy, appears on the scene, this time as the theoretician of the "rules of theology," that is, of the method whereby religious knowledge, like every other discipline of the mind, is organized and constructed in accordance with internal principles that impart to it both the appearance and value of a science. Alain no more contraposes reason and faith than he does the profane and the sacred: he marks the distinction between them so as to unite them. Mindful of the supreme dignity of theology, he has Nature remark, *Non adversa, sed diversa sentimus.* A number of spiritual leaders were to express alarm at the confidence thus shown in reason; but the century of Albert the Great, Bonaventura, and Thomas Aquinas was to prove them wrong.

IV

The first generation of Chartrians were so taken up with their "philosophy of the world" that they seem to have considered man only in relation to Nature, viewing him as a homogeneous unit even at the spiritual level. In their eyes man was a "microcosm"—the theme was a traditional one of antiquity and a source of inspiration for the scholars of Chartres who revitalized it to include even theology in which they paid more attention to the act of creation than to the grace of Redemption. This is a far cry indeed from Augustine's view of man rapt in his inner drama and preoccupied with the history of his own conscience and the collective history of mankind.

That this parallelistic concept of man and nature would bring new vitality to religion had already been made clear by the intellectual mysticism of the Greek fathers, Origen and Gregory of Nyssa, the import of which was slowly to emerge in the course of the whole twelfth century. Once again the Porretani were to find themselves in the forefront of those who welcomed these new religious ideas, notwithstanding the hostility prevailing in the Augustinian-dominated world of the West: God is present in His creatures and the *forma essendi* of their very being; hence His creatures are good since they exist in and by so deep-rooted an association. But it also brought a new vitality to philosophy, for at the same time as they unsuccessfully attempted to fit the theory of the Soul of the World into the Christian doctrine, the Chartrians saw man's dignity in his ability to evolve ideas presenting both an intelligent and divine explanation for all things. And finally, it brought a new vitality to science, since the physical and physiological structure of man comprehends the four elements of the universe, adapted to man's nature.

But both the pagan and the Christian Greeks had perceived how, within the unity of man and cosmos, man distinguishes himself from the cosmos and determines his position by opposition: one's presence to oneself is distinct from one's presence in the world. Whether expressed through the idealism of the Platonists or the empiricism of Aristotle, the Socratic call to Know Thyself had combined an irreducible psychology with a physics of the soul. But the Platonism of the Chartrians, limited as it was to the image presented in the first chapters of the *Timaeus*, was unaware of the resources of this spiritual philosophy. This gave their opponents a decided advantage, for without recourse to any Christian Socratism their spiritual experience provided them with an acute sense of the inner self the absence of which in men like William of Conches unleashed a stream of violent and justified criticism at Citeaux. It was not Chartres that produced those innumerable treatises *De natura animae, De spiritu et anima, De unione corporis et spiritus,* reflecting the intense spiritual and scientific curiosity of the many circles of the twelfth century, and employed by the Cistercians and Victorines to give support to the psychological analyses they

produced in such abundance. St. Bernard was indeed at another frontier of the Christian world.

Only with the next generation was this Christian phenome-
nology of the spirit to receive attention by a John of Salisbury,
who was no doubt drawn to this sphere of thought by the
very eclecticism of his temperament. But we should note that
he traced its origins back to the experience of the early
Fathers much more than to the theories of the philosophers.
In no sense, however, did he adopt the fundamental conceptions animating the St. Bernard doctrine of free will, *De
gratia et libero arbitrio,* in which the supreme experience of
Augustine yielded new vintages in the climate of Cîteaux.
From Alain of Lille to Simon of Tournai, in fact, the
Porretani resolutely and steadfastly supported the position
of the *philosophi* as against that of the *theologi:* their analysis
of freedom rested completely on the definition formulated by
Boethius the philosopher, as he was called—*Liberum arbi-
trium est liberum de voluntate judicium*—and not at all on the
Augustinian definition circulated at the time by Pierre Lom-
bard.

Here once again we find the Chartrian notion of naturalism
encompassing the moral sphere, wherein perfect man is defined by those very laws of nature where virtue awakens
virtuality. So that if Venus participates in the work of Nature,
as recounted in the moral of the *De planctu Naturae,* this is
not really an act of evil lust unless a breach of fidelity to
nature itself is involved; for the presence of God is actively
manifest even in the forces of carnal desire. The twelfth
century was to be imbued, in different forms, with this
humanism, and it was Chartres that imparted to it its first
philosophical justification.[4] For this justification, the utilization of the rich sources of antiquity provided the instrument;
but it was the acute sensitivity to the world and the experi-

----

[4] On the developments of secular morality based on natural law
alongside supernatural morality, cf. the works of Ph. Delhaye, particularly "L'enseignement, de la philosophie morale au douzième siècle,"
in *Mediaeval Studies,* II (1949), pp. 77-99, and "Une adaptation du
'Des officiis' au douzième siècle: le 'Moralium dogma philosophorum'"
in *Recherches de théologie ancienne et médiévale,* XVI (1949) 227-
258.

This is the refraction in teaching of the books on the phenomena of
desacralization that occurred in institutions and public morals and even
ordinary contracts, which passed from *de jure* and sacred laws (*jus-
jurandum*) to law regulated by legislation and juridical sanctions
(*jus*).

ence of things, including Christian grace, that gave it its initiative. As John of Salisbury said, *Rerum experientia est magistra intelligentiae.*

TRANSLATED FROM THE FRENCH
BY PAULINE BENTLEY

BIBLIOGRAPHY

On the Renaissance of the twelfth century, Ch. H. Haskins, *The Renaissance of the Twelfth Century* (Cambridge: Harvard University Press, 1927); G. Paré, A Brunet, P. Tremblay, *La Renaissance du XIIe siècle. Les écoles et l'enseignement* (Paris, Ottawa: 1933: P. Renucci, Paris: 1954).

On the Schools at Chartres, A. Clerval, *Les écoles de Chartres au Moyen Age* (Paris: 1895).

On the second generation of Chartrians, R. L. Poole, "The Masters of the Schools at Paris and Chartres in John of Salisbury's Time," in *English Historical Review*, XXV (1920), 321-42; Cf. C. J. Webb, *Prolegomena*, in his edition of John of Salisbury's *Polycraticus* (Oxford: 1909); H. Liebeschutz, *Medieval Humanism in the Life and Writings of John of Salisbury* (London: Warburg Institute, 1950).

On the disciples of Gilbert de la Porrée, the *Porretani,* subject of numerous recent works, see critical bibliography laid down by E. Bertola, "La scuola di Gilberto de le Porreo," in *Saggi e studi di filosofia medioevale* (Padua: 1951), 19-34.

On the philosophy of nature at Chartres, E. Gilson, "La cosmogonie de Bernardus Silvestris," in *Archives d'histoire doctrinale et littéraire du moyen âge,* III (1928), 5-24; J. M. Parent, *La doctrine de la création dans l'Ecole de Chartres* (Paris-Ottawa: 1938); G. Raynaud de Lage, *Alain de Lille, poète du XIIe siècle* (Paris-Montreal: 1951); T. Gregory, "L'idea della natura nella scuola di Chartres," in *Giornale critico della filosofia italiana* (1952), 433-42.

PART THREE

Science, Religion, Humanism

ITALIAN RENAISSANCE HUMANISM*

Nicola Abbagnano

I. THE PROBLEM OF HUMANISM

From the second half of the fourteenth century onward,
writers, historians, moralists, and politicians in Italy unanimously insisted on a radical change demonstrated in man's
attitude toward the world and toward life. They were convinced that a new epoch had begun that constituted a radical
break with the medieval world; and they endeavored to clarify
for themselves the significance of this change. They ascribed
it to the "rebirth" of a spirit that man had already possessed in
the Classical Age and that had been lost during the Middle
Ages: a spirit of freedom by which man vindicates his rational autonomy, recognizes himself as deeply implanted in
nature and in history, and determines to make these his
dominion. This "rebirth" was, from the point of view of these
writers, a return to antiquity, a reappropriation of capacities
and powers the ancients (i.e., the Greeks and Romans) had
possessed and exercised: a return, however, that consisted not
in a simple *repetition* of antiquity, but in a resumption and
continuation of all that the ancient world had achieved. Such
convictions were expressed, in one form or another, by numerous figures of the Italian Renaissance; and it may be said that

* *Journal of World History*, VII, 2.

every new discovery of documentary material enables us to realize more completely the degree to which these convictions were shared by writers and personalities of the epoch.

Such testimony is corroborated by important cultural phenomena: the birth of a new art, splendid in the variety and value of its expressions; of a new conception of the world; of a science destined to bear fruit throughout subsequent centuries right up until the present day: of a new way of understanding history, politics, and relationships between men in general. For a long, long time such testimony was taken literally and served as a basis for determining the division of Western civilization into historical periods. With Italian Humanism began that modern age of civilization of which we, today, are the heirs and direct descendants.

Not always, however, have contemporary historians accepted the declarations of the Italian Humanists to the letter. Some of them, as was their right and even, in a certain sense, their duty, have questioned those declarations and submitted them to the test: going so far as to deny or, at least, to mitigate the sharp dichotomy the Humanists placed between their epoch and that which preceded it—thus weakening the originality of the Renaissance and strengthening its historical continuity with the past. The Humanists prided themselves on having discovered the formative human value of the liberal arts, that is, disciplines such as poetry, rhetoric, and history which the ancients maintained to be proper to free men. But had the Middle Ages really ignored these disciplines? Certainly not, if one takes into account the constant study of such disciplines in that period and their vital role in forming and developing medieval culture. The Humanists declared themselves hostile to the problems proper to medieval philosophy and considered them abstruse and useless. With what then were their own writings concerned? With the soul, with God, with providence, with predestination and human freedom; that is to say, with the same problems as were debated in the Middle Ages, to which, moreover, they found by and large the same solutions. The Humanists were hostile to medieval science and in particular to Aristotelian physics, in which they perceived only a complex of abstruse concepts expressed in barbaric form. Yet it was precisely in medieval Aristotelianism and in particular in its fourteenth-century variant that the founders of modern science, Leonardo, Copernicus, Galileo, found their major inspiration; on account of its polemics against the physics of the Aristotelians, Renaissance Humanism was an obstacle rather than an aid to the formation of the new science.

Such contentions are characteristic of Renaissance studies of the last few decades, intended above all to correct the image that the Renaissance had projected about itself and that historians of the nineteenth century substantially accepted. They are not completely arbitrary and devoid of foundation since they are based on new investigations, new readings, and newly discovered texts and documents. They cannot be ignored, therefore, in a study that proposes to illustrate the contribution of the Renaissance Humanism to the history of Western culture. A synthetic picture of this contribution can be sketched only by bringing to the fore the fundamental themes around which revolved the reflections of Renaissance writers. At the same time, the picture will include a critique, or rather a re-evaluation of the more recent theses to which we have just referred.

II. The Discovery of Man

Renaissance Humanism is often credited with having discovered or rediscovered "the value of man." This expression meant above all the value of man as a terrestrial or earthly being implanted in the world of nature and history, capable of forging his own destiny therein. The man credited with this value was a finite, rational being whose participation in nature and society was neither a sentence nor an exile but an instrument of freedom, and he could, therefore, accomplish in nature and among men his development and his happiness.

It is commonly held that the medieval conception of the relationships between man and the world drew its inspiration from Aristotelianism. Actually, it corresponded substantially to the Stoic conception according to which the world was a necessary and perfect order, in which each thing had its place and function, and was maintained in this place or this function by an infallible force. All that man could and must do was conform to this order. Even his free choice could be usefully employed only in view of this conformity. Therefore, the fundamental institutions of the medieval world—the Empire, the Church, Feudalism—appeared as the guardians of the cosmic order in all things concerning man and his world. Their main object was to make all those material and spiritual goods to which man could aspire (from truth to his daily bread) appear to derive from the order to which he belonged; that is, from those hierarchies that were the interpreters and custodians of this order.

The signs of the reawakening of commerce and of the arts shown in the eleventh century, voyages of discovery and trade, provoked the first crisis of the medieval conception of cosmic order. They provided factual evidence that it was possible for the individual to acquire for himself the goods he needed, increasing and defending them by his own activity and thanks to the collaboration of others. Hierarchical power gradually began to appear as a limit or a threat, rather than as a help or guarantee to the human capacity to acquire or enjoy the goods indispensable to man. The struggle for municipal autonomy, for liberation from the restrictions of feudalism, was substantially based on man's confidence in himself, in his capacity to provide for his needs and to organize himself into autonomous communities making better provision for his own defense than the hierarchies imposed from above. The so-called discovery of man by Humanism was nothing but the philosophic expression or conceptual recognition of capacities that man had already attributed to himself centuries before and that he had already exercised and was exercising in those cities that were the cradle of Humanism. As is often the case, the philosophic elaboration arrived somewhat tardily upon the scene in order to express and generalize a human experience that had already borne fruit in the fields of economics, politics, and art. Seen from this angle the geographic connection of Italian Humanism with the great Italian cities and, above all, with Florence, where the exercise of new economic and political activities had been, and was still, more open, more free, and more mature than elsewhere, acquires its true significance.

The exaltation of human freedom by Giannozzo Manetti, Pico della Mirandola, Marsilio Ficino, was an act of faith in the powers that man was discovering and rediscovering in himself, an act of faith in his capacity to shape his world, to modify and to better it indefinitely. Pico della Mirandola has expressed this act of faith in a well-known passage:

"I have given you, Adam"—so says God—"neither a predetermined place, nor a particular aspect nor special prerogatives, so that you may take and keep that place, that aspect, those prerogatives that you desire all by your own choice and advice. The limitations to the nature of other beings are contained within my prescribed laws. You shall determine your own nature, without being constrained by any barrier, by means of your own freedom to whose power I have entrusted you. I have placed you in the midst of the world so that from there you might better see what is in the world. I have made you neither heavenly nor earthly, neither mortal nor immortal in order that, like a free and sovereign artifice, you may mold and sculpt yourself into that form you will have chosen for yourself."

This freedom, which is the absence of determinism and the capacity for self-determination, contains the highest exaltation of the dignity of man as such. It is an optimistic exaltation that ignores many limitations, restrictions, and conditions to which (as we know today) human freedom to self-determination is subjected. But it expresses man's confidence in himself, that is to say, in his autonomous powers, and the urge to exercise such powers. Men of the modern world have never since been completely without this confidence and this urge, and even today every victory, every forward step seems to be conditioned by them.

III. Man in Nature

Since the capacity for self-determination, the freedom that the Renaissance exalts in man is a power man possesses in regard to himself, to other men and to things, it is a worldly power. This implies on the one hand a basic bond with the world of nature and on the other hand a second bond—no less essential—with society and with history. These themes occur frequently in the writings of the Humanists and of the Italian Renaissance philosophers.

If by naturalism we mean the conviction that man is part of nature, that nature is his dominion, that the aspects that bind him to nature—corporeity, needs, feelings—are so essential to him that he can neither ignore nor leave them out of consideration, we can certainly speak of a Renaissance naturalism. The writers of the Renaissance indeed exalted the "spirit" of man, which is the object of his powers of freedom, but they did not forget the body and all that pertains to the body. The recognition of the value of pleasure so common among the Humanists and their aversion toward medieval asceticism clearly demonstrated a new evaluation of man's natural aspects. "Epicurus," said Cosmo Raimondi, "places the supreme good in pleasure because he has looked deeply into the force of nature and understood that we were born and have been formed by nature in such a way that nothing is more fitting than to have all the members of the body sound and healthy and to keep them in this condition free from spiritual or bodily evil." The *De voluptate* of Lorenzo Valla is the major document on the importance attributed to pleasure as the relationship that binds man to the body and to all bodily things. Valla even elaborated an ethic of pleasure by reducing virtue itself to a choice of pleasures: the man who comports himself well is the man who puts the greatest advantage before the least and the least disadvantage before the greatest. As a natural being, man, according to Valla, is neither God nor angel; and even when he would prefer not to be exposed to daily dangers, he should not forget that if he could avoid these dangers, he would be immortal; and immortality is something he cannot ask of nature nor can nature grant it to him. In an extreme and paradoxical form, Valla also expressed the new evaluation of the carnal aspect of man: "From the human standpoint prostitutes are more meritorious than sanctimonious and continent virgins."

The Renaissance popularity of Epicurus, whom the Middle Ages had considered to be the philosopher of impiety, is due to this new attitude toward nature. He then emerged as a master of human wisdom, a philosopher who had seen man in his true nature. Nor was the Renaissance slow to defend the pleasure of the fleeting moment, pleasure as an end in itself, as defined by Aristippus; but parallel with this we find, in Ficino for example, the exaltation of pleasure as a universal cosmic force, as the joy that makes the universe expand and consolidate itself.

The aversion toward medieval asceticism was the obvious counterpart of this attitude. The Middle Ages were perhaps (and even this may be superfluous) not so addicted to asceticism as the Humanists imagined. Asceticism was, however, undoubtedly a path toward moral perfection, and this is precisely what the Humanists denied. Coluccio Salutati and

Giannozzo Manetti, Poggio Bracciolini and Lorenzo Valla all engaged with equal vigor, though in various keys, in polemics against asceticism and that monastic life that adopted it as its ideal. In his *De professione religiosorum*, Lorenzo Valla denies any religious superiority to monastic life. The life of Christ, he says, is imitated not only by those who belong to religious orders but by those who, both inside and outside the ranks of the clergy, dedicate their activity to God.

IV. MAN IN SOCIETY

The other aspect of man's earthliness is that social and political character that binds him to the human community by the same essential bond that binds him to nature. This was a favorite theme, particularly with Florentine Humanists, who actively participated in the political life of their city. Discussions concerning the superiority of the active life over the speculative and of moral philosophy over physics and metaphysics merely provide further illustration of this theme. In his *De nobilitate legum et medicinae*, Coluccio Salutati declared that he gladly left to the propagandist of pure speculation all other truths, as long as he was left with science of all things human. And he preferred laws that concerned men and their interrelationships to medicine and natural sciences in general, which are concerned with things. Leonardo Bruni in the *Isogagicon moralis disciplinae* affirmed that "Moral philosophy is, so to speak, all ours. Therefore those who neglect it and give themselves to physics seem in a way to occupy themselves with extraneous matters and to neglect the pertinent." These words do not express, as is sometimes held, the aversion or contempt of the Humanists for inquiry into nature, but rather their insistence for reasons of polemics on an aspect of human life that medieval philosophy seemed to have unjustly neglected. It was this polemic urge that persuaded the same Leonardo Bruni to translate the *Nicomachean Ethics*, the *Politics*, and the economic books of Aristotle. These translations seemed to him to be the best means of entering into possession of the knowledge that antiquity had possessed and employed but that had long been disregarded. In the preface to his version of the *Politics*, Bruni said:

> The more fully goodness is diffused the more divine it should be considered. Because man is a weak animal and only receives from civil society that completion and perfection which he does not himself possess, no discipline is better adapted to him than that which permits him to understand what society is, what the state is and how civil society survives or perishes. It seems to me that whoever ignores these things both ignores himself and shows contempt for the precept of the most wise God.

Matteo Palmieri's *Della vita civile* and Bartolomeo Sacchi's *De optima cive* illustrate substantially the same concepts. The success of the *Nicomachean Ethics* in the fifteenth century was a result of this rediscovery of the political nature of man—a rediscovery that often was not just a simple theoretical recognition but an effective urge toward political activity. The Humanists desired a return to Aristotle the moralist and rhetorician but declared themselves hostile to Aristotle the physicist. The latter was the representative of the philosophy that leaves man, his needs and his nature, out of consideration; he is the philosopher of absolute and immutable order where there is no room for freedom and for man's initiative. Aristotle the moralist, on the other hand, was the ancient master of wisdom—the man who fully expressed the virtues and the vices of man as a political animal and determined the conditions and forms of civil society. Aristotle the moralist was also he who recognized the value of money as indispensable for the well-being of the individual and for the life and preservation of society. And on this the Humanists happily insisted, considering contempt for money a manifestation of medieval asceticism founded upon the ignorance of man's true nature.

The political domain was thus freed of all metaphysical or theological subjection. It was Machiavelli who carried this trend to its logical conclusion. His unprejudiced attitude toward the choices offered to the contemporary Italian politician was based on the conviction that the limits of political activity were defined by the very nature of this activity. The political task does not need to draw its own morality from outside—the norm that justifies it and imposes its limits upon it. It was justified by its intrinsic task of leading men to an orderly and free form of society, and its limits were determined by the chances of success presented in the means employed.

The recognition of freedom as the capacity for autonomous initiative, as the possibility of planning individual and social life; the positive evolution of the natural aspects of man (pleasure, feeling, sensuality) and of his economic and political activity—this is what the Humanists found in the ancient world and what they did not find in the medieval world. The return to antiquity was considered by them, therefore, as the indispensable instrument for regaining possession of capacities that had already yielded excellent results in the history of man and could still be utilized for the happiness of the human race.

V. THE RETURN TO ORIGINS

This return to Antiquity was also understood as *a return to the beginning:* the return to that which gives strength and life to everything and on which depends the preservation and perfection of every being. The return to the beginning was a Neoplatonic concept. It is no wonder, therefore, that it was theorized, above all, by the Platonists of the Renaissance (Ficino, Pico). But it was also explicitly defended by naturalistic philosophers (Bruno, Campanella) and by Machiavelli, who pointed to a "reduction to beginnings" as the only way in which communities seek restoration and thus escape decadence and ruin; for all beginnings, said Machiavelli, have in themselves some goodness from which things regain their vitality and primitive force.

In classical Neoplatonism, the return to the beginning was plainly a religious concept. The beginning is God and the return to God is the fulfillment of man's true destiny. This consisted in retracing backward the emanative process through which beings had moved away from God; in mounting the slope once more; in attempting to identify oneself with God. Such an interpretation was not foreign to the writers of the Renaissance. The Neoplatonists, especially, both repeated it and adopted it for their own. But the return to the beginnings also assumed, in the Renaissance, a human and historical meaning according to which the "beginning" to which one must return is not God but the earthly origin of man and the human world. This is, without doubt, the sense in which Machiavelli spoke of the "reduction to beginnings" as a renewal of the human community. In his *De ente et uno* in addition to the return to the absolute beginning—i.e., God —Pico della Mirandola also admits man's return to his own beginning, i.e., to man himself in whom his earthly happiness resides. This return of man to his own beginning is substantially a return to what man *has been,* a return to his distant but more authentic past, to the origins of his history. Obviously the origins of human history go beyond the classical world to which, above all, Renaissance writers looked; but they held that it was precisely in the classical world that the exercise of those powers that originally assured man a privileged place in the world had found mature and perfect expression. The writers of the Renaissance commonly held that religious revelation, the hermetic and mysterio-physical doctrines, classical philosophy, and Christianity were aspects or moments of a unique human wisdom that constituted precisely that "beginning," to which all knowledge and man's very conduct must be referred. We shall see the impact of this conviction on their idea of religion and religious tolerance. Meanwhile the first consequence of such a "return to beginnings" was a vital interest in the past—an interest that was not mere erudite curiosity, but an element or condition of life itself. It was not only a question of studying and interpreting ancient texts, of writing genuine Latin purged of medieval deformations, of enjoying those refinements that familiarity with the classical world offered to the language, customs, and habits of the man of the world. It was rather a question of taking full stock of the achievements, of the ancients, so as to repeat them or to realize them more fully.

Every epoch lives within a tradition, a cultural heritage, in which it sees embodied the fundamental values that inspire its attitudes. But tradition is never, especially in an age of transition or renewal, an inheritance passively or automatically transmitted. It is the *choice* of an inheritance. The Humanists rejected the medieval inheritance and chose that of the classical world as that in which they saw embodied those fundamental values dearest to their hearts. Their major preoccupation was to revive this inheritance as an instrument of education, that is, of human and social formation. The privilege they accorded to the so-called humanities, that is to say, to poetry, rhetoric, history, ethics, and politics, was based on the conviction, also inherited from the ancients, that these were the only disciplines that educated man as such, enabling him to enter into possession of his true capacities. This conviction may today be considered too restrictive, but it cannot be interpreted merely as a prejudice of the literate. The humanities were not, for the Humanists, a field for brilliant but useless exercises or a spurious refinement to be flaunted in fashionable circles. These were the only tools they knew capable of forming a man of dignity and freedom committed to the construction of a just and happy world. There is no doubt that Humanism (like every other period of Western history) was not entirely guiltless of literary gymnastics, a certain preciosity of erudite inquiry, of a temptation to disguise, under the formal merits of the language of literature or art, the lack of a serious or profitable human purpose. Nor is there any doubt that these decadent aspects predominated and became more evident when, in the seventeenth century, the political and civil decadence of Italy rendered almost impossible the exercise of those activities that the Humanists of the preceding centuries had exalted in the ancient world. Meanwhile, Italian Renaissance Humanism had already borne fruits even outside Italy; and in Italy itself the new spirit of initiative and freedom that the Renaissance had revived was bearing fruit in science.

VI. The Discovery of Perspective

One of the most important conquests of this period, that of the *historical dimension* of events, was due to the return to antiquity, the keynote of classical Humanism.

The Middle Ages had been completely ignorant of this dimension. It is true that they recognized and utilized classical culture; but they utilized it by assimilating it and making it contemporary. For the writers of the Middle Ages, facts, personalities, and doctrines did not have a precise, individual, unique aspect. Their only validity was that accorded them in the universe of discourse in which these writers moved. Geography and chronology as instruments of historiographic verification were useless from this point of view. Each personality or doctrine moved in a timeless sphere—that delineated by the fundamental interests of the epoch, and therefore apparently contemporary to this sphere.

With its interest in antiquity, in true antiquity, not that transmitted by a deformed tradition, Renaissance Humanism achieved for the first time an attitude of *historical perspective,* that is, of detachment and differentiation of the historical object from the historiographic present. Platonists and Aristotelians were subject to controversy in the Renaissance, but they aroused a common interest in the discovery of the true Plato or true Aristotle, that is, of the genuine doctrine of their founders, not deformed or disguised by the medieval "barbarians." Philological exigence was not an accidental or formal aspect of Humanism but a constituent element. The need for discovering texts and restoring them to their authentic form by studying and collating the codices was accompanied by the need to discover the authentic meaning of poetry or the philosophic or religious truth they contained. Without philological research there was no Humanism, properly speaking, but merely a general attitude in favor of the defense of classical culture, which can be found in all epochs and is therefore not characteristic of any particular one.

The defense of classical eloquence was a defense of the genuine language of Classicism against the deformation it suffered in the Middle Ages, and an attempt to restore it to its original form. The discovery of documentary falsifications, of false attributions—the attempt to understand literary and philosophic figures in their own setting, in their chronological perspective—was the fundamental aspect of the historic character of Humanism. Doubtless, Humanism succeeded only partially or imperfectly in this task of historic restoration; this is, moreover, a task that is never finished, but presents itself again and again in historiographic work. But Humanism realized the value of such a task, and initiated and pursued it, leaving it as a legacy to modern culture. The eighteenth-century Enlightenment subsequently effected the decisive step along the road leading to modern historiographic investigation.

The importance of this aspect of the Renaissance can never be overestimated. Historiographic perspective makes possible the separation of the past from the present, i.e., the recognition of the differentiation and individuality of the past and the investigation of those features and conditions that determine this individuality and uniqueness; and finally the consciousness of the originality of the past in regard to ourselves and our own originality in regard to the past.

The discovery of historical perspective was with respect to time what the optical perspective of Renaissance painting was with respect to space. It was the faculty of realizing the *distance* between one object and another, and between objects and the person who is considering them; hence the capacity to understand them in their proper place, in their differentiation from others, in their true individuality. The meaning of human personality, as the original and autonomous center of the organization of various aspects of life, is conditioned by perspective in this sense. The importance that the modern world attributes to human personality is a consequence of an attitude adopted for the first time by Renaissance Humanism.

VII. RELIGIOUS PEACE

For all its aversion to asceticism and theology, the Renaissance was not antireligious in character. Those who insist on the continuity that binds it in this sense to the Middle Ages are right in the sense that there is no sign of any attempt on the part of Renaissance writers to diminish the value of religion in general, and of Christianity in particular, or to advance doctrines or points of view openly irreconcilable with those of traditional religion. Discussions on God and Providence, on the soul, its immortality and freedom, even though conducted according to traditional form, obviously had another aim—that of understanding and justifying the capacity for human initiative in the world. This capacity for initiative was defended above all in the religious domain. The Humanistic defense of religion was characterized by two distinctive features: recognition of the civil function of religion and toleration.

The civil function of religion was based on the correspondence between the heavenly city and the earthly city. The civil life of man found its ideal and norm in the city of the saints, in the harmony and happiness proper to the superterrestrial world. On the other hand, the harmony and happiness of the superterrestrial world were not given sufficient importance, according to the Humanists, if man were not urged to achieve them as far as possible during his life on earth. In his *De Dignitate et Excellentia Hominis,* Giannozzo Manetti summarizes and reaffirms the most common Humanistic themes on this question. Manetti sees in the Bible not only the announcement of superterrestrial, but also earthly happiness. Religion, according to Manetti, was trust in the positive value of the work of man, in the success of this work, and in the reward it will obtain in the future life. Manetti reached the point of declaring the nonauthenticity of such writings as *Ecclesiastes,* which seemed to him to belie that joyful and optimistic conception of earthly life he held as essential to religion. The task of religion, therefore, for him as for Lorenzo Valla and many others, was to encourage and support man in the tasks of civil life, in work, in political activity, and in philosophical inquiry.

On the other hand, Humanist religion was profoundly permeated by a spirit of toleration. The concept of tolerance, reaffirmed in the modern world as a result of the religious wars of the sixteenth and seventeenth centuries, implies the possibility of the peaceful coexistence of the various religious faiths while acknowledging their existing differences and recognizing their mutual irreductibility. The Humanists' attitude of religious toleration derives, rather, from their conviction of the fundamental unity of mankind's religious beliefs—of the possibility, therefore, of universal religious concord. This religious peace was founded, according to the Humanists, on the essential identity of philosophy and religion. "Does Paul teach anything more than was taught by Plato?" asked Leonardo Bruni. All the Humanists were willing to accept or actually did accept the standpoint of the Fathers of the Church: Christianity merely brought to fulfillment and expressed in the highest form that same wisdom that ancient philosophy had elaborated. Therefore the same Reason that supported and guided this philosophy became the Word Incarnate. These concepts are clearly expressed by Marsilio Ficino in the *De Christiana Religione* of 1474. In this work, Ficino enunciated both the principle of unity and that of the diversity of the various religions of the world: "Divine Providence," he said, "does not permit that there be at any time any region in the world devoid of all religion, but rather that there be different modes of worship at different times and in different places." Pico della Mirandola was the standard-bearer and inspired prophet of a "regenerative peace" that would reconcile all philosophies and all religions. His *Oratio de dignitate hominis* (originally intended to be called *Carmen de pace*) proposed to lay the foundations of a universal peace by showing the fundamental accord between Platonism and Aristotelianism and between these two doctrines and the other philosophies of antiquity, as well as that of the Cabala, magic, Patristicism, Scholasticism, and the entire world of philosophy with Christianity and religious revelation. Certainly the belief in this universal reconciliation founded on the fundamental unity of human wisdom in its various manifestations can rightly be considered chimerical. But the confidence in the possibility of such a peace meant the renunciation of irreconcilable conflicts, and of the struggle between religion and philosophy, between different religions and different philosophies; the Humanists considered this renunciation the end of theological hatred and intolerance.

VIII. Origins of Experimental Science

With the recognition of the essential and determinative character of man's relationship with nature, Humanism had established the fundamental premises of modern experimental investigation. There has lately been some insistence on the importance of the contribution made by some fourteenth-century Scholastics to the formation of modern science, by their critique of fundamental Aristotelic theories like the movement of the stars and projectiles. These contributions, together with the hostility of the Humanists toward Aristotle the physicist and toward Scholastic speculation on physics and metaphysics in general, sometimes lead to the conclusion that the development of modern science is more closely connected with traditional Aristotelianism than with Humanism.

We have already seen, however (Section 4), how the aversion to the physics of Aristotle and the preference accorded to his ethics were for the Humanists a direct polemic means of accentuating the importance they wished to accord the moral disciplines held indispensable to guide the activities of man. This polemical motive did not imply an aversion to nature or to investigation or to the direct observation of nature that Renaissance art, so intimately related with the

Humanistic movement, proclaimed as its foundation, guide, and ideal. Scientific investigation, as demonstrated in the intuitions of Leonardo and in the works of Galileo, was an investigation based on observation and experiment. Observation and experiment are not things that can simply be announced and registered; they cannot remain in the phase of mere ideas, but must be actually undertaken and carried to a conclusion. They cannot, however, be undertaken and terminated if they are not supported by a vital interest—an interest that can be constituted only by the conviction that man is solidly implanted in the world of nature and that his best and most characteristic cognitive powers are those deriving from his relationship with nature. When Galileo declared that "experience of the senses" was the only other source of knowledge besides mathematical reasoning, he clearly indicated the change of direction that is the origin of the experimental basis of modern science. Before him Bernardino Telesio, though not actually engaging in the work of inquiry, had affirmed in the *De rerum natura juxta propria principia* that the essential principles of the natural world, those that alone afford an explanation of it, are the "sense principles," which establish the equation between "what nature manifests" and "what the senses perceive." To return to the experience of the senses, to question it and make it explicit constitute the only way, from this point of view, to arrive at the explanation of nature by nature, i.e., without recourse to principles foreign to nature itself. This autonomy of the natural world, which is the basic assumption of every experimental investigation, was a major aspect of the Humanistic attitude that endeavored to understand every phenomenon in relation to its constitutive elements and its intrinsic value. Thus, from a general point of view, we may say that for the development of an experimental investigation of nature, Humanism established the necessary conditions, which are:

(1) that man is not a provisional guest of nature but himself a natural being who makes nature his dominion;

(2) that man, as a natural being, has both the interest and capacity to know nature;

(3) that nature can be questioned and understood only by means of those instruments which she herself furnishes to man.

These, obviously, are general rather than determinant conditions and therefore cannot provide an explanation for all the characteristics prerequisite to the foundation of modern science. These characteristics were determined by other factors for which Renaissance Humanism was also mainly responsible. The first was supplied by precisely that "return to antiquity" that was the hallmark of Humanism. The return to antiquity led to the revival of doctrines and texts that had been neglected for centuries, like the heliocentric theories of the Pythagoreans, the works of Archimedes, of the geographers, astronomers, and doctors of antiquity. Often these classical texts supplied the inspiration or cue for new discoveries, notably in the case of Archimedes, from whom Galileo frequently drew his inspiration. On the other hand, Renaissance Aristotelianism, while it provoked a new and freer reading of Aristotle, usually elaborated, in opposition to his theologico-miraculous doctrines, the concept of an immutable and necessary natural order founded on the causal chain of events. This concept came to constitute the general scheme of scientific investigation. Magic, which the Renaissance brought once more to the fore, was accepted and disseminated, and contributed toward determining the active and operative character of modern science: that which consists in dominating and subjugating natural forces to turn them to the service of man. Finally, from Platonism and ancient Pythagoreanism science derived that other fundamental premise on which Leonardo, Copernicus, and Galileo all insisted, namely that nature is written in mathematical figures and that the language proper to science is that of mathematics.

Humanism was present, directly or indirectly, in one or other of the essential aspects of every one of these factors, which in various degrees and in various ways conditioned the beginnings of experimental science in Europe. Among such factors may and, indeed, must be included the critiques the Scholastics of the fourteenth century (Ockham, Buridan, Albert of Saxony, Nicholas of Oresme) had directed against certain fundamental points of Aristotelian physics. It should not be forgotten that such critiques derived from the empirical orientation that, thanks to Ockham, came to predominate late Scholasticism at a time when, as a result of the acknowledged impossibility of the task of interpreting and defending theological truths, philosophy was made available for other objects and interests. These critiques derive their value, therefore, not from association with traditional Aristotelianism but from being anti-Aristotelian and constituting the first manifestation of that rebellion against Aristotelianism that, in the second half of the same century and in the next, gave birth to Humanism. They constitute, therefore, not the bond between Aristotelianism and science but, on the contrary, the first break in the traditional Aristotelian ranks. What was lacking from the Aristotelianism of the fourteenth century (as well as from a major part of that of Renaissance) was that recognition of the *naturality* of man and his capacity for knowing that is the indispensable condition of every experimental investigation of nature. Seen from this standpoint Aristotelianism could not supply science with any vital impulse or motive. Only the Humanistic rebellion could realize that radical change of perspective from which scientific investigation and a new conception of the world was born.

This conception—to which Platonists like Nicholas of Cusa and Ficino, naturalistic philosophers like Telesio and Bruno, scientists like Copernicus and Galileo all contributed equally —was the exact antithesis of the Aristotelian concept. The world was not a finite or conclusive *totality* but an infinite *whole* open in every direction. Its order was not finalistic but causal, and consisted not in the perfection of the whole and of the parts but in the necessary chain of events. Man was not the being in whom culminated the teleology of the universe, and whose destiny was therefore entrusted to this teleology, but a natural being among other natural beings who, moreover, possessed the capacity to plan and realize his own destiny. Human understanding of the world was not a fixed and closed system, but the result of constantly renewed attempts that had to be continuously submitted to the test. The instrument of this understanding was not a superterrestrial and infallible reason, but a complex of natural, fallible, perfectible powers. Such were the features of an overall conception that remains at the basis of our science and our civilization. Such a conception was the product of that Italian Renaissance Humanism, which may be said to have ushered in —for better or for worse—the modern world, with all its risks and its achievements.

TRANSLATED FROM THE ITALIAN
BY NINO F. LANGIULLI

BIBLIOGRAPHY

Note: This bibliography refers only to authors whose opinions have been mentioned in the text.

I.

Almost all the nineteenth-century literature on Humanism exalts the originality of Humanism and reaffirms its break with the Middle Ages. This is the theme of the famous works of Burckhardt, Dilthey, Voigt, and also of Cassirer in *Individuum und Kosmos in der Philosophie der Renaissance*, 1927. G. Toffanin, on the other hand, insists on the continuity of Humanism with the Middle Ages in *Storia dell' umanismo*, 1933. For a more balanced critical interpretation, see the works of Eugenio Garin, mentioned below. On the derivation of modern science from medieval Aristotelianism, see works mentioned in Section 8.

II.

On this theme the work of J. Burckhardt, *Die Kultur der Renaissance in Italien*, 1860, is still a classic. Cf. also especially Garin, *Medioevo e Rinascimento*, 1954.

III.

All the literature on Humanism insists on its naturalistic aspect. See E. Garin, *L'umanesimo italiano*, 1952.

IV.

This is another aspect of Humanism that is unanimously recognized. Cf. especially E. Garin, *La cultura filosofica del Rinascimento italiano*, 1961.

V.

This aspect of the thought of Humanism has been less frequently studied. Cf. K. Burdach, *Riforma, Rinascimento e Umanesimo*, Italian translation, 1935; and N. Abbagnano, *Storia della filosofia*, II, 1961, Ch. I and following.

VI.

On the growth of the historiographical perspective in the Renaissance, see especially the three books by Garin mentioned above.

VII.

On the religious ideal of the Renaissance see the research by E. Garin in the first part of *La cultura filosofica del Rinascimento italiano*.

VIII.

The link between the origins of science and medieval Aristotelianism was established for the first time by P. Duhem in his famous *Etudes sur Léonard de Vinci,* 1906-13, and subsequently developed by numerous authors, amongst whom see especially M. Clagett, *The Science of Mechanics in the Middle Ages* (Madison, Wisconsin; London: Oxford, 1959) and John H. Randall, Jr., *The School of Padua and the Emergence of Modern Science,* 1961. Other authors have claimed that there was a contrast between science and Humanism, such as Toffanin in his *Storia dell'umanismo,* op. cit., and more recently Zilsel in the *International Encyclopedia of Unified Science,* II, 8 (1941). For a reassessment of the problem see the article by E. Garin, "Gli umanisti e la scienza," in *Rivista di Filosofia,* 1961, 3.

SCIENCE AND REFORMATION*

R. Hooykaas

Statistical research has established that among the *foreign members* of the Royal Society (in 1829 and in 1869) and the Académie des Sciences (from 1666 to 1883) the Protestants far outnumbered the Roman Catholics. Likewise it has been found that, although in the sixteenth century the Protestants in the southern Netherlands formed but a very small part of the population, their scientific production in quantity and quality surpassed that of Roman Catholic authors, whereas after their expulsion science in Belgium had some difficulties and in the eighteenth century was practically nonexistent. It has also been pointed out that among the group of ten scientists who during the English Commonwealth formed the nucleus that would afterward grow into the Royal Society, seven were decidedly Puritan, whereas on the list of members of the Royal Society of 1663 62 percent (42 of the 68 for whom the religious affiliation is known) *were clearly Puritan,* a percentage still more striking because Puritans constituted a minority of the population.

Efforts have been made to explain this predilection for observational and experimental sciences by the economic ideals of the class to which those Protestants (mainly Calvinists) belonged. Indeed the utilitarian interest in applied science often bore relation to the fact that the investigators belonged to the rising middle class.

* Journal of World History, III, 1.

The flourishing of exact sciences and technology in Holland about 1600 may be attributed to the expansion of the trade, industry, and navigation of that province, which had no clergy in the proper sense (a reformed minister is not a priest) and almost no nobility. But at the same time there was a great interest in the study of languages (classical and Oriental), botany and zoology, which are not directly "useful." Probably it will always remain impossible to decide whether their economic interests or their religion was first in urging the scientists of England and Holland to research; in any case the religious share in the rapid growth of science is easily underestimated by those modern historians who cannot imagine that religion was the paramount interest of large groups of the population in the sixteenth and seventeenth centuries and who, consequently, do not take seriously the evidences of religious convictions in the works of the great scientists.

For an age in which the religious sanction was necessary to make anything socially acceptable, it made a great difference whether science was condemned, merely tolerated, or positively encouraged by religion.

There is nothing in the dogmas of the three main divisions of Western Christianity—Roman Catholicism, Lutheranism, and Calvinism—to discourage scientific research; great scientists will be found among all three. Yet they do not all three encourage scientific research to the same degree. Max Weber's idea that a special form of the doctrine of election ("Bewährungsglaube," i.e., the belief that performance of "works" is a sign of election) led to a special attitude in economic and, consequently, in scientific endeavor among the Calvinists, has found little favor with experts on Calvinism. Apart from this explanation, however, which indeed seems to oversimplify matters, the work of Weber and especially that of Merton has established the fact that the Reformed (Calvinists, Zwinglians) because of their "innerweltliche Askese" (an intramundane asceticism) were very much inclined toward science. Here a general attitude, an ethical conception of the human task on earth rather than a special dogma seems to have been the main incentive.

In the present paper we will try to expound how the religious attitude of so-called "ascetic" Protestantism, which more or less stood under Calvin's influence, furthered the development of science.

Love of nature

All three confessions held that contemplation of nature may lead the mind to God, the Maker of all things; on the other hand, there was also a general warning that the study of nature may turn the mind away from God, as it will become absorbed in visible things and in secondary, natural causes, forgetting the invisible things and the great Primary Cause. Both views could be corroborated by biblical quotations, and it is evident that a thoroughgoing scientific investigation was liable to be regarded from the latter point of view. When the Middle Ages sought edification in nature, it was for the purpose of illustrating spiritual truths, not of conducting scientific study. In cases where a scientific study of nature was recommended as useful to religion (Thomas Aquinas), it was natural philosophy in the Aristotelian sense and not observational, experimental science that was intended.

The new, humanistic movement showed little inclination to appreciate nature for its own sake. In the works of the Humanists "we do not hear the whisper of the winds nor the song of the birds," and Petrarch, who was in this respect an exception in spite of his esthetic appreciation of nature, spoke scornfully about scientific research. The overgreat admiration for the ancients led to attempts to reconstruct science on the data borrowed from the oldest sources. In many cases the authority of Aristotle was replaced by other authorities, preferably the most ancient (Hippocrates instead of Galen; Galen instead of Avicenna; the genuine Aristotle instead of his medieval interpreters; Plato, Democritus, or "Pythagoras" instead of Aristotle).

A really positive evaluation of nature and of the scientific investigation of nature was furthered by the Reformation. The number of sixteenth-century botanists in central and northern Europe who were of the reformed faith is indeed remarkable. The "German Fathers of Botany," Otto Brunfels († 1534), Jerome Bock (1498-1554), and Leonhart Fuchs (1501-1566) were zealous Protestants; Clusius (1526-1609), Dodoens (1517-1585), Jean and Gaspart Bauhin (1560-1624), de l'Obel (1538-1616) belonged to the Reformed Church; William Turner (1508-1568), "the true pioneer of natural history in England," had a share in the introduction

of Calvinism into England. The same independence of thought
that led many botanists to throw in their lot with the spiritual
reformers of their day also led them to discard many of the
superstitious beliefs connected with plants (astrology, signa-
tures), though they were not quite free from it. Many of the
early Protestant botanists and zoologists (Clusius, de l'Obel,
Pierre Pena, Jean Bauhin, Felix Platter, Volcker Coiter)
were for some time pupils of the great naturalist Guillaume
Rondelet (1507-1566), one of the leaders of the Reformed
in southern France. Some of them stood in immediate contact with the Reformers: Platter with Calvin, Konrad Gesner,
the great Zürich naturalist, with Bullinger, Clusius with
Melanchthon, Turner with Hugh Latimer, Johannes à Lasco,
and Thomas Cranmer. All these authors show a wholehearted
acceptance of nature in which they recognize the work of
God's hands. Volcker Coiter (1534-1576), one of the founders
of embryology and comparative anatomy, "the most religious
anatomist of the sixteenth century," never tired of praising
God on account of the wonderful adaptation of animal structure, and Clusius testified that botanical discoveries gave him
as much joy as if he had found a prodigious treasure. Bernard
Palissy (1510-1590), the famous Huguenot potter, reveals
throughout his works a sympathetic love for the earth and
the trees, often maltreated by the laborers; he passionately
admired the plants "even the most despised." These early
Protestants shared the deep love and admiration of animals
and plants of which the Psalms, the Book of Job, and the
Gospels give testimony and which is also evident in the works
of Luther and Calvin.

But love of nature does not necessarily include love of the
science of nature, and from this latter does not necessarily
ensue appreciation of the experimental and observational
method of scientific research. Therefore we have to consider
why the Reformers believed that science ought to be cultivated
(viz., *to the glory of God* and *to the benefit of mankind*) and
how this should be done, according to them (viz., *in an
empirical way, in spite of human authorities,* and *by using our
hands*).

I

The glory of God

The predilection for scientific research in Protestant circles may be largely explained by the great emphasis laid by Reformed theology upon the central theme: "the glory of God." This has been beautifully worded by Kepler (1571-1630), when he said that being priests of God to the Book of Nature, the astronomers ought to have in their minds not the glory of their own intellect, but above anything else the glory of God (1598).

The Reformed confessions emphasize that God reveals Himself in Scripture and in Nature, "which is before our eyes as a beautiful book, in which all created things, large and small, are like letters, showing the invisible things of God." Recommendation of pious contemplation, however, does not necessarily imply an urge to scientific research. The latter was often regarded as a real danger to religion, not only by medieval asceticism but also by some spiritualistic sects of the sixteenth century (Anabaptists). Reformed theology maintained in opposition to this belief that the duty of glorifying God on account of His works should be performed by all faculties, not only by the eyes but also by the intellect. Calvin deemed those who neglect the study of nature as guilty as those who, when investigating God's works, forget the Creator. He sharply reproved "phantastic" opponents of science as being only fit to make men proud and not as leading to a "knowledge of God and the conduct of ordinary life." Again and again he testified his positive appreciation of scientific research as penetrating deeper into the wonders of nature than mere contemplation. And he does not mean the speculative "physics" of his time, but the real sciences (in the modern sense) of that epoch—astronomy and anatomy, which revealed the secrets of the macrocosm and the microcosm.

His followers, even the most conservative among them (like

G. Voetius), were enthusiastic supporters of science and learning. Reformed theology not only tolerated scientific research (this had also been done by Roman Catholic and Lutheran theology), but even demanded it.

The duty of scientific investigation of nature was not regarded as a hard law; it was enjoyed as a duty of love, as is clearly shown in the works of Robert Recorde (c. 1510-1558), L. Fuchs, Thomas Digges (1545-1595), B. Palissy, J. Kepler, and Philips van Lansbergen (1561-1632). Sometimes it was even exaggerated: perhaps as a consequence of a growing but as yet unconscious rationalism, it was often propounded in the sixteenth century that rational scientific investigation is a higher fulfilment of the divine command than mere contemplation. Thomas Browne and Robert Boyle believed that the scientist performs the duty of glorifying God better than anyone else: a "learned admiration," a "philosophical worship" is the highest act of religion. They were not aware of the fact that thus they were conceiving a new separate priesthood, to wit the priests to the Book of Nature, for they sincerely believed that the cultivation of science does not require much special training and talent: "here is enough business for minds of all sizes" (Sprat, 1667). Yet earlier investigators, while recognizing with Calvin that the scientist looks deeper into God's work, did not conclude that, consequently, the better he accomplishes his duty of glorifying God. They considered the question from the standpoint of the parable of the talents, which played an important role in their ethics (e.g., Palissy; van Lansbergen). He who has the talent and the occasion for doing research has the duty to exploit his talent.[1] Consequently, Kepler was of the opinion that the unlearned who praises God only for what is seen by the eyes does not do Him less honor than the astronomer to whom God gave also the eye of reason to see more clearly (1609).

The general priesthood of believers

On the other hand, the conception that everybody ought to glorify God by discovering His wisdom, power, and glory in

---

[1] Cf. Calvin's *Commentary on Genesis* I: 16, where he says that "they who have leisure and ability" ought not to neglect astronomical research.

creation according to his *talents* meant that the competency and right to do scientific work did not belong exclusively to a certain class of people.

The Protestant doctrine of the priesthood of all believers proclaimed not only the *right,* but even the *duty* of everybody (who was able to do so) to read the Book of Scripture for himself. As a consequence, likewise the right and duty to read the Book of Nature, without regard to the authority of the fathers of natural philosophy—Aristotle, Pliny, Ptolemy, Galen—was put forward. While fully acknowledging the value of specialized biblical scholarship, the Reformers had nevertheless maintained that the meaning of Scripture is self-evident on essential points and, accordingly, that nobody can be excused by delegating the responsibility for reading Scripture to the hierarchy. In the same way everybody, in principle and according to his capacities, might be a priest to the Book of Creation, in defiance sometimes of the ancient authorities. When Palissy was derided because of his ignorance of the classical languages and hence of the scientific books written therein, he proudly answered that he had obtained his knowledge through the anatomy of nature and not through reading books, for "I have had no book but heaven and earth and it is given to every man to know and read this beautiful book." The belief that everyone should read the Book of Nature according to his capacities supported the defenders of the "new" science when they called upon the unlearned to contribute to the knowledge of natural history, geography, and physics by communicating their observations on birds and flowers, on ebb and flood tide, on celestial phenomena and the inclination of the magnetic needle. Travelers and mariners especially were invited to do so. Because of the experimental character of the "new philosophy" the manual workers were invited to contribute their skill and knowledge, for it was a "philosophy of hands" more than a "philosophy of words and notions."

The general priesthood of believers is perhaps the only specifically Protestant doctrine that was sometimes consciously, sometimes unconsciously, used to back up science. In any case this doctrine had a large share in framing Protestant thought.

The benefit of mankind

The glory of God and the benefit of mankind are as closely connected in Christian theology as the two tables of the Law, summarized by Christ as the duty of love for God and our neighbors. Therefore the insistence of Reformed theology on the benefit that may come to mankind from useful inventions in medicine and technique is not a manifestation of the capitalistic mentality of a rising merchant class that hides its mammonistic intentions behind a pious pretense. Here again genuine love for God and one's fellow beings is the main driving force. Even Francis Bacon (1561-1626), often represented as the patron of utilitarianism, was largely inspired by religious motives. He refused to mix up science and theology, but his Calvinistic religion shines out on the pages of his nontheological works. He cited St. Paul in order to proclaim that knowledge without love is vain and that the scientist demonstrates love through the production of works, which are not done for mental satisfaction alone. "La science pour la science" is totally opposed to Reformed ethics; the glory of God and the invention of useful things to lessen the burdens of human life are the final aims of science. Pierre de la Ramée (Petrus Ramus, 1515-1572) defined each science by its application: "geometry is the art of measuring well," etc. Not the knowledge of things but their useful application is, according to him, the aim of science, and Kepler afterward nicknamed him a "usuarius." His influence on Puritanism was very great: it was especially felt in Cambridge and Harvard. Milton, Ames, and Rudolf Snellius were among his followers. It seems, however, that the utilitarian tendencies of Puritan science were not *caused* by the philosophies of their heroes Ramus and Bacon, but that these scholars only gave an able expression of feelings that were already widespread independently of them.

In Holland, during the Eighty Years' War, Reformed ministers, inspired by religious and social motives, furthered scientific schemes, especially those of value for the development of industry (windmills) and navigation. These were necessary to continue the war against Spain, the success of which was closely linked with the economic and naval power of the Netherlands. Dr. Isaac Beeckman (1588-1637) in

Dordrecht founded the first meteorological station in Europe with the help of the town magistrate. There he made observations with the minister Colvius. The minister Philips van Lansbergen spent his time on astronomy, generously supported by the Estates of Zeeland; the minister Plancius (1552-1622) at Amsterdam, one of the ablest geographers of his time, delivered lectures on astronomy and cartography from the pulpit of the Zeedijk Chapel, and was the driving force behind the efforts of the Hollanders to find a new way to the Indies.

In England Leonard Digges (c. 1530-1563) and his son, Thomas, both zealous Protestants, wrote in the vernacular to further astronomy, geodesy, etc. Thomas Digges even abandoned pure mathematics; in order to employ them in the service of prince and country, he reduced the "sciences mathematicall from demonstrative contemplations to experimentall actions." In 1588 Thomas Hood delivered lectures in London on geometry and astronomy for soldiers, artisans, and mariners. At Gresham College, founded in London in 1597, lectures on divinity, music, geometry, astronomy were to be delivered in English and Latin. In Rotterdam Beeckman, together with a physician, a mill-builder, and a mathematician, founded a "Collegium Mechanicum" in order to give gratuitous advice to the town magistrates on the emendation of the harbor, shipbuilding, mill-building, and drainage, and he planned lectures on mechanical problems in the vernacular "for the benefit of carpenters, masons, skippers, and other burghers."

II

Empiricism

The Reformers wanted to keep exclusively to the record of divine revelation as written down in the Bible. They wished to abolish what they considered rationalistic, superfluous additions to the biblical revelation and to return to the pure source. A parallel attitude was assumed toward the Book of

Creation. In the interpretation of nature the same sense of responsibility prevailed as in the exegesis of Scripture: they were anxious not to deviate from the true meaning of the Bible, so they felt religiously bound to nature. Here also they considered themselves to be on holy ground, confronted with a book of God that had to be accepted even when not completely understood. It was sacrilege to make it conformable to human reason, which, after the Fall, is always prone to blur and distort the facts in order to satisfy its own pride. This faithfulness to a reality, which may even be incomprehensible, becomes evident in Francis Bacon's opinion that being tied to facts prevents the divagations of human reason and fantasy: "The understanding left to itself ought always to be suspected." "The wit and mind of man, if it work upon matter, which is the contemplation of the creatures of God, worketh according to the stuff and is limited thereby, but if it work upon itself, as a spider worketh his web, then it is endless, and brings forth indeed cobwebs of learning." The same attitude was prevalent in Gilbert (1540-1603), who founded his science primarily upon observation and experiment, because "it is easy for men of acute intellect, apart from experiments and practice, to err." Christian religion, they believed, is a religion of facts; it bears a historical character. In the same way, natural science is founded upon facts, however much they may transcend human understanding. In their anti-rationalism the spirit of the Reformation and the spirit of experimental science show a close affinity. In accordance with biblical theology Bacon ascribed rationalistic aspirations to the hubris that lies at the bottom of all revolt against God; by following the dictates of our own reason and imposing our ideas upon nature instead of religiously seeking to discover how it pleased God to make things, we have lost our dominion over nature. There was a distrust of general systems, excogitated by the human brain and, consequently, investigation of particular things was encouraged.

Protestant theology was perfectly aware of this resemblance between its own spirit and that of experimental science, and it often regarded the latter as an aid to religion. The Puritan army chaplain John Webster considered it an advantage of the experimental "science of facts" above the old "speculative science of notions and words," that the students "may not grow proud with the brood of their own brains," and Thomas Sprat compared the qualities of a good Christian to those of a good experimental philosopher: both doubt their own thoughts and acknowledge their own ignorance.

The religious submission to facts sometimes led to quite unexpected results. Kepler was thoroughly imbued with Platonism and, accordingly, he was *a priori* convinced of the truth of the dogma of the circular and uniform movement of the celestial bodies. Yet, after a heavy inner struggle, he abandoned this prejudice, which had never before been doubted, not even by Copernicus and Galileo, because of a small difference of eight minutes, and propounded non-uniform motion in elliptic orbits. This was the birth of really modern astronomy (Copernicus was only restoring the "very ancient," so-called Pythagorean, tradition instead of the younger Aristotelian one). Without exaggeration he could state that "these eight minutes paved the way for a reformation of the whole of astronomy."

Angelo Sala (1576-1637), an Italian reformed refugee, who was physician to the Stadthouder of Holland and to the Duke of Mecklenburg, had less difficulty in abandoning old prejudices, as he was first of all an experimenter with little inclination to speculation. He analyzed and synthesized copper vitriol and demonstrated the identity of artificial and natural vitriol (*Anatomia vitrioli,* 617). In this way he overthrew the general prejudice, deeply imbedded in medieval and ancient science, that the products of nature cannot be made by art. Sala rejected the speculative chemistry of his day, "for chemistry occupies itself only with things that may be touched by human hands and it consists only in concrete proofs."

Palissy, the Huguenot martyr, repeated throughout his works "I was there," "I saw that"; he promised to satisfy the senses of sight and touch to everyone who might visit his collection, where within two hours more might be learned by contemplation of the displayed objects than by fifty years of study of the theories and opinions of the ancient philosophers.

In the same way Gilbert pretended that his philosophy was proved by "real demonstrations and by experiments manifestly apparent to the senses," and Bacon's main objection to the Greeks was that they relied more upon reason than upon immediate observation of nature (their philosophy is "talkative," not "generative"; it bears contention instead of fruit); truth ought not to be sought in the mind, but in the world. Palissy praised experiences as being prior to theory; it has the first and the last word: "Practice brought forth theory"; "by

practice I find . . . the theory of many philosophers, even of
the most ancient and the most renowned, to be false." Another
artisan, the instrument maker Robert Norman (1581),
promised to base his arguments on magnetism not upon
conjectures and imagination, but only upon experience, reason, and demonstration; according to him experiments are
"reason's finger," pointing to truth.

This empiricism led the experimental scientists to a mild
skepticism, even toward their own theories. The geographical
discoveries had exploded all philosophical reasoning about
the division of land and water and about the inhabited
parts of the earth. Here bare facts overthrew all clever
theories. The unexpected discovery of countries with human
inhabitants, animals, and plants never dreamed of proved the
possibility of the seemingly marvelous and corroborated the
religious acknowledgment of God's infinite power. As William Watts remarked: the *thoughts* of the philosophers were
contradicted by the *unexpected observations* of the navigators.
As age-old prejudices crumbled down, a remarkable freedom
of thought and openness toward new inventions and discoveries was created. The seventeenth-century scientists liked
to say that there are no "columns of Hercules," no *ne plus
ultra* in philosophy. This led them, especially the followers of
Bacon (who very often were Puritans or, like Bacon himself,
were influenced by Puritanism), to propound audacious
hypotheses. Precisely the fact that hypotheses were regarded
as only provisory, and that, consequently, a suspension of
judgment was indispensable until experience had confirmed
a supposition, caused this freedom of theorizing.

Isaac Beeckman, the Calvinist rector of the Latin School
at Dort, accepted the Copernican hypothesis as probable, but
did not consider it an established truth. The Puritan clergyman Henry Gellibrand (well-known for his magnetical experiments) assumed the same attitude; he sees no escape from
Copernicanism, however much it contradicts everything
considered as "rational" up to his time; it easily leads us "to
the consideration of the imbecillity of Man's apprehension, as
not able rightly to conceive of this admirable opifice of God
or frame of the world, without falling foule on so great an
absurdity." The Puritan divine John Wilkins, a bold thinker,
said that not everything marvelous should be considered be-
forehand as supernatural; it is one of the tasks of natural
science to reduce the apparently supernatural to the natural.
As Beeckman had put it before him: theology goes from non-

270 EVOLUTION OF SCIENCE

wonder to wonder, science from wonder to nonwonder. Anti-rationalism on a religious basis evidently did not mean gullibility toward the supernatural. This aloofness was perhaps the very consequence of the fact that these intensively religious people satisfied their religious demands by means of Scriptural revelation and did not want a substitute for it in systems of natural philosophy. This becomes evident in Beeckman. He was one of the first defenders of atomism (both Descartes and Gassendi were influenced by him), but this atomism did not have a quasi-religious significance for him. It was only a physical hypothesis more satisfactory than scholasticism, but in his opinion it did not even answer every physical question, let alone metaphysical ones. The same critical attitude toward his own theories prevailed with the "sceptical chymist" Robert Boyle, whose free thought and mild skepticism were closely connected with his religious faith. This attitude was extremely favorable for the development of natural science, but it destroyed the magnificent illusions of the Middle Ages as well as those of the seventeenth century (Cartesianism). A conservative theologian, Alexander Ross, rightly complained that the new philosophers had left the old and known path and had reduced Aristotle's "comely order" into the old chaos. The new philosophy could not be better characterized: an adventurous quest for truth, even when harmonious illusions were destroyed by it.

It should be pointed out that an *empiricism* founded upon a theological basis was not new. It had been anticipated by those defenders of *Augustinian theology* who, like Bishop Tempier in 1277 and Nicole Oresme in 1377, maintained the possibility of marvelous natural phenomena that seemed impossible to scholastic rationalism. The theological background of the Reformed scientists had much in common with theirs; the difference was only that science had progressed since then and that the appreciation of scientific research had grown immensely.

The empiristic tendency was perhaps strongest among the Puritans of the Commonwealth, many of whom, though Calvinistic in theology, in many respects deviated from continental Calvinists and from early Puritans by their bolder conceptions of political and ecclesiastical freedom and in their stronger bias toward science and even against the humanities. John Webster demanded "laboratories as well as libraries" in behalf of the academic youth, in order that "they may not be idly trained up in notions, speculations, and verbal disputes, but may learn to inure their hands to labour." John Hall, in his proposal for reform of the universities, rejected "formal logick" as leading to vain disputes, and metaphysics as "abstrusely abstract" and thus far remote from use. He felt more sympathy with mathematics and natural philosophy, but his knowledge of the latter was derived not from books but from "experiences." Evidently Ramus had influenced him. Ramus was against deductive logic, rhetoric, etc.; he wanted to start from actual practice and to state the rules observed therein. In the same way John Webster opposed the teaching of formal grammar, because grammar may be learned much better from reading and conversation, and Jean Dury wished that logic should be taught not in an abstract way but "by examples of every kind and in concreto."

The Puritan educationists particularly stressed the value of concrete examples, phenomena, material aspects. Their passionate desire to substitute truth for imagination could easily lead to a rejection of the literary aspects of education as "vanities," when the counterbalancing influence of their biblical background, which with them was still all-pervading, gradually grew weaker. But at first any excessive enthusiasm for scientific education was opposed by such moderate Puritans as John Wilkins. Seth Ward recognized that "verbal exercises" should be replaced by observations and experiments and that more attention should be given to chemistry, agriculture, etc., but the academies he regarded as having a more general character that made it necessary for them to give assistance to those who want to study theology and languages and literature. This moderate attitude prevailed in England even during the Commonwealth, and certainly also in New England. It was recognized that experimental science should have a more prominent place, but that humanistic studies also are important. On the Continent (and here the Netherlands, where the Reformed Church—ruled on presbyterian principles —was the only one officially recognized, offer the best example) this same attitude was prevalent. The position of science here never was such a bone of contention as in England, but neither was it so much a matter of popular and theological emotion as in England. Yet the interest in science was so great in Holland that it was put up as an example to his countrymen by the English apologist of science, Thomas Sprat.

It seems, however, that there was no country where the fate of the scientific movement was so closely and so generally connected with religion as in England, and undoubtedly the most ardent apologists of freedom of science on religious motives were amongst the English Puritans. Science formed an integral part of their idea of a *civitas Dei*.

The Reformed were criticized by their Lutheran brethren because of their "this-worldliness" and because of their zest for "works." Indeed, they wanted to animate every department of life by the ferment of Christian religion. They did not believe that the Kingdom of God could be founded on earth; their real fatherland was in Heaven. And yet they considered this life as a preparatory stage for the life to come, a stage in which they had to act *as if* the Kingdom could already be realized. They went to New England "to found the perfect society . . . and never expected it to be perfect, but only the best that fallible men could make." This comprehensive view of life, so characteristic of Calvinism, was never more consciously conceived than by the English Puritans, and when they founded their commonwealth many of them forgot all theological reserve and genuinely believed that the *Kingdom of God on earth* was nearer than ever before. Milton belonged to these optimists; John Hall was another one. All good things having been accomplished, only the establishment of "learned piety" was still lacking. He wrote to Parliament: "If you will now make good our hopes in this one thing, you will put an end to all our wishes, and settle us in a condition which will somewhat resemble that eternall fruition which we all breath after, a time of prayses." The difficulties of the time should not dissuade Parliament from this work of peace, for there is the illustrious example of Holland, which, while struggling with a sad war and not yet wholly free from a "perfidious and horrid Tyrant," showed "prodigal magnificence for learning." The "discovery of a new world full of knowledge" seemed quite near, "God surely . . . begins a fuller manifestation of himselfe" and that manifestation was largely by means of scientific discovery.

The Puritan enterprise of establishing a commonwealth wherein Christianity would not be a matter of Sunday worship alone, but should penetrate social ethics, economics, politics as well as science, was shipwrecked. Yet some remnants were saved and used to construct the edifice of post-Restoration England with its firmly established experimental science.

"Enthusiasm" and science

When Calvin wrote against those "phantastic people" who decry all sciences because they would only make man arrogant and lead him away from God, he was thinking of spiritualists like the Anabaptists. In the upheaval of the English Civil War such spiritualistic sects came to the fore and in 1653 Parliament even considered the suppression of universities as heathenish and unnecessary. However, the majority "gave a stop to their frenzy." In 1657 Cromwell had to protect Oxford against Anabaptist hostility. The members of the spiritualistic sects like the Quakers in England, the Labadists and the Mennonites in Holland, were not very friendly toward human learning in general. Their aversion to school theology was of the same nature as that of some otherwise very culturally inclined Puritans (like Webster); their dislike of metaphysical philosophy they shared with all opponents of rationalism, their indifference to science took its origin in a type of asceticism that approached monastic "ausserweltliche Askese." But the Mennonites had, before 1620, already ceased their opposition to learning, whereas the Quakers soon took an active interest in applied science.

On the other hand, many conservative clergymen, supported by political reactionaries, were more afraid of science than most sectarians. They regarded it as a danger to the established church, and after the Restoration of the Stuarts, Joseph Glanvill, Robert Boyle, and Thomas Sprat did much to refute their arguments, especially as the charge of puritanism ("enthusiasm" or "fanaticism") as well as that of deism and atheism was made against the "virtuosi." Now it has already been made evident that those who were most radical in their return to "Scripture alone" in theology (to wit, the Reformed, Zwinglians, and Calvinists, or, in general, the puritanically minded) were also most radical in their support of a direct inquiry into nature by experiment and observation, which was the ideal of the Royal Society, which was founded shortly after the Restoration. Consequently it is small wonder that after 1660 "fanaticism" and "new learning" were decried as cognate vices by High Church divines (like Robert South) and by the playwrights and "wits" who vied with each other in hatred of the Puritans. At the beginning of the republican

period it had been just the reverse: the Puritans then were
accused by the High Church party of destroying all learning;
they were called "Goths and Vandals." They were then all
deliberately identified with some left-wing extremists. The
Puritan government, however, furthered scientific investigations in the Baconian sense, as is evident from the fact that
some of the most important founders of the Royal Society had
been appointed at Oxford during the Commonwealth (Wilkins,
1648; Wallis, 1649; Goddard, 1651; Petty, 1651). In 1653
Parliament appointed a committee "for the advancement of
learning" (of which the Puritan physicians Sydenham and
Goddard were members). The Protector Richard (1658) also
had the intention to advance "useful learning," and in New
England the Puritan clergy were foremost in their promotion
of new astronomy and science. Thus it was impossible to
maintain that the Puritans hated every kind of learning, and
therefore after the Restoration the charge was reversed and
they were accused of loving science too much.

It is tragicomical that on this occasion the *defenders* of
science identified "Puritanism" with the "enthusiasts," the
zealots of 1650, in order to demonstrate that science was
quite fashionable and had nothing to do with Puritanism.
Sprat, who took up the cause of science against its detractors,
did his best to prove that "enthusiasm" was obnoxious to
science, but that the true Church of England doctrine alone
could and should foster it. People like Sprat, often "trimmers"
(ex-Puritans) themselves, knew perfectly well that most
Puritans had as violent a dislike of "enthusiasm" as their High
Church antagonists. "Solid learning," secular as well as
sacred, was dear to them.

III

Authority in science

Experience versus reason was the background of empiricism. This includes also experience versus the reason of the
ancients, experience versus authority. The opposition to human

authority appealed very strongly to the Reformed. Their mind had been trained to the idea that one has to find out the truth for oneself and that there ought to be independence of human authority in order that the submission to divine authority be the more complete. The general laicization must have influenced also their scientific attitude. New ideas could easily get hold of them, and were at least not rejected because of their nonconformity to traditional beliefs.[2] No ecclesiastical censure on books and scientific ideas was officially applied by a central body of discipline, and scholastic philosophy was not officially connected with theology. When for example the great Dutch theologian Gisbertus Voetius (1588-1676) defended the Aristotelian philosophy as a necessary support of orthodox Protestant theology, his opponents of the Cocceian party either divorced philosophy from theology, or inclined to Cartesianism. When Voetius regarded the geocentric world picture as the only one compatible with Scripture, the no less orthodox Cocceians freely adhered to Copernicanism without interference of synods or church consistories.

In spite of their reverence for the Fathers of the Church, the Reformers never forsook a critical and free attitude toward them. Likewise the Protestant scientists liked to point out against their Romish opponents who recognized "Tradition" as well as Scripture as a source of revelation, how many mistakes the Church Fathers and the popes had made in scientific matters. The Reformation might signify to some of its adherents a return to the church of the first centuries, but to the majority it was a return to Scripture. In the same way many naturalists were not content with rejecting medieval commentators but also wished to be free from classical antiquity, as they wanted to return to Nature herself. Of course this led to exaggeration, but on the whole this iconoclasm was healthy for the development of science. It was necessary that criticism of the ancients and consciousness of the value of the present age should replace the adoration of the past.

Many Protestants could not wholly free themselves from the spirit of Humanism; it was difficult for them to purify their thoughts of the influence of their university education. Beza and Melanchthon, the immediate successors of the two great Reformers, even returned to *scholasticism*. Perhaps it may be said that the scientists often were more thoroughly Protestant

---

[2] Except, of course, Protestant scholasticism (see below under "Copernicanism").

than the theologians. Kepler, who profoundly admired Plato, obeyed "divine revelation" rather than the "divine philosopher," not only in metaphysical questions but also when accepting elliptic orbits. He was a devoted Lutheran, but Luther's authority did not move him to accept the Lutheran doctrine of Holy Supper. This same freedom he maintained in scientific questions: "Holy Lactantius, who denied that the earth is spherical; holy Augustine who acknowledged the sphericity of the earth, but denied the existence of antipodes; holy the Officium that recognized the antipodes, but rejects the motion of the earth . . . but holier yet is to me Truth, which reveals that the earth is a small sphere, that antipodes exist, and that the earth is moving."

Palissy, the founder of paleontology and agricultural science, declared "the Ancients were as human as the moderns, and they may have erred like us." The same opposition to the authority of the ancients is evident in the works of Norman, Gilbert, Wilkins, and many other English writers. Especially the "Philosophia Libera" (1621) of the clergyman Nathaniel Carpenter (a protégé of the Calvinist archbishop Usher) was a plea for liberty of scientific research and freedom from authority.

The reformation of science

The adherents of new philosophy and those of new theology were both accused of forsaking ancient traditions and rashly accepting dangerous novelties. On the other hand, the scientists of the period themselves were keenly aware of the fact that there was a connection between the liberation of theology from ecclesiastical and philosophical tradition by the Reformation and the liberation of science from ancient authority through the New Learning. Both were considered a return to the original and truly ancient and authentic source of knowledge. When speaking of Paracelsus the physician Richard Bostocke (1585) said: "He was not the author and inventour of this arte as the followers of the Ethnickes phisicke doe imagine . . . no more then Wicklife, Luther, Oecolampadius, Swinglius, Calvin, etc. were the Author and inventors of the Gospell and religion in Christes Church, when they restored it to his puritie, according to Gods word," and he made the same comparison with Copernicus.

Bostocke compared the cause of true religion, which was oppressed because only interpretations in accordance with Scotus and Aquinas were allowed, with the cause of true chemistry, agreeing with experience, which was eclipsed by the "sophisticall stuffe" of Aristotle, Galen, and Avicenna.

Aristotle, often considered as the common enemy to Reformed theology and the new science, was called a "pope in philosophy," and the "new philosophers" warned against the custom of quoting his text as if they had Scriptural authority.

Thomas Culpeper (1655) gathered in a few sentences some typical aspects of the Reformation and their parallels in the new science, to wit, the antiauthoritarian character of both, and the collegiate character of their activities in synods and scientific societies. And John Hall, like Noah Biggs, was of the opinion that after ecclesiastical and political reform "this last piece of reformation" ought to be the "reformation of learning."

After the Reformation the Latitudinarians in the Anglican church went on to compare the Reformation with the New Learning; according to Sprat, they have much in common, both of them "passing by the corrupt copies, and referring themselves to the perfect originals for their instruction; the one to the Scripture, the other to the large volumes of the creatures."

Puritans and authority in science

The Puritans of the sixteenth century as well as their opponents (until about 1630) of the "Anglican" type generally were Calvinist in doctrine. However, in their desire to abolish episcopacy and to keep the Sabbath very strictly, they went further than Calvin, who did not think it necessary to impose the Genevan form of church government on churches abroad and who adhered to more liberal views on Sabbatical rest. Gradually many Puritans, by the persecution they underwent, were driven into a certain extremism, so that the Puritanism that shook off the yoke of Charles I and Archbishop William Laud contained sections more radical than the Presbyterian or moderately Episcopalian Puritans who started the movement. In these groups laicization, so important for natural science, had progressed furthest, and the dislike of authorities in theology and science was strongest. As uncompromisingly as some Puritans combated the introduction of alien elements in biblical theology, they withstood the adulteration of science by speculative ingredients. They were the most intrepid defenders of scientific freedom, which they regarded as a necessary supplement to theological freedom. Both should be liberated from Aristotle and scholasticism. Noah Biggs (1651) asked for an "Academy of Philosophick freedom," and Webster remembered those "valiant champions who have stood up to maintain truth against the impetuous torrent of antiquity, authority, and universality of opinion" and demanded a "philosophical liberty to be bound to the authority of none, but truth it self."

The Puritans when dealing with theological and ethical issues were inclined to reject anything not sanctioned by the Bible; especially scholasticism seemed to them popish and half-heathenish. One step further and Aristotelian natural philosophy was also condemned because of its heathen origin. This could be a strong argument to the Protestant mind, especially to people like Biggs, Webster, and William Dell. The disciples of Paracelsus made liberal use of it; the title of Bostocke's work is a whole program: "the difference between the auncient Physicke, first taught by the godly forefathers, consisting in unitie peace and concords and the latter Phisicke proceeding from Idolaters, Ethnickes, and Heathen: as Gallen, and such other consisting in dualitie, discorde, and contrarietie." The fact that Biggs and Webster, like Bostocke seventy years earlier, were not only apologists of experimental, Baconian learning, but also of Paracelsus, proves that they had a tendency to mysticism of a kind not congenial to Calvinism. This becomes evident in their attitude to "learned divinity." Continuing a venerable tradition from the Middle Ages to Luther and Calvin, they opposed the blending of biblical doctrine with pagan philosophy, but they went much further in that they joined the "spiritualists" in their rejection of a "learned ministry." On the other hand, the conservatives seemed to forget the danger, both to science and theology, that was hidden in the connection with Aristotelian philosophy. The Netherlands Reformed theologian Voetius was too much in need of the help of scholastic philosophy in his combat against Cartesianism, atomism, and Copernicanism to bother about its pagan or "Romish" origin. And, like Alexander Ross, he was of the opinion that the very cause of science and religion demanded unswerving loyalty to Aristotle.

In general, however, the *via media* was chosen. What was

acceptable in the ancients was accepted, and at the same time it was felt that contemporary science was at least equal and in many respects superior to that of antiquity. The doctrine of "common grace," which plays such an important role in Calvin's theology, may have been influential in warning Protestants against a rigorous and wholesale rejection of the ancients on religious grounds. According to Calvin the Fall had done most damage to mankind in religious and ethical respects (here only a very faint glimmer of light has been left in "natural" man), but the intellectual faculties were comparatively little impaired. He was too realistic to extend the situation of religion to all departments of life only for analogy's sake; he believed that outside the sphere of the Church, truth had been revealed in a general way in degrees differing according to the subject. He was of the opinion that we owe much to the heathen in the arts and sciences, and on the grounds of the Bible and of common experience he refused to consider this contribution worthless. According to Calvin the light of truth often shines clearly in the heathen and "if we hold the Spirit of God to be the only source of Truth, we will neither reject, nor despise this truth wherever it may reveal itself, provided we do not wish to offend the Spirit of God." In this moderate attitude most Reformed scholars persisted, though deviations to one or the other side occurred. They shook off the yoke of systems and selected from the pagan or Roman Catholic past everything that, according to them, could stand the test of Scripture and "reality." As the Calvinist poet Johan de Brune (1657) put it: "Wheresoever Truth may be, were it in a Turk or Tatar, it must be cherished . . . let us seek the honeycomb even within the lion's mouth."

Manual labor

The love for experimental science and the technological interest of the Reformed were closely interwoven with their ethical evaluation of manual labor. Experimentation often derives the choice as well as the solution of its problems from the crafts, and now that the speculative occupations were to a certain extent devaluated, there was, even amongst the learned, less disrespect for manual labor. In principle manual labor had never been slighted by Jewish and Christian ethics as it had been in late antiquity and, perhaps under the influence thereof, by the humanists.

In a beautiful poem the sixteenth-century clergyman George Herbert expressed the Christian attitude to labor. "For Thy sake" is the tincture that makes the meanest labor bright; this clause "makes drudgery divine," even the sweeping of a room.

The Reformed matrimonial service of the Netherlands calls upon the husband to "labor faithfully and diligently in his Divine calling," and this was certainly more than a pious phrase. Isaac Beeckman, although a theologian and a medical doctor, did not deem it below his dignity to be a chandler and manufacturer of water conduits. He found therein abundant occasions for experiments in mechanics, hydrostatics, and hydrodynamics, and he abandoned this profession only when the headmastership of a Latin school seemed to offer more leisure for pursuing scientific investigations. Esteem for manual labor and diligence in "industries" were regarded as the main causes for the increased wealth of the Hollanders and the improvement of their minds; they "not only disgraced, but terrified their neighbors by their industry."

Agriculture also was extolled by this ethical conception. Palissy was proud of being an artisan and he urged the sons of the rural nobility to spend their energy on agricultural inventions instead of idling away their time, for agriculture is "a right labour, worthy of being honoured." Of all manual labor that of the peasant was held in the greatest contempt; Palissy gave it a scientific background (he is now regarded as one of the founders of agricultural chemistry), as he was of the opinion that "there is no occupation for which more science is required." Bacon stigmatized the opinion that the dignity of the mind should be impaired through occupation with material things; he stressed the importance of the mechanical arts, like chemistry and agriculture.

The conservatives, on the other hand, thought they could not better disqualify new ideas than by pointing out that they were accepted only by artisans. William Barlowe declared that arguments for the rotation of the earth, like those of Mark Ridley, "may goe current in a mechanicall Trades-man shop, yet they are very insufficient to bee allowed for good by men of learning." The Roman Catholic Canon Libertus Fromondus (of Antwerp) emphasized that the Copernican theory was especially favored by the heretics of Holland and Zeeland (and not by the Catholics of Spain and Portugal), and that amongst them only the seafarers, not the really learned, upheld it. That manual labor was little appreciated by the conservatives is demonstrated by their using this argument (which was not entirely just).

The experimental and empirical character of the new science made the cooperation of the craftsmen indispensable. More than the philosophers they were confronted with hard facts. Confidence in wrong theories on ebb and flood tide or on the magnetic needle could cause a disastrous end of a sailor's life. Therefore, the advocates of "new philosophy" mocked their opponents for shunning manual operations and extolled the simple artisan as being nearer the truth. And did not the craftsmen have every reason for their growing self-esteem? Had not the first effective blow to traditional science been delivered by the seafarers who crossed the Torrid Zone, discovered the inhabitants of the Southern Hemisphere (against the opinion of Greek philosophers as well as that of Christian Church Fathers), and found a new world with plants and animals unheard of in the books of Greek and medieval naturalists? Not a new theory but simple *facts,* discovered by simple people, overthrew the old philosophy. The same was true of experimentation: "Simple workmen were capable of convicting of error all great men who are called philosophers" (Pascal).

The artificers were not reluctant in proving their claims; sometimes they were even rather provocative. Palissy lamented the fact that he did not know Latin, because this prevented him from detecting the errors of the philosophical works that had not been translated, and he warned his readers against the "crooked theories of vain philosophies." Robert Norman (1581) was hardly less defiant. Some learned people had written that mechanics and mariners should not meddle with scientific questions, and Norman replied that the scholars in their studies amongst their books can imagine far-fetched theories, "yet there are in this land diverse Mechanicians, that in their severall faculties and professions, have the use of those arts at their fingers ends, and can applie them to their severall purposes, as effectuallie, and more readilie, than those that would most condemne them."

The new philosophy needed the cooperation of the "learned" (mathematicians) with the artificers, and very often this was indeed accomplished. John Dee, Robert Recorde, Thomas Digges, Petrus Plancius, Isaac Beeckman, all men who had university training, entered into friendly collaboration with artificers who wrote on experimental science, like John Blagrave (instrument-maker), William Bourne (writer on navigation), William Borough and Robert Norman (writers on magnetism), William Jansz Blaeu (cartographer), *et al.* In some cases the trained mathematicians came from the class of artificers (e.g. Beeckman) or they were in an intermediate position: engineers without university education (Simon Stevin). But whether they belonged to that class or not, they shared its ideals of the emancipation of the manual workers, and this could only be beneficial to the new science. Bacon's ideal was an England in which wealth rested in the hands of "merchants, burghers, tradesmen, freeholders, farmers in the country"; an evident example was found "in our neighbours of the Low Countries, who could never have endured and continued so inestimable and insupportable charges . . . by their mechanical industry, were it not that their wealth was dispersed in many hands" of people of "inferior conditions." He wanted not only material goods, however, but also intellectual goods more equally divided, as the sixteenth-century scientists, mentioned above, had already advocated.

It was felt that the manual workers ought to have some scientific training, but also that people of the higher classes should not shun manual work. Just as Palissy wanted the young noblemen to invent tools for agriculture, William Petty (1648) wanted children of the highest rank to be taught some manual occupation to enable them to make experiments and become patrons of science. Even the Restoration could not wholly subdue this "democratic" spirit of the new science. According to the optimistic Sprat, "Philosophy will then attain to perfection, when either the Mechanic Labourers shall have philosophical heads, or the Philosophers shall have Mechanical Hands." In the Royal Society "the tradesman, the merchant, the scholar" represented a "union of Men's Hands and Reasons" and preferred "Works before Words." The society realized an ideal much alive since Bacon, and that Gresham College was its meeting place was significant of the old union of Puritanism and science. Since its foundation in 1597 Gresham College had been a meeting place of the learned artificers, astronomers, and physicists of London—a true center of the "new philosophy" but also of Puritanism: two of its professors, Samuel Foster and Henry Gellibrand, were in trouble during the Laudian persecution of Puritanism.

IV

The source of natural science

To the modern reader it seems self-evident that the science of nature should be founded upon the observation of nature, the stellar universe, the earth, the plants, and animals. Yet other possibilities presented themselves in the sixteenth century, namely (1) the writings of the ancients, (2) immediate enlightenment, (3) rational reflection, and (4) Holy Scripture. Therefore, further consideration is needed to explain why the Reformed in general had chosen the Book of Creation as the fifth possibility.

1. The Reformed were sometimes enticed by the writings of the ancients. Bookish people were attracted by the parallel between the return to the oldest documents of Christian religion and the oldest documents of human science. In general, however, this humanistic attitude did not prevail.

2. As to the second possibility, just as some people founded their religion largely upon divine illumination by the Spirit (Anabaptists, Quakers), there were theosophists who expected scientific enlightenment from an immediate insight into the hidden workings of nature. Renaissance mysticism (neo-pythagorism, hermetism, alchemy) furthered the idea that man (microcosm) by a sympathetic feeling could immediately grasp the inner essence of the universe (macrocosm). Kepler's rejection of the scientific esotericism of the Rosicrucian Robert Fludd was paralleled by the attitude of the Reformers toward the "enthusiasts" and theosophists.

3. The third way to science, that of logical deduction from innate ideas, had little attraction for people who attributed small value to "natural theology" because of their distrust of "unaided" reason. Bacon's violent opposition to logic-spinning in science was a reflection of the Puritan attitude and, consequently, was much appreciated by the Puritans. Sometimes, however, the dislike of Aristotelianism was so

great that Cartesianism was welcomed as an ally against it (Webster, Hall). However, those, like Boyle, who really carried on scientific research, were less enthusiastic, as they were afraid that a heavier yoke would be laid upon them by this liberator. They accepted mechanical explanations in general but recognized that Descartes' physical explanations were "chimerical" (Chr. Huygens). This opinion prevailed since the triumph of Newton, who was, in principle, a Baconian. The preface to the second edition of the *Principia,* written by the Rev. Roger Cotes (1713) with Newton's approval, could have been written by any Puritan scientist of the school of Bacon. According to Cotes, the business of true philosophy is to seek after those laws actually chosen by God to form the world, not those He might have chosen, had He so pleased. He opposed Descartes, who was "presumptuous enough to think that he can find the true principles of physics and the laws of natural things by the force alone of his own mind, and the internal light of his reason."

4. The fourth possibility presented the greatest temptation to the Reformed. Because of their principle of founding theology and ethics (and often politics also) upon Scripture, it was easy to draw the parallel of founding science too upon Scriptural data. Scientific research, then, only served to elaborate and to detail a discipline of which the principles were already known by the exegesis of the Bible.

In the first centuries of the Christian era some of the Fathers, in their reaction to pagan philosophy, wanted natural philosophy to be based upon the Bible, whereas others tried to demonstrate that the Greek world picture indeed was in the Bible. Both lines were followed by Protestants. Protestant scholasticism (L. Daneau, 1576; G. Voetius, 1636) clung to Bible texts in order to refute the theories concerning the movement of the earth; Protestant antischolasticism quoted Bible texts in evidence of a peculiar doctrine of elements. Scripture thus proved to be a two-edged sword when drawn into scientific controversies.

The tendency to build up a "Mosaic" science, that is, a science founded mainly on texts from Genesis, was particularly strong amongst the alchemists and the Paracelsists. The charge that Paracelsus was an innovator was answered by the countercharge that scholastic philosophy was heathenish whereas Paracelsus founded his doctrine upon Scripture, a more reliable and also more ancient foundation. Paracelsus put forward the definition: "What generates is an element" (*"Als ist das ein Element das da gebieret"*), evidently an allusion to Genesis I: 11, 21, 24. The Huguenot physician Joseph du Chesne (1593; 1605) consequently excluded air and fire from the elements because they are not mentioned in Genesis as "bringing forth" things, and "we prefer to follow the divine Seer rather than the heathen philosopher." Richard Bostocke (1585), Thomas Tymme (1612), and Noah Biggs (1653) also stressed the biblical character of Paracelsism as a contrast with the heathenish character of scholasticism. Sometimes, reference to Bible texts seemed advantageous even to Copernican astronomers, as in the case of the Calvinist astronomer John Bainbridge (1618), who (with reference to the text that the heavens will wax old as doth a garment) explained the natural origin of comets in the heavens. On this occasion the heathenism of Greek and scholastic philosophy was also used as an argument.

On the other hand, the Copernican system could easily be rejected by referring to passages in the Bible (Joshua 20: 12-13; Ps 19: 6-7; Ps 104: 5; Eccles. I: 4-5). Therefore, to prevent theological opposition, the Lutheran Pastor Andreas Osiander inserted a preface to Copernicus' *"De revolutionibus"* (1543) in which the Copernican theory was represented as a merely mathematical hypothesis with no pretensions to any physical truth. Luther and Melanchthon were against the Copernican system as not being in accordance with the Bible; Melanchthon's rejection was also inspired by his scholasticism. Yet there was no violent hostility. Rheticus, the first disciple of Copernicus, was professor of astronomy at Wittenberg; Michael Mästlin, who initiated Kepler into the secrets of the Copernican system, taught at Tübingen. The Danish astronomer Tycho Brahe, in order to agree with the Bible, propounded an intermediate system (a geocentric universe with the sun and the moon revolving about the earth and the five planets about the sun). After the condemnation of the doctrine of the motion of the earth by Rome (in 1616) and the trial of Galileo (1633) because of its conflict with the biblical text, Roman Catholic authors often accepted the Tychonian system. Many Protestants followed Gilbert and Origanus, who modified this latter system by admitting the daily rotation of the earth (Edw. Wright, Fr. Godwin, M. Ridley, N. Carpenter). It could be expected that those Protestants with whom biblicism was the strongest, i.e., the Puritans, would be the staunchest opponents of the motion of the earth. Yet, the reverse is true. In England Th. Digges (1573), John Bainbridge (1618), Henry Gellibrand (1634), John Wallis, and John Wilkins (1640) were Puritan supporters of the Copernican system, and this open-mindedness to new and bold ideas went even further. In 1576 Digges put forward the theory that the fixed stars are at varying distances beyond the orb of Saturn, thereby breaking through the closed, spherical universe that Copernicus had not abandoned and that Kepler and Galileo would adhere to. Not the Italian freethinker Giordano Bruno, but Thomas Digges was the first to propound this audacious hypothesis. Wilkins also accepted the idea of an infinite universe; he ascribed the opposition of Copernicus to servility to the ancients and to the fear of deviation from the exegesis of Scripture phrases as given by "the supposed infallible Church."

Calvinism and Copernicanism

The main reason for the open attitude of so many Reformed authors toward the movement of the earth seems to be that their biblicism was related only to religious (historical, ethical, ecclesiastical) aspects, not to scientific topics. As a rule they gave little room to "Mosaic" science and sought indeed the data of science in the Book of Creation. One of the reasons for this must have been the example set by Calvin, their greatest theological teacher. First of all, it is important that Calvin, notwithstanding his severe critique on Greek philosophers, did not reject everything that originated with the heathen, but carefully tested each of their ideas on its own merits. In principle, the same was done by those conservative theologians (Roman Catholic as well as Protestant) who put the Aristotelian world system to the test of Scripture and were of the opinion that there was perfect agreement. Calvin, however, saw more clearly than any of his contemporaries that the world picture of the Bible conflicted with the Aristotelian system. He remarked that Genesis speaks of one expanse, whereas the Aristotelian astronomers make a distinction of spheres. He pointed out that Genesis calls the sun and moon the "great lights," whereas the astronomers prove by conclusive reasons that the little star of Saturn is greater than the moon. Yet Calvin did not reject the current astronomical system. As a layman in astronomy he accepted the almost unanimous beliefs of the astronomers. The cause of the difference between "Moses" and astronomy is, according to him, that Moses wrote in a popular style; he only described what all ordinary persons endowed with common sense are able to understand, whereas the astronomers investigate whatever the sagacity of the human mind can comprehend. Thus Calvin's manner of exegesis of "scientific" texts in the Bible is closely connected with the generally accepted Protestant doctrine that the biblical revelation is accessible to everyone. According to him, the Holy Spirit opens a common school for the learned and the unlearned and therefore chooses what is intelligible to all. If Moses had spoken in a scientific way, the uneducated might have pleaded in excuse that such subjects were beyond their capacity. Therefore Moses adapted his writing to common use. "He who would learn astronomy and other recondite arts, let him go elsewhere."

Consequently, it is to Calvin's great credit that he recognized the discrepancy between the scientific world system of his days and the biblical text, and secondly that he did not repudiate the results of scientific research on that account. It is quite irrelevant that Calvin did not know the Copernican system.[3] If the Aristotelian system is not in the Bible and yet may be true, the Scriptural argument for the rejection of every other astronomical system is without value; from the religious point of view the old system henceforth loses its advantages over the Copernican system.

Calvin's influence is evident in the preface to Gilbert's *De magnete* (1600) by Edward Wright. Kepler defended the Copernican system with almost the same arguments, as did the reformed pastor Philips van Lansbergen (1619; 1629) and his son, Jacob van Lansbergen (1632). P. van Lansber-

---

[3] The quotations attributed to him by A. D. White, *A History of the Warfare of Science with Theology* (London; 1896), p. 127 (between quotation marks!) which are repeated by many authors on Calvinism, offer one more example to show that many historians pass judgment on Calvin without having a serious knowledge of his works. Moreover, an equitable judgment on Calvin is not possible without comparing his ideas with those of his contemporaries and predecessors. "Many would be glad to damn and dismiss Calvin by a reference to Servetus; but no man ought to be judged solely by his worst acts. The advocates to tolerance do not always exercise that virtue . . . even toward the intolerant of the past, to whom 19th century liberalism was a thing wholly unknown." "Calvin's intolerance has usually been exaggerated and the range of his tolerance has been overlooked." (J. T. McNeill, *The History and Character of Calvinism* (New York and London: Oxford, 1954), pp. 228-229. The execution of Servet was approved by the Catholics, by the mild Bullinger (Zwinglian) and the gentle Melanchthon (Lutheran).

gen's work was published with the support of the strongly
Calvinistic Estates of Zeeland; it was applauded by the poet
and "Pensionaris" Jacob Cats, the poet Johan de Brune, and
the secretary to the Synod of Dordt, Daniel Heinsius. Simon
Stevin and Isaac Beeckman were Copernicans, and the most
influential reformed theologian of the first half of the seventeenth century, André Rivet, did not deem the Copernican
system contrary to Scripture.

This sufficiently demonstrates that when Calvinism in Holland was in its heyday, it did nothing to prevent Copernicanism.[4] During the Cartesian controversy that raged in
Holland in the middle of the seventeenth century, the Voetian
party tried to discredit Cartesianism and Copernicanism by
connecting them with Arminianism and libertinism. This fact
may perhaps have helped to establish the now prevailing
opinion that Arminians and libertines showed more inclination toward the new hypothesis than the orthodox Reformed, an opinion, however, that is not confirmed by the
facts.

It should be stressed however, that by no means did all
Reformed writers on theology agree with Calvin's method of
exegesis. Many of them adhered to scholastic philosophy, and
for that reason were prompted to a traditional exegesis (Zan-
chi, Daneau, du Bartas, Voetius). The famous independent
theologian John Owen was against the Copernican system on
purely biblical grounds.

G. Voetius, the first rector of the University of Utrecht,
deemed scholastic philosophy the only philosophy conformable to Scripture. Moreover, he was of the opinion that "Holy
Scripture teaches not only what is necessary to salvation, but
also lays down the . . . principles of all other good sciences
and arts; the Copernican system is in flat contradiction with
the text and the intention of the Bible. If the Holy Spirit
accommodated Himself to the ordinary people, He would
tell a lie on behalf of the common people. When recom-
mending commentators on Genesis, Voetius especially mentioned Pereira S. J. On the other hand, his opponents within
the Reformed Church, the Cocceians, had a predilection for
Calvin's accommodation theory and were, in general, Coperni-

---

[4] A. D. White's verdict that "the Calvinistic Church" in Holland was
at first strongly against the whole new system but that "Calvinism even
in its stronghold was powerless against it" is based on ignorance of
the real situation. The Reformed Church did not meddle with the
Copernican question. Cf. A. D. White, *op. cit.,* p. 150.

cans. Calvin was, according to Dean Farrar, "one of the greatest interpreters of Scripture who ever lived." His exegesis was not only scholarly and remarkably free from prejudice, but he was also very careful not to arrive too soon to an apodictical conclusion. Therefore, John Donne preferred him to Melanchthon because "Calvin will say, It seems to be thus, Melanchthon, It can be no otherwise but thus. But the best men are but problematical, only the Holy Ghost seals with infallibility." This is also the highest praise one could bestow on a scientist. Possibly Calvin by his manner of exegesis of Scripture indirectly influenced his followers who devoted themselves to the exegesis of nature.

There is a tendency to contrast the presumably milder and more cultural attitude of High Church Anglicanism and Roman Catholicism to a conventional caricature of Puritanism and Calvinism as a cold, unemotional, static orthodoxy. "Calvinism has usually been discussed in an atmosphere of controversy and has often been judged, even by academicians, with slender reference to the evidence."[5]

The myth of the Puritan hatred of music and art has been exploded by P. A. Scholes; that Calvin and Puritanism had a stimulating influence upon science has been made evident by several recent studies. "Puritanism was an important factor . . . in promoting the type of thinking that helped to arouse interest in science" (Stimson). "Calvinism or puritanism or ascetic protestantism generally . . . played no small part in arousing a sustained interest in science." "The happy marriage of these two movements was based on an intrinsic compatibility" (Merton). The religion of the Reformed neither regarded grace as an addition to nature, nor as an antithesis to it, but closely intertwined them. Consequently, a radical renewal of every department of life—church and state, individual and society, morals and science—was their aim. It seems evident that they achieved considerable success with respect to science.

<hr />

[5] McNeill, *op. cit.*, p. vii; R. H. Tawney (*Religion and the Rise of Capitalism*, London; Pelican, 1938) accuses Puritans of mourning a lost paradise, whereas Anglicans and Catholics saw the earth in a heavenly light (p. 228). Thus Tawney commits the same error of generalizing too much, an error of which he accuses Weber (p. xi; 313). He charges Puritans with a lack of social solidarity (p. 270) and also condemns the Calvinist defense of the poor as being "without compassion" (p. 139). Cf. Mac Neill, p. 419, "this judgment could have been reached only by ignoring a great body of evidence."

BIBLIOGRAPHY

This article is a summary of a book the author has almost finished, dealing with this subject. The author wishes to thank Dr. Douglas Johnson Cheam (Surrey), and Dr. Joseph Needham, ScD, F.R.S., for their kind help in making accessible the treasures of English libraries on his last visit to their country.

Important studies on Puritanism and science are the articles of D. Stimson and especially R. K. Merton's "Science, Technology and Society in 17th Century England." The doctor's thesis of C. E. A. Turner, "The Puritan Contribution to Scientific Education in the 17th Century" (Fac. of Science, History of Education, University of London, 1952), has not been printed. Many valuable data will be found in R. J. Jones, *Ancients and Moderns* (St. Louis: Washington University Press, 1935); P. H. Kocher, *Science and Religion in Elizabethan England* (San Marino, Calif.: Huntington Library, 1953); P. Miller, *The New England Mind* (Cambridge: Harvard University Press, 1953); and also in the work of C. E. Raven, *John Ray, Naturalist* (London and New York: Cambridge University Press, 1950).

The articles of J. Pelseneer deal exclusively with the situation in Belgium. S. F. Mason (*Main Currents of Scientific Thought*, New York: Abelard Schuman, 1954; London: Routledge, Kegan Paul, 1953), also gives attention to the relations of science and reformation. R. Hooykaas wrote about "Robert Boyle," Isaac Beeckman, Pascal, and Kepler in connection with the problem of science and religion. The article about "Science and Theology in the Middle Ages" (*Free University Quarterly*, III, 1954, pp. 77-163) could be regarded as an introduction to the present article.

Of a more popular character is the valuable work of B. Farrington on *Francis Bacon* (New York: Henry Schuman, 1949; London: Lawrence & Wishart, 1951). About Calvinism in general the books of J. T. McNeill, *The History and Character of Calvinism,* and A. Lecerf, *Etudes calvinistes* (Paris: 1949), give reliable information.

Ed. note: See Preface, p. XIV.

CATHOLICISM, PROTESTANTISM, AND THE DEVELOPMENT OF SCIENCE IN THE SIXTEENTH AND SEVENTEENTH CENTURIES*

François Russo, S.J.

The influence of religious beliefs and attitudes on the development of science is one of the most interesting chapters in the history of the subject. Moreover, its discussion calls for exceptional tact, as the field is one where prejudice is particularly rife, and the facts are not easy to discover. How did the individual conscience succeed in combining religious and scientific activity, and what were the dominant factors in the creative progress of the scientist? These are hard questions to answer.

It is a subject worthy of investigation, however, being of fundamental importance to the history of thought, more especially in the period with which we shall have to deal—the sixteenth and seventeenth centuries, with particular reference to the hundred years from 1550-1650, when Christendom was shaken by a dangerous religious crisis, chiefly due to the birth of Protestantism and the subsequent Catholic reformation. This was also the period in which modern science began to take shape.

I shall not attempt to cover the problem in its entirety. My aim will be to undertake, in the light of the existing literature

* *Journal of World History*, III, 4.

on the subject, particularly the writings of the Protestant historians, a critical examination of the conclusions hitherto advanced and the methods by which they were reached, and to help to fill in some considerable gaps by providing brief but accurate particulars. This may result in a fairer estimate —since it will be better balanced—of the part played by Catholicism and Protestantism, respectively, in the development of modern science.[1]

Lack of balance and of a really systematic approach to the subject, leading to unjustified conclusions, seem to me to be the worst defects of current studies of the problem. These are particularly evident in the recent history of science by S. F. Mason, where one chapter, dealing with the scientific revolution and the reformation, juxtaposes correct statements with various conclusions not justified by the premises, and which has no corresponding chapter on the Catholic contribution to scientific progress.

A similar criticism may be brought against *Science and Reformation,* the much more thorough and original study by Professor Hooykaas,[2] to which I shall often have occasion to refer. Here, in particular, the author, striving to demonstrate the favorable opportunities offered to scientific development by Protestant thought, more than once creates the impression, without furnishing any proof, that this beneficent effect of Protestantism was specifically due to the manner in which it differed from Catholicism.

Other writers, and more especially J. Pelseneer, have attempted to dismiss the question in a few pages. The paper by Mr. Pelseneer, though he has a high reputation as a historian of science, is really disconcerting in its brevity and oversimplification. I will touch on this again later.[3]

[1] Readers are referred, once and for all, to the following works: my own *Bibliographie d'histoire des sciences et des techniques* (Paris: Hermann, 1954; multigraphed supplement, 1955). This mentions the studies on which the present paper is based, and gives the titles of the principal works by the scholars to whom it refers and of the most important studies written about them.

A. C. Crombie, *Augustin to Galileo. The History of Science* A.D. *400-1500* (London, 1952).

A. Wolf, *A History of Science, Technology and Philosophy in the 17th Century.*

[2] cf. *supra.,* R. Hooykaas, "Science and Reformation."

[3] J. Pelseneer, "La Réforme et l'origine de la science moderne," *Revue de l'Université de Bruxelles* (July-August 1954), 12 pages. In this the author quotes from articles he has published in other reviews, including *Lychnos.*

Although, owing to the complexity of the problem, differences of opinion tend to persist among historians as to the interpretation of some of the facts, it at least seems possible that a great measure of agreement could be reached regarding the methodological requirements for the study of the question—in other words, as to the precise nature of the aim. I propose first of all to strive to define this, for the purpose of widening an outlook that seems to me to have been, until now, extremely narrow.

Methodological Preliminaries

The religious attitude seems liable to influence scientific development in at least two ways, which call for preliminary consideration—firstly, through the eagerness for a knowledge of nature that is prompted by the Christian faith, and secondly through the manner in which the demands of orthodoxy are reconciled with the freedom of research the scientist must have. The great merit of R. Hooykaas is that he gives careful thought to both these points, from the Protestant angle. My purpose will be to criticize some points of his article and to submit a similar study in respect to Catholicism; the material for this already exists in bulky and learned works, which I shall try to summarize.

After determining what there is in the religious attitudes of Protestantism and Catholicism that serves as an incitement to cultivate the sciences, it remains to be discovered whether those attitudes have any *direct influence* on the elaboration of the *scientific method*—an important question. Science cannot be developed merely by an encouraging attitude. It must be provided with technical means of developing, and a method is the foremost of these. It was the creation of a method that made modern science possible in the first place. So we ought to ascertain to what extent the religious attitude, whether Protestant or Catholic, influenced the formation of that method. R. Hooykaas does not seem to have paid sufficient attention to this point.

There remains the more immediate problem of discovering what part was played by Protestantism and Catholicism respectively in the actual *inventions* that contributed to the advancement of science. This naturally leads us to inquire to what persuasion the various scientists to whom we owe the creation of modern science have belonged. But it should be noted—a point Protestant historians have somewhat neglected —that before we can infer from these results that a particular creed has had an *active influence* on scientific progress, we have to make sure, in considering each individual scientist, that his faith had some notable influence on his discoveries. As I pointed out just now, this is not an easy matter to decide, though it must be agreed that to ascertain what religious belief a scientist holds provides a valuable clue.

But how is this to be ascertained? J. Pelseneer, making use of the interesting work of Candolle, uses a general method— he compiles statistics for all scientists, irrespective of their subject of study. This leads to grave difficulties. Whom are we to select as genuine scientists? Like Candolle, J. Pelseneer, followed in this by R. Hooykaas, takes them from the lists of members and correspondents of the academies of science. These particulars are certainly significant; but they are by no means entirely satisfactory. Should not the aim be to arrive at a weighted average? But how is this to be done?

Furthermore, statistics for the period with which we are concerned are insufficient, for the scientific associations did not take really definite shape until the latter half of the seventeenth century.

Moreover, this overall method needs to be supplemented by statistics for each separate discipline—which are probably the most important and incidentally the easiest to compile; for there is general agreement as to the names of those who have made decisive contributions to the different branches of science. One is surprised to find that in this respect the Protestant historians have nothing but arbitrary selections to offer, though it would have been easy to approach the task *systematically*.

Again, though the most important point for our purpose is to discover to what creed the leading scientists belonged, we should not overlook the efforts made to spread a knowledge of science, particularly during the period of education. A scientist's tendencies will depend to a great extent on the environment in which he was brought up, and especially on the scientific teaching he received in his young days. The parts played by Protestantism and Catholicism in this respect must consequently be ascertained. One regrets that J. Pelseneer, R. Hooykaas, and the other Protestant historians did not pay more attention to these points.

Since my investigation deals chiefly with Catholicism, it must pay special attention to the part played by clerics in scientific progress. Here there may be illuminating and hitherto somewhat neglected particulars to be gleaned regarding the interest in science displayed by the Catholic Church.

Such are the main lines of the survey I propose to make; for everything connected with Protestantism I need only refer readers to the very important article by R. Hooykaas —that is, to the extent I feel able to agree with him.

I. Humanism and Scientific Development

Though it is not the immediate subject of this study, the influence of Humanism on scientific progress deserves to be considered here, for Humanism, being closely bound up with religious history, was one of the most important channels through which religious thought affected that progress.

Humanism, a very complex movement, may be regarded in its widest sense as a reaction against the dialectical excesses of a scholasticism that had to a great extent become fossilized and ingrown; as an intense eagerness to become acquainted with the cultural wealth contained in the writings of an earlier age and—though to a less extent—with nature in its infinite variety; as a desire to develop all the potentialities of human intelligence and sensitivity; and as an urge to challenge traditional maxims that had until then been too meekly accepted. It is true that Humanism is concerned with science in only a few of its aspects. The exaggerated erudition, the intellectual profligacy that led men to the most insensate studies—such as magic, astrology, and alchemy—had nothing to contribute to science. Literary and esthetic Humanism, too, were little concerned with scientific matters; many Humanists were turned aside from the constructive study of nature and from rational learning, on which modern science is based, by their preoccupation with imitating the ancients, their concentration on book learning, and their inordinately grandiloquent and poetical concept of culture.

But in the sixteenth century especially, a considerable body of literary Humanism was taking nature and the cosmos as its study. This movement, which was strongest in France, helped to restore the tradition of the Hexamerons, which had come down from the Fathers of the Church, while careful, at the same time, to absorb the recent findings of science. It produced works of no great literary value and of indifferent scientific interest; but it provided an outlet and, as such, was a factor favorable to science.

The form of Humanism current among physicians—again, chiefly in the sixteenth century—was, however, a close association of literary and scientific interests. I will mention its most noteworthy representatives later on.

We also have to thank literary Humanism for the publication of the scientific writings of the ancients, particularly those of Archimedes and Apollonius, with which the Middle Ages had had no firsthand acquaintance and which were to exert such a great influence over the development of mathematics and mechanics.

Humanism also endowed scientific thought with means of expression that were certainly of great value to its development.

Nor should the present-day custom of specialization make us forget that an appreciable number of Humanists were both "literary" and "scientific" in their interests, so that science and literature spurred each other to fresh progress in one and the same writer.

As R. Hooykaas has rightly pointed out, Humanism gained unquestionable support from Protestantism. The reawakened feeling for the Bible, the deep sense of the sovereignty of God, and the intense religious sentiment that are such notable features of Protestantism certainly helped to promote the study of nature, which was recognized as God's handiwork, a manifestation of Providence in which the beauty of His creation was to be admired. It is clear that many Protestant scientists, particularly Kepler, were impelled in their investigations by religious motives. But—a point perhaps not sufficiently stressed by R. Hooykaas—Protestantism also manifests a kind of disapproval for a world it regards as corrupt, and even a degree of pessimism, which was certainly not propitious to science.

As we know, the Catholic attitude toward Humanism was at first somewhat reserved. The Catholic Church noted with alarm that some Humanists were serving the cause of the Reformation by attributing such importance to Holy Writ that tradition was neglected. Moreover, Humanism, more especially at Padua, had a tendency toward pantheism and Platonism that was unacceptable to orthodox Catholics.

So the Catholic Church could not accept Humanism without reservation. But neither did it spurn the Humanists, as several Protestant historians have alleged. It is true that in 1528 and 1529 Noël Beda, the uncompromising Syndic of the Faculty of Theology, supported by Antoine de Gouvea, the principal of the celebrated Collège de Montaigu, fiercely accused Erasmus and Lefèvre d'Etaples of being Lutherans. But another tendency in Catholicism continued to take a much more favorable view of Humanism.

In this effort on the part of Catholicism to accept all the good features of Humanism and reconcile it with traditional philosophy, the Company of Jesus was destined to play a decisive part, and thus did much to further the development of science.

Ignatius de Loyola, the founder of the Company of Jesus, gave great prominence to the humanities in the program he drew up for the intellectual training of the members of the Company, and later for the boys who came to study in its colleges. Those colleges soon arose in great numbers throughout the Catholic countries of Europe. Ignatius did a special service to science by rejecting the erudite embellishments of Humanism about which the contemporaries of Erasmus and Rabelais were so enthusiastic and by demanding a sober, lucid expression of thought. This was the origin of the educational tradition that was to provide a sound, balanced training for coming generations that produced many scientists, including René Descartes, a pupil at the Collège of La Flèche, where his early experience of intellectual life gave him a sense of method and a lucidity that left their mark on his later work.

It was not only the prevailing atmosphere of the day that led Catholics, and especially the Company of Jesus, to welcome Humanism. Fundamental reasons of a religious character were turning the Catholic mind toward rational knowledge and particularly toward the study of nature. For it is not only among the Protestants of the sixteenth and seventeenth centuries that we find admiration for creation as God's handiwork, together with a realization of the religious importance of familiarity with nature. The spiritual attitude of St. Ignatius Loyola, who commanded his flock to "find God in all things" and was dominated by the wish to glorify and serve Him in all things, no doubt illustrates the deepest and most imperative motive for furthering the advancement of science. Moreover—to refer briefly to an extremely complex question—it may be noted that Catholicism has the advantage of Protestantism inasmuch as an optimistic view of the creation and of the tasks confronting mankind permeates its whole tradition and is displayed, more particularly, in the teachings of the learned Thomas Aquinas. This was an important factor, tending to enhance Catholic respect for science.

This dynamic spirit underlies the Humanism of many secular scholars and even more clerics, among whom the members of the Company of Jesus are particularly prominent—men such as Father Richeome, whose infectious enthusiasm for geography is displayed in his *Trois discours sur la religion catholique* (1597), Father Fournier (1591-1652), who gives us a complete encyclopedia of marine phenomena in his *Hydrographie* (1643), a lively yet extremely lucid work that enjoyed a wide circulation; Peiresc (1580-1637), who was magistrate, astronomer, and physician; Father Mersenne (1588-1648), a Minim Friar who corresponded with all the learned men in Europe and was ready to tackle any problem; Father Athanasius Kircher (1602-1680), whose tremendous output testifies to a limitless curiosity that, though perhaps slightly undisciplined, has a certain scientific value and whose correspondence, still unpublished, is also very extensive; Huet (1639-1710), Archbishop of Avranches, who lent his energies to the Academy at Caen and was interested in theology, poetry, and physics; and Father Milliet of Chales (1621-1678), whose *Mundus mathematicus* (1674) sets forth in three huge folios all that was then known about mathematics, mechanics, geography, magnetism, stonecutting, military architecture, hydrostatics, navigation, optics, music, pyrotechnics, and astronomy.[4]

[4] Here one cannot fail to be reminded of Pascal. His case, surely, was the exact contrary of that of the Humanists mentioned above. After his conversion, on the night of November 23, 1654, his scientific pursuits came practically to an end, which forms a very strange contrast to his extraordinary activity in previous years. Facts are facts: Pascal gave up his scientific work more or less completely for the sake of theological and religious activities. The reader may consult the excellent book on this subject by Pierre Humbert, *Pascal savant* (Paris: Albin Michel, 1947). I will simply point out that Pascal's abandonment of science is partly attributable to a tendency, derived from the Jansenists, toward pessimism and a contempt for Nature—something the Catholic Church has always striven against.

Humanism of this type, with its emphasis on science, prompted the first teaching curricula drawn up for the Jesuit colleges. A dominant role in the elaboration of the scientific part of these programs was played by Father Clavius (1538-1612), a professor in the Roman college, which produced a great number of eminent Jesuit scientists, some of whom will be mentioned later.

It is worthwhile quoting the defense of "mathematics" (as will be seen from the passage in question, the subject was then taken in a very wide sense) brought forward by Clavius in 1586 in answer to some of his colleagues whose tastes were too exclusively literary:

> Mathematics inform poets about the rising and setting of the heavenly bodies and historians as to the position and distance of different places; to philosophers they offer firm examples for demonstration; to politicians, truly admirable methods for conducting their business in private life and in war; to physicians they teach the manner and diversity of celestial movements, of the light, of colors, of transparent bodies, of sounds; to metaphysicians, the number of the spheres and the intelligences; to theologians, the principal parts of the divine creation; to jurists and experts in canon law they teach computation; not to speak of the services rendered by the work of mathematicians to the State, to medicine, to navigation and agriculture. We must therefore strive to ensure that mathematics shall prosper in our colleges as well as other subjects.

The new scientific information is liberally represented, as well as more traditional views, in the exhaustive commentary on Aristotle that—because it was written at Coimbre—is known as the *Conimbricenses* and that was for a long time the basic handbook of the Jesuit colleges.

This same Humanistic trend is found among missionaries as well, and in very vigorous form. They combined zeal for winning souls with great curiosity about the new lands where, unlike the lay travelers, they made long sojourns; their descriptions make valuable source material for ethnography, natural sciences, and physical geography. The account of the "Indies" given by Father Acosta in his *Historia natural y moral de las Indias* (Seville: 1590), which in the course of time was translated into French, Italian, and Dutch, is a masterpiece of observation and precision, of genuine scientific value. In

China the Jesuit missionaries embarked upon immense astronomical, geographical, and botanical projects inspired by the same spirit; their work does not constitute an essential contribution to scientific progress, but it had unquestionable scientific interest and was of extraordinary help in spreading a knowledge of science. I will describe some of their activities later.

II. The Scientist's Freedom of Research

It is quite evident that science can only develop in an atmosphere of intellectual freedom. What is not so evident is the justice of the claim made by certain Protestant historians, that in the sixteenth and seventeenth centuries that atmosphere was provided only by Protestantism, Catholicism having, by its authoritarian and dogmatic attitude, set up a barrier against scientific research. Not that this oversimplified view is accepted by all Protestant historians. R. Hooykaas, for instance, is much more subtle in his approach to the subject; nevertheless, it seems to me that in dealing with the history of the sciences at the time of the Reformation he gives too much credit to the Protestants, as against the Catholics, where freedom for scientific work is concerned.

The religious authorities, whether Protestant or Catholic, were inclined during the sixteenth and seventeenth centuries to make regrettable sorties into fields that did not concern them; after the Council of Trent these were perhaps at times a little more emphatic on the Catholic side, owing to the fear that heresy might creep in under cover of the new scientific concepts.

So far as Protestantism is concerned, we have more than one example of interference, or of a general attitude hardly calculated to promote the advancement of the sciences. Even Candolle, a Protestant who cannot be accused of lacking sympathy for that creed, remarks that as long as the authoritarian principle was dominant in Geneva—which means from 1535 to 1735—no Genevan citizen gained real distinction in science. Whereas as soon as a more liberal system was introduced the sciences began to flourish.

Although there is no absolute proof, it would appear that in certain Catholic countries, above all in Belgium and Austria, one of the chief causes of the lack of scientific vitality was the authoritarian political system, with its close connection between the temporal and religious powers. But it would be unfair to blame the Church itself—its doctrine and spiritual principles—for a state of things that was to a great extent due to political circumstances. This is shown by the fact that in France, a country with a Catholic majority but where the political system was more liberal, the sciences developed without hindrance.

It must also be observed that during the period with which we are concerned, and in respect to Protestantism and Catholicism alike, science experienced difficulty in escaping from the leading strings in which it was maintained by theology and metaphysics, neither of which had arrived at a sufficiently clear differentiation between the strictly religious and philosophical fields and that of positive science.

For instance, owing to the unfortunate prevalence of conventional ideas, progressive astronomers were confronted on more than one occasion with the statement that the theory of Copernicus could not be reconciled with the Scriptures. Protestants and Catholics were in the same boat over this. Indeed, the Protestants were perhaps in slightly the more awkward position of the two, owing to the strictly literal interpretation of the Scriptures into which they were forced by their rejection of tradition.

Among the Protestants, Luther made pronouncements fiercely hostile to Copernicus, as did Melanchthon in his *Physics,* which appeared in 1552. Tycho Brahe felt obliged to reject the views of Copernicus, out of respect for Holy Writ. Kepler had difficulty in getting his *Mysterium cosmographicum* into print (1596) and had to cut out a chapter on reconciling heliocentrism with the Scriptures. And in 1607, for reasons which, even if not based directly on the Scriptures, were in any case theological, he was hard put to bring out his account of the Comet of 1607, owing to the serious objections raised by the Lutheran University of Leipzig.

The case of Galileo

The significance, implications, and consequences of the condemnation of Galileo should obviously be considered as part of the general problem of what freedom the religious authorities allowed to scientists. Without embarking upon yet another detailed account of the case, I will touch on a few basic points regarding the causes and effects of the judgment.

It cannot be denied that in passing sentence on Galileo the Roman authorities were allowing the religious power to encroach to some extent upon the field of science; but we have to grasp the fact that although Galileo's intuition was correct and most of his criticism of Aristotelianism justified, the arguments he brought forward in support of Copernicus's theory were inconclusive. Not until the latter half of the seventeenth century could heliocentrism be said to pass unchallenged. For instance, in 1633, Mersenne—though well informed of the latest developments in astronomy—was very hesitant, as were many other scientists, whose views covered a wide range. Moreover, by refusing—quite rightly—to put forward his opinions in the form of a hypothesis, Galileo shocked the theologians whose views on the *nature* of astronomic facts were still bound up with the general theological system. This being so, to abandon the ancient astronomic concepts might have spread considerable confusion in the ranks of the faithful. All these are explanations rather than excuses for the behavior of the Roman theologians, for if they had been more openminded about the problems raised by scientific progress, and if their "technical" advisers—for the most part Jesuits belonging to the Roman College, and in particular Fathers Scheiner and Grienberger—had been bolder in expressing definite views (as they were in a position to do, owing to their competence and the heliocentric convictions they already held, and as it was their plain duty to do), the condemnation of Galileo might have been avoided.

But however regrettable the sentence passed on him—which did not involve the infallible head of the Church—its effect on scientific development in the Catholic countries was not so disastrous as has frequently been asserted. Galileo himself was able to continue his work after being sentenced; in 1638 he published his great work, *Discorsi e dimonstrazioni matematiche intorno a due nuove scienze*—in Holland, it is true, but without ill results for himself. In France, where, owing to the comparative freedom of the Church, the decree of 1633 was never published, so that greater liberty existed, Descartes—a believer in Copernicus—wrote to Mersenne in April, 1634, saying that he would have "the right to maintain that what the Roman Inquisition decided did not automatically become an article of faith"; but he was cautious enough to mark time, and gave up the publication of his *Traité du monde,* on which he had been working from 1630 to 1633. It can hardly be said that Descartes' scientific activity was impeded by the decree of 1633.

Although the Jesuits in France did not teach the theories of Copernicus, they frequently expressed sympathy for them. They kept to the compromises adopted by Tycho Brahe, but certain theses presented in public at La Flèche in 1642 agreed in stating that no demonstration could definitely prove that Copernicus was mistaken in his views. Father Fabri declared that "if conclusive evidence were to be found in favor of Copernicus's system, the Church would make no difficulty about recognizing that the [conflicting] passages [of the Scriptures] were to be taken in a metaphorical sense." In 1665, Father Bertet caused it to be proclaimed at Grenoble that the astronomic systems of Tycho Brahe and Copernicus were equivalent from the mathematical standpoint. Father Milliet of Chales wrote that "Copernicus has made his system seem so probable that several others now follow him, and it is an admirable thing that this hypothesis should account so precisely for all appearances." In 1688, at Grenoble, the Jesuits were still teaching that the earth did not move; but they included the statement that *non physicae principiis sed Sacris Litteris repugnat system copernicum.*

It can thus be seen that the schools were open to the ideas of Copernicus at a fairly early stage. As for the work of the scientists themselves, it would be very hard to prove that in the Catholic countries it was retarded by the judgment passed on Galileo. This expressed no objection to astronomical observations, as I will show later, and the great progress made by science during this period was of too technical a nature to be affected by the Roman prohibitions, which were chiefly of a cosmological character.

The authority of the ancients and of the schoolmen

Scientific development necessarily entailed, to a great extent, the rejection of the authority of the ancients, which had often been excessive and frequently in contradiction to the facts, and also the rejection of a method of deduction and a series of concepts that led in many cases to abstract reasoning in which there was nothing really coherent.

As R. Hooykaas correctly points out, Protestantism played an indisputable part in this healthy reaction—one not unconnected with its readiness to combat tradition and the methods of the schoolmen and restore direct contact with the Scriptures. But, as R. Hooykaas also shows, this reaction against the classics and the schoolmen was not complete and unanimous among the Protestants; and the Catholics were far from displaying such unyielding conservatism as some people tend to believe.

True, the Council of Trent helped to restore Aristotle and the schoolmen to favor, but not to an extent that deprived any Catholics concerned with science of their freedom to discuss the traditional views.

Father Richeome had full liberty to question Aristotle's theory of climates. In his *Trois discours sur la Religion Catholique,* he writes:

> From ancient times until our own day it was universally held as a thing certain, and not without reasoning and probable conjecture, that the torrid zone was uninhabitable by reason of the great and burning heat of the sun's rays, which passed directly above it twice in the year. Yet the experience of our own century, *bold and curious above all past centuries,* [my italics] teaches us not only that several parts of that roasted zone are by no means excessive in heat, but more, that they are the most temperate in the world.

Father Scheiner, who discovered sun spots at the same time as Galileo, never got into trouble, though the discovery struck a very serious blow at the traditional doctrine of the incorruptibility of the heavens.

Then there is the case of Vesalius, the critic of Galen, who was indeed very bitterly attacked—but by the university authorities, not by the Church, which left him perfectly free to work out the novel ideas that had such far-reaching influence.

Furthermore, by preserving the principles of Aristotelian philosophy and by dissuading Catholics from rash and unbridled speculation—this latter through the Index, drawn up by the Council of Trent at its last sessions (1559-1561)—the Church helped to maintain a background of healthy rationalism which was bound to assist scientific development. As H. Hauser remarks, scientists, thus put on their guard against excessive speculation, were the more inclined to turn to experimental methods, and this too was definitely in the interest of scientific progress.[5]

III. Religious Attitudes and the Growth of the Scientific Spirit

As I said just now, if science is to develop, a favorable atmosphere is not the only necessity; there must also be a method. This grew up chiefly in the first half of the seventeenth century. Did the religious attitude directly influence its growth? It is hard to say. Causality is particularly difficult to trace where these spiritual attitudes are involved. The Protestant writers who have taken up the problem have failed, in my opinion, to give it sufficient time and thought. Here again, I make no claim to present a full study of the question, and shall confine myself to a few hints that may serve as a guide.

Law and logic in nature

Modern science would never have been possible without the recognition that in nature there are certain constants, that natural phenomena are connected by permanent relationships. It will be remembered that sixteenth-century Humanism showed one trend that was in complete opposition to this, and that at one time it almost carried the day—when men like Cardan and Giordano Bruno lapsed into a naturalistic pantheism, a panpsychism, according to which the universe was a hodgepodge of uncoordinated wonders, and Paracelsus inclined toward a form of mysticism most unpropitious to a clear understanding of phenomena.

Speaking more generally, the sixteenth century—and even the seventeenth, though to a lesser degree—had great difficulty in making room for any rational study of nature; people saw miracles on every hand, and many phenomena we

---

[5] H. Hauser, "Science et philosophie après le Concile de Trente," *Scientia*, 1935 (I), pp. 192-201.

now know to be entirely "mechanical" were then believed to spring from some mysterious vital forces.

The movement that ultimately set itself to establishing a more rational and positive attitude was one of great complexity. It went beyond the strictly methodological problem of science and took in metaphysical and religious questions. From one angle it seems indistinguishable from the freethinking, atheistic trend. In this respect M. Busson's well-known book gives many particulars that help to explain the growth of the modern scientific spirit,[6] showing that from this point of view it was unconnected with the religious crisis that ultimately gave birth to Protestantism. But at the same time there developed in the Christian world a campaign—based on the most traditional views as to the relationship between faith and reason—to defend the rational study of nature and thus preserve that belief in the transcendence of the divine influence that had been impaired by the Paduan's ideas on the immanence of the psyche and by the exaggerated tendency to regard nature as a conglomeration of mysterious and unaccountable phenomena. Catholicism had the principal share in this reaction, for it was better able than Protestantism to put reason in its right place.

One should note that though the demands of faith and science made it necessary to combat the vague mysticism that came very much into fashion during the sixteenth century, that same mysticism—chiefly in the form of a revived interest in Plato—assisted the trend toward a quantitative, numerical understanding of facts that is a fundamental factor of modern science. Its influence on Galileo and Kepler is very evident. This, again, has no direct bearing on the crisis in the Church at the time of the Reformation.

---

[6] See *Les Sources et le développement du rationalisme dans la littérature française de la Renaissance* (1533-1601), especially pp. 226-32 and 440-46. M. Busson makes a very penetrating analysis of the manner in which the faith of certain Catholics was distorted into childish credulity, and of the discussions on the theme of miracles. The sixteenth century was still far from any clear differentiation between a metaphysical determinism that leaves no room for divine intervention or human liberty, and a system of natural laws recognized by a methodology deterministic in origin, which confines itself to its level of understanding of phenomena and is thus perfectly compatible with religious faith. Analyses of the same kind are devoted to the seventeenth century in M. Busson's two other books, *La pensée religieuse de Charron à Pascal* (Paris: Vrin, 1933) and *La Religion des classiques, 1660-1685* (Paris: Presses Universitaires, 1948). See also V. Monod, *Dieu dans l'Univers*. (Paris: 1933).

Experiment

The growth of modern science was also contingent upon greater attention to experiment. Here there is a point to be made clear. It is true that the urge to experiment implies a spirit of observation, a desire to take facts into account and pay more attention to them than was done by the schoolmen with their exaggerated confidence in deduction and in the statements of the ancients.

It is perfectly fair to consider that the inclination for observation and experiment first revealed in the sixteenth century and continued in the seventeenth was favorable to the development of modern science. R. Hooykaas mentions many Protestant scientists who tended in that direction. But I can see nothing *specifically* Protestant about it. Considerable experiment was going on among Catholics as well, particularly in Italy, as I shall show later when discussing the development of the various disciplines. Outstanding experimenters on the Protestant side were Gilbert, Palissy, Harvey, Kepler, Boyle, Hooke, Huygens, and Van Leeuwenhoek, and on the Catholic side Vesalius, Galileo, Torricelli, Pascal, Mariotte, and Roberval.

This revival of the taste for observation was due to rather complex reasons. One of its principal causes was undoubtedly nominalism, as, indeed, R. Hooykaas mentions; in the case of Nicolas Oresme, for instance, it was a reaction against the rigid scholastic rationalism that neglected the concrete, the individual. But the movement set in before the Protestant Reformation; though Protestantism supported it for its own reasons, the trend is not essential to the Protestant religion as such, and it played an important part in Catholic thought as well.

This attraction toward facts is also, to a great extent, due to the great discoveries made in the sixteenth century. Here Protestantism has no claim to precedence over Catholicism. On the contrary, the Catholic missionary movement seems to have played an especially important part in the matter.[7]

[7] See the basic work by G. Atkinson, *Les Nouveaux horizons de la Renaissance française* (Paris: Droz, 1935), which shows the influence of geographical discoveries and particularly mentions (p. 419) the lack of interest shown by the Protestants in these discoveries.

It must be acknowledged, however, that the sciences involving observation were particularly popular, especially from the seventeenth century onward, in the Protestant countries, above all the Netherlands and England.

But the experimental spirit necessary to the modern scientific attitude was not built up merely by accumulating observations. It is axiomatic that the observation of nature shall be guided by ideas, prompted by the desire to marshal facts in a rational manner, and that every theory shall be subjected to the test of experiment. As Alexander Koyré has so brilliantly demonstrated, modern science might be said in many respects to have developed in *conflict* with the facts, in defiance of appearances. Scientific thought has occasionally been compelled to set the facts aside for the moment in order to work out a rational theory. This state of things is not emphasized in the study by R. Hooykaas, who, broadly speaking, arrives at the following set of equations: Protestantism=experiment; experiment=modern science. As I have already pointed out, the first of these equations is open to question. The second is even more so; in favoring empiricism, the Protestants were not making nearly so direct a contribution to the emergence of modern science as R. Hooykaas believes. They may even have retarded it now and then. It may be true, as R. Hooykaas states, that in their antirationalism the spirit of the Reformation and that of experimental science are closely linked, but it is not certain that antirationalism really helped to produce modern science. It was, indeed, desirable to combat the view of science as solely a matter of deduction, because deduction was based on a number of preconceived, rudimentary ideas, derived from a rough assemblage of tangible experiences; but room should have been left for a more subtle rationalism, closer to the realities taught by experiment. It is by no means self-evident that Protestantism, as such—or Catholicism either, for that matter—had any direct influence here.

We should also take a cautious attitude toward the methodological pronouncements of certain scientists, for one cannot always be certain that they constitute an accurate reflection of the speakers' attitude toward science, or have made an effective contribution to scientific progress. In this connection, R. Hooykaas, like some other historians, seems to attach undue importance to the views of Bacon and Bernard Palissy concerning experiment.

Our chief concern must be to understand the progress of the intellectual attitude that led from astronomy as it was before Copernicus to Newton's celestial mechanics. For the spirit of modern science emerged largely during that period. Studying this evolution, as A. Koyré has done so ably, we find that religious opinion—whether Protestant or Catholic—had no direct influence upon it. Awareness of the respective roles of fact and reasoning faculty in scientific knowledge developed as the result of a train of thought that owed little to religious motivation.

IV. THE RESPECTIVE CONTRIBUTIONS OF CATHOLICS AND PROTESTANTS TO THE PROGRESS OF SCIENCE

Having considered the influence exerted by Catholicism and Protestantism respectively on the development of a form of Humanism receptive to science, on the scientist's freedom of research, and on the formation of the scientific method, we now come to the question of the parts played by Protestants and Catholics in scientific progress. I will not repeat what I have already said in my preliminary remarks on methodology as to the difficulty of deciding, on the strength of such observations as can be made in this way, whether there was or was not any connection between the religious attitude—Protestant or Catholic—and the progress of science.

As I have already remarked, the general statistics for scientists, drawn up by Candolle and drawn upon by J. Pelseneer, should be used with great caution; in any case they do not begin until 1666, when the Paris Académie des Sciences was founded, and are consequently of little help for the period with which we are dealing. They do, however, confirm one important point—that the Spanish contribution to scientific progress was extremely slight. Spanish historians themselves admit the fact. Spain's only contributions of any importance—and even those are not fundamental—were made in the sphere of the natural sciences; and to lend weight even to this statement we are compelled to couple the name of one genuine Catholic Spaniard, Francisco Vallès (1520-1592), who did remarkable work in epidemiology, with those of a Jewish doctor, Antonio Gomez Pereira, who lived in the first half of the sixteenth century, and a "heretic," Michel Servet (1509-1553), a nonconformist Protestant who was burned at Geneva on Calvin's orders.

Though the fact of Spain's deficiencies is undeniable, some caution should be observed in suggesting explanations for this state of affairs. I will not pause to refute Candolle's oversimple view that it was due chiefly to the Inquisition. Nobody can seriously maintain that the Spanish Inquisition was censorious to a degree that made it impossible for Spaniards even to study geometry, optics, or botany. The cause of the weakness appears to be mainly cultural. The Spanish are above all a spiritual, artistic, and literary people. Should we hold this against them? Surely there should be some variety in the cultural attitudes of different nations—regrettable though it may be that this indifference to science should have been carried so far.

As for the other countries, there is no need of statistics to show that, broadly speaking, it is incorrect to claim that the Protestant countries far outdistanced the Catholic ones in the field of scientific activity. Taking the population figures into account, it may be admitted that the balance is slightly in favor of the Protestants. But are statistics of this kind valid in cultural matters? In any case, to mention a general impression to which I will return later when discussing individual fields of study, it may safely be said that the countries with a majority of Catholics, such as France, and those that were entirely Catholic, such as Italy, contributed at least as much to the progress of science as did the Protestant countries, foremost of which were England and the Netherlands. It should be remembered that scientific activity in Italy was exceptionally brilliant, at least up to 1650. Omitting the well-known names to which I shall return later on, we may recall the universities of Padua and Bologna, the famous Accademia dei Lincei in Rome—which was forced to close in 1651—and, in the latter half of the seventeenth century, the Accademia del Cimento, at Florence. The vitality of science in France, where it was pursued almost solely by Catholics, is too well known to require stressing. It is, however, true that after the middle of the seventeenth century the scientific movement in France and Italy showed some decline in vigor, though this was not as marked as Protestant historians have asserted, and that on the other hand there was a considerable increase of scientific activity in England and the Netherlands. But the analysis given in previous sections points to the conclusion that this was due not to religious but to cultural and economic causes. This statement, of course, needs to be confirmed by further elaboration, for which this brief study allows no space. We should look into the possibility that scientific progress may have been impeded by the fact that in the Catholic countries the university education of clergy and monks was under the more or less direct control of the ecclesiastical authorities—as, for instance, in France at the Sorbonne—and made very little allowance for the progress of scientific thought. One suspects that this was the case, but in the present state of knowledge it is impossible to be absolutely positive. Similar inquiry should be made into the censorship of books before publication. It seems likely that interesting unpublished documents on this subject might be forthcoming.

Let us now turn to what is in my opinion the most important aspect of the matter—one that I am surprised to see was somewhat neglected by R. Hooykaas and J. Pelseneer —the investigation *subject by subject* of the part played by Protestants and Catholics, respectively, in the progress of science.

I shall not attempt to cover the whole range of subjects, but only the most important among them, with special reference to those in which particularly striking advances were made during the period with which we are concerned. This means reviewing, in succession, mathematics, astronomy, mechanics, optics, electricity, the sciences dealing with the soil and with biology (botany, zoology, human anatomy, physiology), and finally the applied physical sciences. I shall refer only to the most distinguished scientists in each branch. But as I said in my introductory remarks on methodology, I shall also give some brief particulars of the contribution made to progress in these subjects by the clergy and more especially by the Company of Jesus, whose scientific activity covered a field the extent of which historians have hitherto, perhaps, not fully realized. The fact that, except for the contributions of a few outstanding figures, the results of this activity were not really fundamental should not surprise us, science being, in the ordinary way, not the principal occupation of clerics. But, as already mentioned, it was of great importance to the spread of science and its introduction into education. Protestant education, at least in France, was less open-minded.

Mathematics. The great mathematical advances of the sixteenth and seventeenth centuries were due principally to work in three nations—Italy, France, and England. Unless I am mistaken, the most notable French mathematicians were all Catholics with the exception of Viète, the founder of mod-

312 EVOLUTION OF SCIENCE

ern algebra, who was a Protestant. The English mathematicians were, on the contrary, all Protestants.

The most important contributions made to algebra in the sixteenth century—apart from those of Viète, who was in a class of his own—came from the Italians Cardan (1501-1576), Tartaglia (1505-1557), and Bombelli (1530 — ?). In the seventeenth century advances in algebra were due chiefly to Descartes, to the Englishman Harriot (1560-1621), and to the Frenchman Albert Girard (1595-1632). To Descartes we owe, in particular, the invention of analytical geometry.

Differential and integral calculus owed its first development to the Italian Cavalieri (1598-1647), who was a member of the Order of Jesuati (not Jesuiti), the Frenchman Roberval (1602-1675), the Belgian Jesuit Grégoire de Saint Vincent (1584-1647), Blaise Pascal (1623-1662), Pierre Fermat (1601-1665)—who also made some very penetrating research into the theory of numbers—the Dutch Protestant Huygens (1629-1695), the Englishmen Wallis (1616-1703), James Gregory (1638-1675), and above all, of course, Newton (1642-1727), the German Protestant Leibniz (1646-1716), and the Protestant Jacques Bernouilli, of Basle (1654-1705).

In geometry France takes the lead, with Descartes, Pascal, Desargues (1591-1662), and La Hire (1640-1718).

An invention that came as a sidelight, but that was of great practical importance, was that of logarithms, by the Englishman Napier (or Neper) (1550-1617).

Although, apart from Grégoire de Saint Vincent, the Jesuits had no mathematicians of the first rank, they produced some estimable books and used them in connection with teaching which, though admittedly elementary, they imparted in an intelligent and stimulating manner. The commentary on Euclid by Calvius, which contains a wealth of shrewd observations, had a wide circulation in the learned world as well as in the Jesuit colleges. Mention should also be made of the works of quadratures by Fathers de la Faille (1597-1652) and Guldin (1577-1643), of that by Father Fabri (1606-1685) on the squaring of the cycloid—an important contribution to the progress of infinitesimal calculus—and of the work on the calculation of centers of gravity, by Father Lalouvère (1600-1664). *Récréations mathématiques* (1624), by Father Leurechon (1591-1670) is also not without scientific interest and enjoyed great popularity.

This short review shows us that Catholics and Protestants

alike made contributions to the construction of the science of mathematics in the sixteenth and seventeenth centuries, and that it is hard to say which group played the greater part.

Astronomy and mechanics. The same applies to the admirable discoveries, from Copernicus to Newton, from which modern astronomy and mechanics emerged. After a "revolution" had been effected by Nicolas Copernicus, Canon of Cracow (1473-1543), astronomy made tremendous progress thanks to the Protestant Kepler (1571-1630), whose efforts in the field of science were manifestly supported by mystical inspiration; but it was not he who, strictly speaking, established the celestial mechanism. This achievement resulted from the efforts of the Catholics Descartes and Galileo (1564-1642) and the Protestants Huygens (1629-1695), Hooke (1635-1703), and finally Newton. A considerable, though minor contribution was also made by two Catholics, the Italian Borelli (1608-1679) and the Frenchman Bouillant (1605-1694), who had been converted from Calvinism at the age of twenty-two.

In addition to this major work, the progress of astronomy is denoted by the increasing number of observations, which became much more precise and accurate as instruments were improved and new ones invented. Chief among these was the telescope; the story of its invention is still obscure, but it seems to have been due to the joint efforts of Dutchmen and Italians, and was used for the first time in 1610, by Galileo.

The Jesuits took a great interest in astronomy. They had numerous observatories, the best known of which were at Prague, Rome, and Ingolstadt. But they also made interesting observations in the others, chiefly those in France, such as the observatory attached to their college at Avignon. Father Clavius was chiefly responsible for the reform of the calendar in 1582. Father Scheiner (1575-1650) discovered sunspots in 1610, at the same time as Galileo. Father Zucci (1586-1670) had the first idea of the reflector telescope. In their foreign missions the Jesuits undertook important astronomic work. Especially in China, where they introduced European astronomy and reformed the calendar; leading figures in these considerable undertakings were Fathers Terrentius (1576-1630), a founder member of the Accademia dei Lincei, Schall (1592-1665), and Verbiest (1623-1688). The last of these equipped the imperial observatory at Peking with magnificent instruments, constructed under his supervision and still to be seen there. The Jesuit missionaries were also required to communicate the results of their observations to the European academies, and some of them aroused great interest, especially those dealing with the calculation of longitude.

The Jesuits also distinguished themselves as map-makers; an Italian, Ricci (1552-1610), was the first to correct the gross errors in the depiction of China in sixteenth-century atlases; another Italian, Martini (1614-1661), drew up a map of China in which he reveals a great mastery of technique; it was published at Amsterdam in 1655 with the title *Atlas sinensis* and earned considerable praise.

Optics. Though the greatest advances in optics during the seventeenth century were made by Newton, the work of his predecessors was by no means negligible. Here again it is impossible to say which creed had the advantage of the other. Side by side with the Protestants Snellius (1591-1626), Kepler, Huygens, and Römer (1644-1710) are the names of Catholics such as Descartes, the Jesuit Grimaldi (1631-1663), who was the first to formulate the theory of wave mechanics, the Abbé Mariotte (1620-1684), Malebranche (1638-1715), and Fermat (1601-1665).

Magnetism and electricity. Here again a Protestant name dominates—that of the Englishman Gilbert (1544-1603); but Father Cabeo, a Jesuit (1602-1650), also deserves mention for the important new views set forth in his *Philosophia magnetica.* In addition to the experiments conducted by the Dutch Protestant Otto von Guericke (1602-1686) there were those carried out at Florence by the Accademia del Cimento and continued later by the Royal Society. Here again it seems impossible to give the palm to one creed rather than the other.

Geology, paleontology, mineralogy. Here the great pioneer is a Protestant, Bernard Palissy (1510-1589). At war with dogmatism and facile, conventional views, Palissy put forward ideas about the construction of the earth and the nature of fossils whose originality and accuracy were to remain unappreciated for a long time. More than a century later, the chief progress in the geological sciences was made by a Danish Catholic, Nils Stensen (or Steno) (1638-1686), a convert from Protestantism, who became a priest and ended his life as an archbishop. His *De solido intra solidum naturaliter contento* (Florence, 1669) lays the foundations of stratigraphy and crystallography. This latter discipline also owed noteworthy progress to the Englishman, Hooke, with his celebrated *Micrographia* (1665).

Other, though minor, contributors to this aspect of science

were the English Protestant Martin Lister (1638-1712) and Father Kircher, whom I have already mentioned. In his huge *Mundus subterraneus* (1665, 2 vols., folio) Kircher includes much information that is unscientific and often mythical; but he makes a number of pertinent remarks and above all he had an enthusiastic desire to find out about the nature of the terrestrial globe that was calculated to turn men's minds toward a branch of research to which serious scientists had until then paid scant attention.

Natural sciences. Here again there is no marked superiority of one confession over the other. R. Hooykaas is of course correct in pointing out the importance of the role of Protestants in sixteenth-century botany. There was the German school, with its strong Lutheran affiliations, which included Brunfels (1470-1534), Jerome Bock (1498-1551), and Leonhardt Fuchs (1501-1566); at Basle there was Gaspard Bauhin (1560-1624); l'Escluse (1526-1609), a native of Antwerp who lived in France for a time and spent his last years in England, was probably the most eminent of the Protestant botanists; and at Montpellier there was the Frenchman, l'Obel (1538-1616).

But Catholic Italy produced Mattioli (1500-1577), a very keen observer, Andrea Cesalpino (1519-1603), the greatest of the sixteenth-century botanists, the first to suggest a lucid classification of plants—in his celebrated *De Plantis* (1583), and Aldrovandi (1522-1605), who founded the first botanical garden, at Bologna.

During the seventeenth century there are two outstanding names in botany—the English Protestant John Ray (1627-1705) and the French Catholic Tournefort (1656-1708), who made the greatest contribution to the establishment of a system that was put forward by any botanist before Linnaeus.

The leading sixteenth-century zoologists were the Protestant Gesner (1516-1565) of Basle, and Rondelet (1507-1566), a doctor of Montpellier, declared by R. Hooykaas, following the authority of Arber, to be one of the leaders of the Reformation in southern France, whereas the Protestant historians themselves admit that it is difficult to prove that he ever passed from Catholicism to Protestantism.[8] Rondelet's book on fish, *De piscibus* (1554), is remarkable for the period, and

---

[8] The long article on Rondelet in the Michaux *Biographie universelle* describes his conversion to Protestantism as very dubious. The Haag biographical dictionary, *La France protestante*, is more categorical, but offers no really conclusive evidence.

even Linnaeus referred to it. Mention should also be made of the French Catholic Belon (1517-1564), who is universally recognized as the founder of comparative anatomy.

In human anatomy one name towers above the rest—that of the Belgian Catholic Vésale (1514-1564). Vesalius taught for many years at Padua and also lived for some time in Spain. He wrote the famous *De humani corporis fabrica* (1543). Others who distinguished themselves at Padua were the Italians Fallope (1523-1562) and, still more, his nephew, Fabrizio d'Acquapendente (1537-1619).

The greatest name in surgery is that of the French Protestant Ambroise Paré (1510-1590).

His discovery of the circulation of the blood is the great claim to glory of the English Protestant Harvey (1578-1657). But back in the sixteenth century a pupil of Vesalius, Realdo Colombo (1516-1559), and the Protestant Michel Servet (1511-1553) had discovered the circulation of the blood in the lungs, and Cesalpino the valvules of the veins.

Fabrizio d'Acquapendente may be regarded as the founder of embryology. Research on this subject was considerably stimulated in the seventeenth century by the Italian Redi (1626-1697).

The movement of animals and the functioning of the muscles were the subject of an important book by the Italian Borelli (1608-1679), who, as we have seen, also gained distinction in mechanics and astronomy.

Microscopic biology originated in the seventeenth century, receiving its most important contributions from the Italian Malpighi (1628-1694), who was the first to demonstrate the circulation of the blood in the capillaries, and the Dutch Protestants Swammerdam (1637-1682) and Van Leeuwenhoek (1632-1723). Thanks to the microscope, the latter discovered unicellular living organisms.

Applied physical sciences. I will confine myself, in this immense field, to providing a few particulars to contravert the widespread impression that Protestantism was chiefly responsible for guiding science into practical channels. There is, in my opinion, little justification for this view. Protestant England did, indeed, play an important part in the development of mechanical technology from the seventeenth century onward; but France and Italy also have remarkable achievements to their credit in this respect, as was recently pointed out by Bertrand Gille in his general study entitled *Les problèmes techniques au XVIIᵉ siècle.*

It is also worthwhile to mention the contribution made by clerics, and particularly Jesuits, to applied science. The Jesuits gave a distinctly practical slant to the teaching of science in their own colleges, and also held chairs in numerous French universities where they taught hydrography, training students in marine subjects. They were interested in shipbuilding as well; Father Hoste (1652-1700), for instance, published a *Théorie de la construction des vaisseaux* (Lyon, 1697), which was respected by the technicians. Other Jesuits, such as Father Milliet de Chales, interested themselves in the art of fortification. The construction of machines was the favorite subject of the celebrated Father Schott (1608-1666), and his *Technica curiosa* (Nuremberg, 1664) had a wide circulation. Father Lana-Terzi (1631-1687), an Italian, was one of the chief pioneers of flight.

CONCLUSION

The foregoing account, and the methodological observations that accompany it, has, I hope, shown the great difficulty of determining the influence of religious attitude, whether Protestant or Catholic, on the development of science in the sixteenth and seventeenth centuries, and what share of any such influence was possessed by either creed. To conclude—as J. Pelseneer does after analyzing in a few pages the statistics of scientists in each confession—that "modern science was born of the Reformation" seems to me to make a really excessive departure from the most elementary requirements of the historical method. The slightly longer consideration given to the subject in this article indicates far less categorical and obvious conclusions, which may be summed up as follows:

1. The Protestant attitude in religion provided, in the majority of cases, but not always, an atmosphere that doubtless fostered scientific progress inasmuch as it encouraged the study of nature and left scientists to work without restriction.

2. Taken as a whole, Catholicism was at least equally receptive toward those branches of science that emanated from its own doctrine and spiritual outlook. The work of the Company of Jesus, in particular, was marked by a Humanism

very favorable to science and not met with to the same extent in Protestantism.

As for freedom of scientific research, though it may sometimes have been unduly restricted owing to religious considerations—the case of Galileo is a notable example of this —there is no evidence that such interference seriously impeded the progress of science. In any case, Protestantism offers similar examples of such methods, which may be imputed, on both sides, to a conventional outlook and a failure to distinguish clearly between the scientific and religious fields.

3. While it is true that the Protestant countries displayed remarkable scientific activity, that of the Catholic countries, or at least of France and Italy, seems to have been equally intense, except perhaps in the case of Italy toward the end of the seventeenth century.

4. There is no really conclusive evidence that scientific activity, whether in Catholic or Protestant countries, was connected with religious attitude. In any case there are cultural and economic factors of at least equal importance to be taken into account.

5. While comprehensive statistics for scientists of the two creeds are difficult to obtain for the period under consideration, and are not very illuminating, it is interesting to investigate the respective parts played by Catholics and Protestants in the advance of the different branches of science. This leads to the conclusion that, numerically speaking, Protestants and Catholics seem to have shared equally in these developments.

6. The preceding conclusion does not necessarily imply that Protestantism and Catholicism influenced scientific development to precisely the same extent, for:

    a. Numerical conclusions give only a rough idea of an infinitely complex situation—viz. the making of discoveries and their exploitation.

    b. It still remains to be determined, for each individual scientist, what was the connection between his religious attitude and the scientific research on which he was engaged. In most cases the connection seems to have been somewhat tenuous.

7. The foregoing conclusion leads us to recognize that, especially from the seventeenth century onward, scientific development became more and more a question of technical method and thus grew fairly independent of religious attitudes. This is another aspect of the process of secularization, the effect of which was to remove scientific demonstration from

the sphere of religion—a process that arose, not from rejection of religious beliefs, but from a more correct understanding of their nature.

In conclusion I should like to express my gratitude to R. Hooykaas. Though I have differed from him on some points, his stimulating views have nevertheless been most helpful. I am glad, too, that by concentrating chiefly on the role of Catholicism in the development of science during the century of the Reformation, my article provides a supplement to his. The two thus combine to form a basis for future amplifications and discussion in an atmosphere of open-mindedness and deep mutual esteem.

TRANSLATED FROM THE FRENCH
BY DAPHNE WOODWARD

SELECTED BIBLIOGRAPHY

D. G. Barraud, *L'humanisme et la médecine*. Paris: Vigot, 1942.

L. Bouyer, *Du protestantisme à l'Eglise*. Paris: Éditions du Cerf, 1954.

M. W. Burke-Gaffney, *Kepler and the Jesuits*. Milwaukee: Bruce, 1943.

A. de Candolle, *Histoire des sciences et des savants depuis deux siècles*. Geneva: 1873.

A. C. Crombie, *Augustine to Galileo. The History of Science* A. D. 400-1500. London: Grey Walls Press, 1952.

F. de Dainville, *La geographie des humanistes*. Paris: Beauchesne 1940.

———, *La naissance de l'humanisme moderne*. Paris: 1940.

———, "Saint Ignace et l'humanisme," *Cahiers Universitaires Catholiques* (June-July, 1956), pp. 458-479.

A. Koyré, "A Documentary History of the Problem of Fall from Kepler to Newton," *Transactions of the American Philosophical Society*, XLV (1955), pp. 329-395.

J. Lecler, *Histoire de la tolérance au siècle de la Reforme*. 2 vols. Paris: Aubier, 1956.

R. Lenoble, *Mersenne et la naissance du mécanisme*. Paris: Vrin, 1942.

S. F. Mason, *A History of the Sciences: Main Currents of Scientific Thought*. London: Routledge, Kegan Paul, 1953. New York: Abelard Schuman, 1954.

R. Mousnier, *Le XVIe et le XVIIe siècles* (*Histoire générale des civilisations*). Paris: 1954.

R. Rouquette, "Ignace de Loyola dans le Paris intellectual du XVIe siècle," *Études* (July-August, 1956), pp. 18-40.

F. Russo, *Bibliographie d'histoire des sciences et des techniques*. Paris: Herman, 1954.

A. F. Schmidt, *La poèsie scientifique en France au XVIe* siècle. Paris: Albin Michel, 1938.

A. Wolf, *A History of Science, Technology and Philosophy in the 16th and 17th Centuries*. 2nd edition, rev. by D. McKie. New York: Macmillan; London: Allen & Unwin, 1950.

Ed. note: See Preface, p. XIV.

PART FOUR

Modern Science

TECHNICAL PROGRESS AND

SOCIETY*

A. A. Zvorikine

The effect of science and technology upon society has in recent years become a much-discussed issue in the world press, if not the most discussed.

There are a number of reasons for this interest in the social consequences of technical progress. On the one hand, profound changes in science and technology and accelerated technical development exert an enormous influence upon people in both socialist and capitalist countries. On the other, technical progress under capitalist conditions, like every scientific and technical invention or discovery, leads to the accentuation of capitalist contradictions. And the utilization of science and technology in the military sphere casts an ominous shadow over the world.

Many books and countless articles have been appearing in capitalist countries about the social consequences arising from the use of atomic energy, about the economic, social, and moral effects of technical progress as a whole and, particularly, of industrial automation.

In the U.S.S.R., the aim of building a material and technical basis for Communism dictates high speeds and scales of scientific and technical progress, resulting in its growing influence on all economic and social aspects of life. Speaking

* Journal of World History, VI, 1.

at the June Plenum of the Soviet Communist Party Central Committee, N. S. Khrushchev laid emphasis upon the social aspect of technical means. In a socialist society, he said, automation possesses not only economic but also vast social significance. Technical progress changes the character of labor, raises the cultural and technical level of working people, and creates the prerequisites of eliminating the difference between manual and mental labor; with automation, man's role is to direct the automatic equipment and instruments, to set them up, and establish their programs and working conditions.

From the foregoing, the theoretical and practical aspects of investigation into the economic and social consequences of technical progress are clear.

In capitalist countries, the heightened role of technology in contemporary society combined with the contradictions its development brings about have made the question of the social consequences of technical progress not only a current topic but a very confused one.

The first and characteristic feature found in most literature written abroad on this subject is the attempt to represent technical advance as the cause of social disorders in modern bourgeois society. Some say that it must be curbed or even halted as something entirely evil. Others hail it and speak of the need to make social relations correspond to the modern technical level, but this is never to be understood in the sense of getting down to rebuilding the whole economic basis of modern bourgeois society, of liquidating private property in the means of production; what they have in mind is some vague capitalist reform that, allegedly, would make it possible to use all the benefits of technical progress to raise man's welfare within the framework of capitalism.

Typical of the views of those who regard technology as hell-born is the Swiss theologian E. Brunner's book *Christianity and Civilization,* in which he says that modern technology means countless millions huddled in huge, soulless cities, a proletariat cut off from Nature, with no real home or friendly neighbors. It means an asphalt culture, monotony, and standardization. These are people, Brunner says, whom the machine has freed from the need to think and desire, and who in their turn must serve it at a prescribed speed and in a stereotyped manner. It means unendurable noise and bustle, unemployment and insecurity, the concentration of productive forces, wealth, and prestige in the hands of a few or their monopolization by state bureaucracy. In Brunner's opinion, it also means the rapid standardization of all national cultures and the destruction of their historic roots. We have cited Brunner rather fully because he shows clearly how phenomena born of modern capitalism, which develops technology in the interests of profit and not of man, are ascribed not to their real author but to technical means in themselves.

Brunner and scientists of like mind have fallen far behind Marx and Engels in their understanding of social phenomena. Marx and Engels gave an even clearer picture of the disastrous results machinery brought to the worker, but at the same time stressed the fact that the cause of the trouble lay not in the machine itself but in its application under capitalist conditions. "There cannot be the slightest doubt," Marx wrote in *Capital*,[1] "that machinery as such is not responsible for 'setting free' the workman from the means of subsistence . . . machinery, considered alone, shortens the hours of labor, but, when in the service of capital, lengthens them . . . in itself it lightens labor, but, when employed by capital, heightens the intensity of labor . . . in itself it is a victory of man over the forces of Nature, but, in the hands of capital, it makes man the slave of those forces . . . in itself it increases the wealth of the producers, but, in the hands of capital, makes them paupers . . ."

The German scientist Alexander Rüstow takes much the same attitude as Brunner. He writes:[2] "The enthusiasm for technical progress so widespread in our day . . . is assuming the character of a demoniac, soulless religion of deliverance, something in the nature of an unrestrained urge to attain record achievements at all costs. And like every theology, this widespread religion of rationalism, by means of paradox and illusory principle, in the final analysis breaks down intellect." When manipulating his ideas of an antagonistic society, Rüstow sees only the undesirable aspect of technical development—which undoubtedly exists, but only in capitalist society: the dulling of the worker's intellect, the fanatical profit-seeking by the capitalist to the detriment of others according to the law of capitalist competition, etc. Here once more we find that the contradictions born of technical development under capitalist conditions are ascribed not to a social system whose framework has become too narrow for technical progress, but to technical progress in itself.

[1] Karl Marx, *Capital* (Moscow: 1955) Vol. I, p. 446.
[2] A. Rüstow, "Kritik des technischen Fortschritts," "Ordo," *Jahrbuch*, IV (1951), p. 384.

It is typical that all these writings, with their lack of understanding of the connection between technical and social phenomena, arise to a considerable extent out of the pessimistic literature that tries to represent the crisis of contemporary capitalist society with its military and economic shocks and its unemployment as being a crisis of mankind, literature asserting that modern civilization, culture, and mankind itself are sliding down to inevitable ruin.

A number of scientists in other lands try to penetrate more deeply into the problems arising from scientific and technical progress. But instead of seeking the social and economic roots of these problems, they generally talk about the "lag" of the humanitarian sciences behind technical progress, a "lag" they consider to be the cause of the social, ethical, and ideological conflicts and difficulties caused by scientific and technical advance. One of the most typical representatives of this point of view is the French economist and sociologist Jean Fourastié, whose works are very widely read in France and other European countries. In his *Le grand espoir du XXe siècle*[3] he says that

> the lag of economic and social sciences behind the natural sciences is one cause of the woes of mankind. In our day technical knowledge leads mankind to unknown horizons. Finding himself between the hopelessly outworn past and the unknown future, man, shorn of his traditions, his ethical principles and his religion . . . and still lacking any philosophy worthy of the new epoch, acts day by day according to shortlived motives, operative for a short period. Man has lost solidity and effectiveness, depth of thought and firmness of principle. He has lost his standard of the possible and the impossible.

Fourastié considers that "a systematic analysis of 'technical progress' would be the Ariadne's thread helping us to find our way in the maze of our times."

The well-known German scientist Friedrich Dessauer gives an enthusiastic estimate of technical progress, linking up profound social changes with the use of nuclear energy, the advance of natural science, and technical development:[4]

[3] Jean Fourastié, *Le grand espoir du XXe siècle* (Paris: 1958) pp. xvii, xix.
[4] *Streit um die Technik* (Frankfurt am Main: 1956).

Man will have greater knowledge, greater abilities. The far distances are drawing close, the time expended on communication lessens. Men can live longer, be stronger. The number of those who are poor, undernourished, and sick will lessen. Deserts will become cultivated land, steppes will blossom into gardens. All this and more will be "for man," not for one single nation, one state or one continent. Everything that historically divides, that politically sunders, everything that is opposite in humanity is of no importance for natural science and technology. For them, no political colorings exist. They turn their face to all people, not to individual nations and not to warring social forms which are handed down from former days.

As we can see, Dessauer—unlike Fourastié—simply retreats from the task of making the social aspect conform to scientific and technical development. He is not, however, entirely successful in this. Passing on to the technical problems connected with automation, he describes the "inflated optimism of the Americans" who claim that now already, and in the future, automation brings benefits to the workers, and also the restrained attitude of Europeans. He refers to the Margate conference attended by 1,100 British and foreign heads of factories, engineers, scientists, and trade-union officials, where it was clearly shown that social conditions do not adapt themselves automatically to scientific and technical possibilities, but in a number of cases become a hindrance to the victorious progress of technical innovation.

Representatives of modern Social-Democratic thought have taken up a rather peculiar position on this question. Many of them are quite willing to concede that technology today is outgrowing the economic relations of capitalism, that it can develop successfully for the benefit of man under socialist relations. But they do not want to take the path of the socialist countries, they offer ideas of the elimination of contradictions between technical means and the social system within the framework of the modern bourgeois state, which in their opinion is even today no longer a class state, but expresses the interests of all strata of society. All this was expressed to a greater or lesser extent at the Munich Congress of the Social-Democratic Party of Germany in 1956. Professor Karl Schmidt, one of the main speakers, said: "Technical means . . . radically change our social system, our political forms and in general all forms of human existence." Apprehensions were expressed at the congress that the new technology would be utilized by the monopolists; Heinrich Deist among others spoke of this. "It is necessary," he said, "to prevent atomic energy and the possibilities of its use from falling into the hands of private capital." It would seem that such statements should lead on to a formulation of the purpose of taking the means of production out of the hands of private capital, or developing the new technical means under conditions of socialism. But instead, it led only to a demand to hand over the leadership of society to those forces to whom the future belonged—i.e., to Social-Democracy. This was the spirit that filled the message of greetings from the party leadership to the delegates at the congress, emphasizing that the results of the Second Industrial Revolution could be fruitful only if Social-Democracy stood at the head of society. And this in spite of the fact that there exists tremendous historic experience in the utilization of science and technology in the interests of man under socialist relations. The Munich Congress of the Social-Democratic Party of Germany did not wish to make use of this experience and adopted a very hazy resolution which gave no real answer to the urgent questions arising from the course of development of modern society. More than that, the trade-union theoreticians of Western Germany are trying to misrepresent the policy of the Communist Party of the Soviet Union on establishing the material and technical basis of Communism and industrial automation. In this respect an article by B. Lewitzky is typical. Alarm about the social consequences of automation is expressed in the latest works by writers whose aim is a purely scientific and technical exposition of automation, but who nevertheless express their apprehension about its social consequences.

One might quote endless examples of the various ideas about the path of social development in view of scientific and technical advance, ranging from appeals to check this advance to assertions that it is this which will save modern capitalism and enable man to enjoy all scientific and technical benefits within the capitalist framework. But this is not the important point; the point is that through all this discordant chorus sober voices are rising with increasing frequency, the voices of more far-sighted investigators.

Capitalism as a social system, they write, has come into a state of irreconcilable contradiction with the level, and still more important—the possibilities—of modern technical development; only socialism as a new and higher social system affords the opportunity to utilize the achievements of science and technology in the interests and for the well-being of man.

Automation and Social Progress, by the English scientist S. Lilley, is typical in this respect. After drawing a clear picture of the contradictions arising out of automation in a capitalist society and tracing concrete ways for easing these contradictions in respect of Britain, Lilley writes at the end of his book:[5]

> There is no ultimate escape from the fact that capitalism, well though it worked in its time, is not a suitable economic structure for making beneficial use of the advanced techniques of today and the even more advanced techniques of tomorrow. Whatever temporary solutions we may find for present difficulties, these solutions will in turn create further problems. Turn and twist as we may, there is no ultimate way forward except that of changing the whole economic system into a socialist one.

The fate of capitalism under conditions of the technical development and advancing productive forces of modern society finds veiled and peculiar expression in general theoretical discussions on the interaction of technology and social relations. There are several typical trends to be observed. Some claim that social phenomena are the direct result of technical development. Others, on the contrary, assert that social phenomena play the leading role, and technical development arises out of them. Others, again, seek a more intricate connection. Let us examine these three trends in greater detail.

There exists a very widespread opinion that all social life is a function of technical development. This opinion is held by representatives of varying trends, from technocrats for whom "technological determinism" is the key to a world outlook, to scientists in various fields who have little thought to spare for the social aspects of science and technology and believe that their development, especially over long periods, has a beneficial effect on mankind. The views of "technological determinism" were very clearly expressed by Leslie White,[6] according to whom "social systems are in a very real sense secondary and subsidiary to technological systems.

[5] S. Lilley, *Automation and Social Progress* (London: Lawrence & Wishert, 1957).

[6] A. L. White, *The Science of Culture* (New York: Farrar, Straus, 1949), p. 365.

In fact a social system may be defined realistically as the organized effort of human beings in the use of the instruments of subsistence, offence and defence, and protection. A social system is a function of a technological system . . . . The technology is the independent variable, the social system is the dependent variable. Social systems are therefore determined by systems of technology." This same point of view is developed by the German physicist Pascual Jordan, one of those few scientists who openly uphold the possible use of atom bombs. In 1956 Jordan published *Der gescheiterte Aufstand*, a book in which among other things he formulated at length his conception of the decisive role played by discoveries and inventions in social and political changes. Taking Liebig's discovery as an example, he illustrates his ideas as follows:[7]

One can hardly foresee an event of greater importance within the next century than Liebig's discovery of artificial fertilizer. Thanks to artificial fertilizer, and to this alone, it was possible to increase the population of Europe. Liebig's discovery was not a result, but on the contrary a condition of the industrialization of Europe and the foundation of all subsequent social and political changes.

The adherents of "technological determinism," as already stated, include scientists who, although unable to ignore the social aspects of scientific and technical progress, do not devote any great amount of thought to these aspects. A notable representative of this school of thought is the American scientist George Harrison of M.I.T. His expressed views have a double aspect: on the one hand he regards the future with optimism, assuming that the approaching or already existing scientific and technical revolution will bring prosperity to mankind, while on the other he, like many other scientists, is disturbed for the destiny of nations and of man, for whom this revolution may well hold a menace.

While firmly believing in the power of science, Harrison writes that "science is coming to determine how much men can eat, how comfortable they are, how hard they must work." He says further: "There is overwhelming evidence that man's scientific achievements with material things can and, because

---

[7] P. Jordan, *Der gescheiterte Aufstand* (Frankfurt am Main: 1956), pp. 41-42.

of his nature, will, in the long run, contribute greatly to his spiritual welfare."[8]

Alongside the defense of "technological determinism" or attempts to avoid any profound theoretical investigation of the social aspects of scientific and technical development, there are also works written in an effort to prove that there is no direct connection between technology on the one hand, and economic and social relations on the other. Typical in this respect are the statements of the prominent German philosopher Karl Jaspers, who tries to prove (in his "Die Atombombe und die Zukunft des Menschen") that the economic and social system of a country plays no part in technical development. While conceding that Marx's thesis on the dominating role of economy in the life of society is of great importance and is generally recognized, he claims that an equally important role is played by the ethical factor, but that no single factor in itself is able to determine the social order. In conclusion he writes:[9]

> Economy, or any other form it may possess, is not absolute. It is no measuring rod for what we are and can become. Economy is probably as necessary as water for an organism, without which the organism would perish. But economy is not everything, just as water does not compose the whole organism. Economy gains meaning only through that for which it exists, and which of course it in itself is not. Economy in itself is permeated by the motives for the sake of which it exists. Therefore, various social orders are possible and exist under an equal technical level."

Here one finds the desire typical of science abroad to avoid investigation of the social aspects of technical progress, to retreat behind the complexity of phenomena and the alleged impossibility of finding any guiding factor in these widely varied phenomena, particularly if this guiding factor is economic.

A recent book in separate articles compares "technological determinism" with "social determinism" (if one may put it that way)—the social conditioning of techniques. In this book a group at the Institute of Social Studies (Dr. H. Th.

---

[8] George Harrison, *What Man Can Be: The Human Side of Sciences* (New York: William Morrow, 1956), p. 1; p. 18.

[9] Karl Jaspers, *Die Atombombe und die Zukunft des Menschen* (Munchen: 1958), pp. 238-239.

Chabot, Dr. J. A. Ponsioen, Dr. J. Veld, Dr. L. J. Zimmerman, Dr. C. A. O van Nieuwenhuijze, Dr. E. A. Campo) briefly outline their views as follows: "If it were permissible to sum up the trend in one single sentence, it would run as follows: gradually a conviction is gaining ground that it would be more correct not to emphasize the social consequences of technical change but to see technical change as a social consequence."[10]

In criticizing scientists who regard technical development as the fundamental cause of changes in economic conditions, the authors emphasize that it is not technical development that determines one (social or economic) aim or another, but on the contrary, it is social aims and economic theories that determine technical development.

One contributor to the collection, S. Bernard, in an interesting article,[11] speaks of the interaction of technical progress and social relations. "The effect of technical progress on social relations," he writes, "is always accompanied by the counter-effect of social phenomena on technical development." The author maintains that "there exists a close interaction between technical and social phenomena in the form of a circle, or better, of a spiral, since this interaction does not coincide in time or space." This interaction of technical development and society, in the author's opinion, can be expressed as follows: "One rising side, which takes its origin from technology and moves towards the social, expresses the social changes in the functions of technical change; the other side, arising from society and moving towards technology, expresses technical changes in the functions of social change." From such concepts the author formulates the content and subject of "sociotechnical research."

An article by Wilbert E. Moore of Princeton University, headed "Measurement of Organizational and Institutional Implications of Changes in Productive Technology," is likewise devoted to technical and social factors. Stressing the extreme importance of research into the problem of the interaction of technical and social factors, Moore writes:[12]

---

[10] *Les implications sociales du progrès technique. Changements techniques, économiques et sociaux (étude theorique)* (Paris: 1959), p. 3.

[11] S. Bernard and H. Janne, "Analyse critique de concepts relatif aux implications sociales des progrès, techniques," *ibid.*, pp. 33-34.

[12] Wilbert Moore, "Measurement of Organizational and Institutional Implications of Changes in Productive Technology," *ibid.*, p. 232.

If changes in productive technology have social consequences, they also have social sources. Technological determinism, including the famous conception of "culture
lag," may be dismissed simply and categorically as having
neither empirical nor theoretical support worth any small
fraction of the attention it has been accorded.

This is the variegated picture of views on relations between
technical progress on the one hand and economic and social
phenomena on the other.

We see that scientists examining the problem in question
note, at the best, one or another of its aspects correctly. The
upholders of "technological determinism" attach decisive importance in modern society to technical development, emphasizing the tremendous possibilities that science and
technology hold for mankind. But because they do not understand the dialectical link between technical development and
economic-social relations, their view does not disclose the real
and objective nature of the interplay of these.

The upholders of "social determinism" likewise fail to see
the dialectical link between technical development and social
relations. In a number of cases they quite correctly stress the
social aspect of technical development, the influence social
life exerts upon it, they correctly criticize the exponents of
"technological determinism," but nevertheless they do not
disclose the objective laws of technical development.

Typical of many statements on the social aspects of tech-
nical development are references to the works of Karl Marx.
Jaspers, as mentioned above, after a courteous reference to
Marx's theory, then discards it utterly.

Professor Balandier, director of the International Bureau
of Research into the Social Implications of Technical Progress,
in an interesting introduction to the collection mentioned
above, also mentions Marxism, although in a very vague
form. "Commentators on Marxist theory," he writes, "have
tried to simplify and misrepresent it, regarding it mainly as
confirmation of technological determinism. This shows how
strong may be the wish to resort to this, the only means of
explaining the complex phenomena operating in modern societies."[13]

It is difficult to reply to such criticism, since it refers to

[13] G. Balandier, Introduction, *ibid.*, p. vii.

Marxist commentators, and these, as we know, can include such as introduce into Marxism ideas directly contrary to those of Marx himself. More definite statements on their attitude to Marxism emanate from the persons mentioned above (Dr. H. Th. Chabot, Dr. J. A. Ponsioen, Dr. J. Veld, Dr. L. J. Zimmerman, Dr. C. A. O. van Nieuwenhuijze, Dr. E. A. Campo), who say that the Marxian system "subjects historical events and social institutions themselves to the explanatory process of economic analysis."[14] Since the authors have not studied the concepts of Marx from his own works, referring only to the Marxist commentator Schumpeter, it should be said at once that "the Marxian system" cannot, of course, be understood from such a general formulation, without further explanation. Three British scientists from the London School of Economics and Political Science write that[15]

> To Marx technology is nearly always part of the total social structure in time: a partly dependent variable. Like Weber, he regards modern industrial technology as a late consequence rather than a cause of "primary capitalist accumulation." Presumably it cannot be introduced into societies where such accumulation has not taken (or is not taking) place. And yet Marx very frequently—though less than Engels—writes as a technological determinist.

They also say:

> At least Marx gives us one clue which is, however obvious, important. Innovation requires innovators; a special, sometimes marginal, group or class, able—potentially at least—to influence and/or dominate in their society. Without such a group . . . a society will remain passive (or be resistant) to technical change and innovation.

We have summarized in detail various interpretations of the interplay between social and technical factors and attempts to draw on the works of Karl Marx to explain this interplay. It must be noted at once that the approach of Marx and Engels to technical questions has of course nothing in common with "technological determinism." Marx and Engels took the

[14] Loc. cit.
[15] R. Firth, F. J. Fischer, and D. G. MacRae, "Social Implications of Technological Changes as Regards Patterns and Models," op. cit., p. 287.

technical level first and foremost as an *indicator* of social relations. Marx formulated this idea exactly and in detail in Volume I of *Capital*. Showing that economic epochs are differentiated not by what is produced but by how it is produced, by what instruments of labor, Marx emphasized that "instruments of labor not only supply a standard of the degree of development to which human labor power has attained, but they are also indicators of the social conditions under which the labor is carried out."[16]

Marx in his theory regards technical progress as a unity of technical and social features. He shows how technical development leads to the development of productive forces, which results in changes in production and economic relations and then in various ideological relations; and how, at the same time, economic and ideological relations in their turn exert an influence on technical development.

Marx shows the profound influence exerted by social relations on technology. One need only take the theory mentioned above, in which technical development derives from the economic and social ends given.

Setting the aim itself, without disclosure of the conditions that give rise to it, means little. Marxism long ago examined this question and included the aim as a motive force of technical progress in its explanation of this. But Marxism derives this aim from objective laws that lie at the basis of one or another formation.

If the accrual of surplus value is the basis of the social system under capitalism, technical progress under that system is linked up with the desire to receive surplus value. This determines the aims of capitalists who, as the British scientists R. Firth, F. J. Fischer, and D. G. MacRae correctly present Marx's view, form a class possessing a dominant influence in capitalist society and specifically a dominant influence on technical progress.

But that is not all. Capitalists in trying to reach their ends are not free to reject technical progress.

It is the compelling force of anarchy in social production that turns the limitless perfectibility of machinery under modern industry into a compulsory law by which every

16 Marx, *op. cit.*, p. 187.

individual industrial capitalist must perfect his machinery more and more, under penalty of ruin.[17]

This is how matters stand with the adaptation of means to given ends. But the strength of the theory of Marx and Engels lies in the fact that it explains the whole multiformity of adaptation to given ends, although this multiformity is basically the concrete expression of economic laws. Marx shows in his works, for instance, that under United States conditions, with an insufficiency of workers and higher wage rates than those obtaining in Europe, capitalists are particularly interested in the introduction of machinery; that in concrete historical conditions of heightened struggle between employers and workers in Britain, capitalists developed machinery with the idea of using it to bring the workers to their knees.

". . . From 1825 onward," Marx[18] writes, "almost all the new inventions were the result of collisions between the worker and the employer, who sought at all costs to depreciate the worker's specialized ability. After each new strike of any importance, there appeared a new machine."

This is, of course, the basic adaptation of means to given ends. There may be countless numbers of other instances, connected for various people with various motives. But to understand the basic line of development, one must be able to define the main direction of adaptation of means to given ends, and that main direction in the final analysis is connected with economic conditions, with the economic laws of social development.

A correct understanding of the relationship between technical and social factors requires first of all a correct philosophical understanding of technology in itself. Technical means are the instruments and means of labor developing in a system of social production. They are an element of productive forces, which together with relations of production forms the economic foundation of society. Technology is based on utilization of the laws of nature. But it is impossible to understand technical development and the social consequences of this development apart from relations of production, from the laws of social development. Natural science speaks of the possibility of using the laws of nature with the assistance of technical knowledge. But the aims and directions of technical

[17] F. Engels, *Anti-Duhring*, (Moscow: 1957), pp. 257-258.
[18] Karl Marx, *The Poverty of Philosophy* (Moscow; 2nd edition), p. 157.

development, its speed, the way in which it influences man—
these and similar questions can be answered only if one takes
its social conditions into account.

The main fallacy in the theory of technical and social relationships widespread in other countries lies just in this
neglect of the social conditions surrounding technical development, in ascribing qualities to technology that are actually
born of the social conditions in which it operates.

The first group of social relations with which technical
development is closely connected are economic relations of
production, which not only change according to technical advance and that of production forces as a whole, but themselves
affect the trend and speed of that advance.

Man is indivisibly connected with technology, as an active
participant in the production process, as the main element
in the productive forces that put technical means into action.
It is therefore natural that technical change exerts a direct
influence on man, on the character and content of his labor,
on his qualification and other aspects of his life; but this
direct influence of technology on man cannot be isolated from
the social conditions of his life. The same technical changes
under socialism and under capitalism will affect man in a
different way.

Technology, however, apart from exerting a direct influence
on man, also affects his life through the development of productive forces.

The level of the development of productive forces determines, as is well known, the character of relations to the
means of production, to the form of property. This is the
main influence exerted by technical means, through the productive forces, on the social relations of man; and the form
of social relations, influenced by the development of production forces, changes—by revolutionary methods in antagonistic societies, and by evolutionary methods under socialism, where the changes in the nature of technical means, the
changes in the productive forces lead to changes in the form
of property and to the transition, for instance, from two forms
of socialist property—the state and collective-farm forms—
to a single Communist form of property.

It is important to stress this aspect of the influence of
technical development through productive forces on social
relations not only because relations to the means of production are highly important social relations, but because if one
is to understand technical development, understand its in-

fluence on other forms of social relations, one must not ignore the predominant forms of property.

But economic production relations as the major form of social relations include a number of others. Technical development leads to alterations in the proportion of social labor and to alterations, as Marx said, in the social combination of the production process. New branches of production appear, changes occur in the relations between individual branches, there are changes in the geographical distribution of production, technical development leads to changes in the type and character of factories, etc.

All this is mirrored, as it were, in social life, all this leads not only to a reconstruction of the production machinery in space and time, but to changes in the status of people, changes in their place of residence, changes in the character of their labor, their training, to many consequences; and these changes, and what is most important, their characteristic concrete features, can be understood only if one takes into account those relations of production within the framework of which they occur.

In addition to the group of economic relations connected with changes in the social combinations of the production process, there is a special group of social relations—the relations of people in the process of daily existence. Just as production includes within itself consumption, so economic relations include relations not only in the sphere of production but in the sphere of daily life. Man, employed in production, must restore his forces, he must have the conditions necessary to satisfy his material, mental, and cultural requirements. The influence of technical means on this group of relations is expressed rather differently from the relations based directly on the production process. Great importance attaches here to the profound changes which modern technology makes in the character of towns, in transport, and in daily living conditions.

The following group of social relations has a fundamentally different nature. If the economic relations defined above may be called material relations formed apart from human consciousness, the other group of relations may be called ideological, as passing through human consciousness. This group includes: (1) political relations linked with the activities of the state, (2) juridical, legal relations, and (3) relations between people connected with various forms of ideology— ethical, esthetic, and with various forms of art.

The influence of scientific and technical progress on these forms of social relations is of a still more complex nature. Class relations, which grow up on one or another economic foundation, are the basis of all ideological relations. Technology exerts a direct influence not so much on the content as on the means and forms of ideological relationships.

On the content of ideological social relations, the scientific-technical revolution exerts a tremendous indirect influence, through the development of productive forces, relations of production, and the whole aggregate of economy and daily life. Developing production advances on to the historic arena new social classes, the bearers of a new ideology. There is destruction or transformation of the old structure of life, the old traditions, and all this finds its reflection in ideological relations.

What are the actual mechanics of the effect exerted by technical development on economic and social relations? The theory of the American sociologist W. Ogburn, criticized recently in an article by N. I. Osmova, is well known.[19] Ogburn's theory may be summarized as follows: Man lives in three environments—(a) natural, (b) social, and (c) technological or technical. The last environment—the material element of culture, is regarded as independently alternating. Under the influence of this independently alternating factor, changes take place in the nonmaterial surroundings (economic and political categories and institutions, ethics, religion, and ideology).

The mechanics of change (adaptation) of social environment in accordance with technology, according to this theory, operate as follows: first comes the local adaptation of life in this or that group to this or that technical change, and some social institutions are altered. Then the total sum of changing conditions in itself gives rise to broader adaptations, etc. What takes place is something like a chain reaction. In one way or another, technical development provides the first impulse toward change, then this development together with the sum of the changes that have already taken place provides a second impulse, after which a broader circle of changes provides the third impulse, etc. Theoreticians of this trend emphasize that the various impulses, coming from various sides, intertwine and influence one another.

[19] N. I. Osmova, "On the So-Called 'Technical Determinism,'" Vestnik Istorii mirovoi kultury, No. 4 (1959), pp. 42-54.

Outwardly, the picture is rather convincing. It is a fact that one must not ignore the influence of technology on all aspects of human life (e.g., in the factory, in agriculture, in transport, in town and village, in daily life). Every invention and discovery that is widely introduced exerts its influence both on individuals and on groups. But it is the task of science, by means of those phenomena that emerge on the surface, to disclose and understand the laws that lie at the basis of the interaction of technical progress and social conditions, to disclose the specific features of this interaction. In the light of the Marxist theory of technical means, expounded above, its natural-scientific and social foundations, the place it holds in the development of productive forces, the mechanics of the interplay between technical and social factors look somewhat different. The operation of technical progress on social conditions, as shown above, may be direct or indirect. But any indirect impact of technology on social life depends, as we have emphasized, not only on technical means but also on those social relations within the framework of which man lives. This interaction has different manifestations in differing social conditions, exerting varying influence on people, on the conditions of their lives.

The main and decisive importance, as we have just said, attaches not to a direct influence but to the profound changes called forth by technical development in the material and technical foundation of society, in the productive forces and the relations of production connected with these. And the various production, property, class relations act back strongly upon technical progress.

An explanation of the general theoretical questions linked up with the interplay and mutual influence of technology and society is a necessary condition for any extensive investigation of the concrete social effects exerted by technical progress on any aspect of human life. But this is a theme in itself.

STRUCTURE AND COMPLEXITY
OF THE UNIVERSE*

Pierre Auger

For many thousands of years the human universe was limited to a few species of animals or vegetables that were sought after as food or prey or feared as enemies. Thus the structure of this universe was like a collection of individual objects that were put into categories and designated by words representing them. Man's brain, like that of other animals, is organized accordingly and presents a remarkable aptitude for distinguishing living species in divers forms and circumstances. However, the world that surrounded primitive man also contained other important albeit nonliving factors, such as rivers, lakes, rocks, mountains, and caves. It was natural that a structure that had proved to be perfectly adequate when applied to living creatures should be enlarged to apply to these other factors: to do this, the individual and definable objects had to be distinguished and names provided to symbolize them. Now—as we know today—such an extension cannot be based on objective reality; it must in consequence grow out of subjective criteria, and it led automatically to anthropocentrism and even to a general anthropomorphism. Nonliving "species" could be defined only through their rela-

*Journal of World History, VI, 3.

tion to Man, thus becoming "relative objects." From the period of their first appearance, this was the case with created things such as tools, dwelling places, works of art. For our present analysis, the essential point is this: primitive man had no way of distinguishing a more or less absolute "objective" object—such as a living creature—from a relative "subjective" object like a tool; to him, they were both objects having the same nature, and he tended to give "life" to a dwelling or a river in the same way as to a savage or domestic animal, and to symbolize one by the other, or by a man. The structure of his universe was thus based on examples of the different types of objects, each individualized and lending itself to a symbolic representation, and its functioning was controlled by the interactions between these objects, including Man himself. To this should be added imaginary and abstract objects, invisible powers and spirits, all of which merely stood for new categories of things participating in the general structure and in the laws of interaction. From this description it can be deduced that the primitive universe was essentially discontinuous and capable of being completely broken down into distinct and individualized elements belonging to a finite number of categories—in short, a "quantified" structure similar to that of language. The notion of number must have developed from this structure, whole numbers being the only ones immediately perceivable. Finally, the importance of the smaller whole numbers—two, three, four, five—came from their constantly being used in enumerating the groups of objects of the same species that surrounded Man in his daily life.

Nevertheless, certain concepts of a continuous sort must of necessity have had a part in this discontinuous universe, particularly with regard to interactions among objects, as well as the changes undergone by the objects themselves without their changing species. In languages, this category is represented principally by verbs. These continuous relationships tend to introduce into the universe elements with a complexity that is different from that based on the "quantified" structure described above. However, upon closer inspection these relationships too are often quantified. Let us take movement, for example: man can be immobile; he may walk, run, or jump. True, one moves from one to another of these conditions by imperceptible degrees; however, not only in language but also in ordinary thinking, movement is made up of a certain number of activities that together form a category. No doubt movement is seen as varying in a continuous manner; it "happens" since the subject moves, but as as soon as possible it is reclassified as discontinuous, and it is in this form that it remains in the memory.

The actual nature of movement—that is, the actual presence of an object in different places at successive periods—is not analyzed in this continuous manner by the human mind (or by animals). An animal or an object that is motionless, on the one hand, and the same animal or object in motion are in reality different things, worthy of different names and considered in a different manner; an action while it is being made and an action after it has been made differ not only quantitatively but also qualitatively; primitive grammar carries traces of this conception. Movements forward and backward in space, entering and leaving, are likewise differentiated.

Lastly, relationships and reciprocal actions between objects generally take the form of a more or less complex structure, with characteristics that can be numbered, named, symbolized, and which is in consequence of a discontinuous or even quantified nature. Relationships such as superiority and inferiority, dependency, interdiction, and obligation, and the intercourse these relationships bring about are actual abstract objects. They may even actually become a part of the concrete objects to which they apply, thus giving them a particular nature and classifying them in the corresponding category. A man is not "a man constrained to obedience, or slavery"; he is a "slave." We speak—and think—of a husband, lord, chief, rich man, nobleman, or outcast as well-defined objects in the structure of the universe, whereas men, deprived of their attributes and considered without a knowledge of the complexity in which they have a part, cannot be distinguished one from another save by continually changing nuances. The same is true of animals, in particular domestic animals, and, finally, of inanimate objects endowed with such and such a quality in the social structure: their name and their symbolism are consequently fixed.

The universe whose structure we have just sketched out is deeply logical and rational. It reveals such a unity in its principles that it is practically unassailable and should either be accepted as it is, as a whole, or be completely rejected. It has great facility of adaptation and allows the mind of primitive man an immediate and satisfactory interpretation of any event, no matter how surprising. However, since this interpretation consists in applying an *a priori* structure—no matter how self-consistent—to the real world, it gives rise to actions the consequences of which can be extremely unpleasant. One might say that primitive society, existing for a long time within a stable milieu, had built up a structural conception of the universe that worked empirically, but that, faced with changes in its surroundings that were too important to be fitted into the normal conception, this society was liable to disastrous reactions, however logical and predictable they might be (at least to a certain extent). If such a society survived the first impact of such a change, it would readapt itself to new conditions by means of an "addition" to its sum of ideas about the complexity of its universe—an "addition" that in no way altered the structure or, at least, the principles of the structure. The primitive universe was adaptable, provided that it was not too slow in changing. When the milieu is stable, progress—or at any rate spontaneous changes—must take place extremely slowly.

II

The shortcomings of the primitive universe were apparent to thinking men from antiquity. One example: motion. The temptation to conceive of motion as including—at its lowest level—immobility was confounded by the discontinuity that separated the two "quantifying" concepts of immobility and motion. To advance beyond this stage, it was necessary to arrive at a completely different concept that had no place in the primitive universe, that of continuous function. The advance of mathematics and the first systematic physical measurements led at last, at the time of the Renaissance, to the development of the conception of continuous laws, of relationships between numbered objects from zero to infinity. The break with the primitive universe, which had remained practically unchanged during the Middle Ages, was not clearly felt; indeed, the structure of the ancient universe was so natural to human thinking that it continued to exist, in almost the same form, side by side with the new, continuous structure, that of functional laws. For that matter, it exists now in daily life, for it applies to language and to the majority of social relationships. One is not *more or less* a son, father, chief, subordinate, cabinet minister, or member of the *Légion d'honneur*. It is still sustained by the whole of the living kingdom, the species of which make up categories having no continuity. However, it became necessary to take into account the fact that other types of objects did not in actuality fall into discontinuous categories, in the same way as living things, or rather, that their individuality was nothing more than a reflection of the individuality of man, who had named them. Whether in the case of tools or furniture, statues of the gods or large rivers, it became evident that here one was dealing with collections of substances having arbitrary and variable form, the parts of which did not have a reciprocal organic interaction, as did those of living beings. In other words, the ancient universe was partly false and partly true, and it became highly important to revise completely the ideas that related to this second sphere in order to have a hope of advancing in the knowledge, interpretation, and utilization of the forces of nature.

In the realm of physical forces, the new universe met with such success that the question arose as to whether it would invade the whole of knowledge and force upon it its continuous laws. In any case, the situation became philosophically difficult as a result of the simultaneous presence of the two kinds of universe: as a matter of fact, the interpretation of natural phenomena often necessitated fitting them together in the same theory. Animal physiology thus made great progress as a result of the systematic intervention of continuous measurement and the establishment of functional laws (similar to the laws governing nonliving systems, natural formations, or constructed machines); at the same time, it became evident that the animal was an indivisible whole, so that those partial systems studied in the living being could never be completely compared to machines.

Phenomena closely related to the notions that formed the basis of the primitive universe also appeared in the field of chemistry. In particular, they proved the existence of chemical species completely distinct from one another and that showed no evidence of continuous action. The very laws that regulated the combinations between these different chemical species introduced numbers and rules so simple that one inevitably equated them with everyday human relationships —preferences or affinities, loves and hates giving rise to sudden changes in relationships, changes of partners, breaks or unions, marriages or divorces.

III

Thus it is that at the end of the nineteenth century we find ourselves in possession of a composite universe the structure of which shows absolute discontinuity between the types and objects making up those classes having simple characteristics. This universe established continuous relationships between these objects, represented by rigorous functional laws and leading to a complete determinism in the chain of events. One might say, from the viewpoint of science, that it contained a heterogenous mixture of two immiscible universes, every crack in the old discontinuous structure having been filled by laws of continuity and statistics of probability that had become indispensable because of all the increasingly precise measurements brought to bear on physical objects. But these laws themselves were incapable of taking into account the discontinuous structure and were, so to speak, only able to flow across it without weakening it.

From the point of view of theory as well as of practice, such a composite universe is extremely useful but much less satisfactory than had been the discontinuous and homogenous universe of antiquity. It was full of contradictions and inconsequences: it was doubtless the way toward something more harmonious, but there was nothing before the turn of the century to indicate how the change would come about or, in particular, whether continuity or discontinuity would win out, whether the last traces of antiquity would be swallowed up by the new world, or whether, on the contrary, the latter would return to the simple harmony of numbers.

The relative importance of the two aspects of the composite universe differed considerably according to the disciplines concerned: according to Linnaeus, natural history is very discontinuous, but Lamarck and Darwin introduced into it an element of continuity. Next, Mendel re-established discontinuity on a more precise basis. Physics was largely dominated by the Newtonian spirit, and since—through its connection with chemistry—it was forced to accept the categories of discontinuous objects and the simple rapports that control the atomic world, it applied statistical laws to them, thus submerging their inconvenient individuality in continuous laws of a thermodynamic nature. Chemistry, as we have seen, was unable to rise above the atomic individuality, which made itself continually evident. The spectroscope lent authority to the discontinuous viewpoint by demonstrating that atoms not only make up units belonging to distinct categories by means of simple groupings among themselves, but that each one gives evidence of discontinuity, as revealed by the streaks in the spectroscope. Furthermore, the orderly arrangement of these streaks led to a suspicion that the simple relationships played a fundamental role. Perhaps astronomy, still classical, was the least affected by these Pythagorean fragments, unalterable and unassimilable little islands lost in the new universe of forces and fields: however, it was not to escape much longer, for astrophysics soon dragged it into the atomic camp.

Was this composite universe a satisfactory one? It could scarcely have been so to the human mind, which was still dreaming of a unity concealed behind the kaleidoscope of reality. The search for this unity was the motive of theoretical and experimental endeavors that produced successful results in many cases: unfortunately, since these endeavors were of necessity carried out along two different lines, depending on whether they dealt with the discontinuous part of the universe or the continuous objects in the universe, they did not and could not as yet bring to light anything tending to unite these two worlds, in juxtaposition, interpenetrating, and yet distinct from each other.

Where discontinuous species were concerned, any uniting factors there might be a prospect of discovering could be sought only in the form of individual, discontinuous elements, present as fundamental structural elements in all known types, whose various combinations and arrangements might account for the properties observed. A firm and natural classification could then be based on them. Chemistry had high hopes for Prout's law, which demonstrated that the weights of the various atoms were approximate whole multiples of the weight of the hydrogen atom. However, the differences between the measured atomic weights and the perfect multiples required by the law remained large. Moreover, these differences seemed not to obey any simple law: a kind of chance seemed to have governed their distribution among all the known elements. The possibility of classifying the numerous chemical elements according to the regular arrangements of Mendeleyev's periodic table led to the supposition of an underlying simplicity: it was extremely tempting to think that the whole thing resulted from a distortion of incomprehensible origin that had been applied to the fundamentally simple structure of these atoms.

When molecules rather than atoms were considered, greater successes were obtained, for even if no new unifying notion was introduced, at least the makeup of all the molecules could be derived by means of combinations and arrangements among the atoms of the known elements. Here, therefore, was the example of a world made up of absolutely distinct individuals forming well-defined categories, and in which each of the individuals was able to be broken down into a certain number—generally small—of individuals belonging to another numerable, natural, discontinuous sphere: that of the atoms. The continuous universe came into play only when attention was given to the properties of groups formed by many atoms or molecules and to the indeterminates that characterized them—temperature, pressure, and other forces.

Attempts at analyzing the other classes making up the discontinuous universe have had varied success, but they have always led to simplification, as in the case of chemical species. Thus crystals, whose discontinuities of a rigorously geometrical form have always attracted great interest, were able to be reduced to extremely simple arrangements similar to the same kinds of groupings of individual elements that make up chemical molecules. The extreme regularity of these arrangements merely raised the geometric simplicity of the elementary groupings themselves, and their reciprocal relationships, to the scale of direct human observation. Here was an example of groups made up of large numbers of individual parts that were free from the laws of continuity: one was dealing with an organization, a *structuration*, in nonliving objects directly perceivable by the senses, and that was simple but complete (that is, no part was without structure).

The other large discontinuous group—in a way, the primordial group, that is, living beings—led, for its part, to a structural conception that seemed completely different. No doubt the final elements of an analysis should be sought out on the atomic or molecular level, but this would not support any fundamental differentiation between living and inanimate things. The discovery of the role played by the cell as the fundamental element of animals and plants was no more than a deceptive unifying force; chromosomes and genes had to be discovered before it finally became possible to discern the substratum of a simplification that was suspected of being very profound. On the other hand, the discovery of the great similarity of the chemical substances making up the bodies of all living beings, from the simplest to the most complex, brought a hint of unity into the almost indescribable variety of the millions of known species. Thus, further away but even more promising, gleamed the hope of being able in some still mysterious way to join the complexity of the structures in the sphere of molecular chemistry with those in the sphere of living things.

The difference between the two discontinuous universes— living and nonliving—still arose from the dynamic characteristic of the former: to protect itself against the disorganizing factors of the environment and, when that environment was sufficiently favorable, to reproduce itself; whereas the most complex chemical molecules remained inert. Should a profound difference in the very nature of these objects be posited, a vital force contained in some and not in others, or should the very complexity of their organization give sufficient evidence for distinguishing them?

The situation during this period can be summed up in a consideration of the two flaws in the scientific universe, the one separating discontinuous objects—molecules and atoms— from the continuous laws of mechanics and physics, and the other separating the world of living organisms from that of nonliving, even where individualized objects such as molecules and crystals are concerned. These two flaws—or cracks —can be bridged in numerous ways: for example, atoms and molecules obey continuous laws, especially when they are considered in large numbers; however, as soon as their internal structure is considered, the flaw appears. On the other hand, living organisms also obey many of the laws of physics and chemistry, but as soon as the question of their being itself, and especially of their reproduction, is raised, the break is unavoidable.

IV

However, during the last years of the nineteenth century, several new causes of dissatisfaction arose. First of all, radioactivity, the discovery of which showed that atoms possessed a complex internal structure. On the other hand, in the field of statistical laws itself—the laws that had seemed to be concerned with the continuous universe, concerning large numbers of atoms and molecules (specific heat, continuous spectrum of emission)—it was seen that these atoms and molecules refused to behave like ordinary objects such as more or less elastic billiard balls or even mechanical or electromagnetic resonators. Electric current itself switched to the enemy camp by taking the form of unitary particles, or electrons. The world of the physicists already found itself on the threshold of an immense change, of a revolution comparable in importance to that brought about by Galileo and Newton.

Big changes were also under way in the domain of living things, changes that tended to entangle more and more tightly the discontinuous and the continuous universes. On the one hand, the Mendelian laws of heredity had led to a more rigorous atomism in the description of the characteristics of the species, bringing them closer to the chemical species. On the other, the application of the continuous laws of physical chemistry were proving themselves of value in all the problems of physiology. The two aspects—continuous and discontinuous—were seen to be closely interwoven in almost every particular case. In neurophysiology, for example, where ordinary electric measurements are used with great success, it was necessary to deal with systems—the neurones—having only two stable states, each completely distinct: like doors, they are either open or shut. The nerve impulse itself was seen as being made up of unitary impulsions, exactly the same whether it be a question of transmitting a sensation or of making a movement.

It was, however, during the year 1900, on December 14th to be exact, that the storm finally broke. On that day, physics entered the predicted new era, and it did so by suddenly breaking with the classical principles. The continuous theories of thermodynamics, too tenuous to keep up with the results of experiments, fell away. Max Planck demonstrated that in the transmission of energy between elementary resonators, atoms, molecules, and the groupings of crystal formations, continuity must be set aside. Bohr later showed that it was no longer possible to apply the laws of electromagnetism to the internal mechanism of atoms. A breach had been made in the wall of continuous laws that would never be repaired. The discontinuous universe awoke and forcefully took over the reputedly impregnable positions held by thermodynamics. Entropy itself, strengthened by its continual and fatal augmentation, was stopped by the crystalline Pythagorism of the atomic edifice.

We have not yet seen the final consequences of this break nor of the discontinuous invasion of fiefs laboriously built up and organized by continuous work during the course of many centuries. On the other hand, the revolution has but moved the frontier, and continuous conceptions have not ceased playing their part in the actual structure of the universe. They will always have a part, for that matter, since they will join together the discontinuous structures when their number becomes very large.

That is how matters stood just after Planck's and Bohr's discoveries in quantum mechanics, to which we may add that of isotopes by Soddy and Aston, which finally settled the old question of atomic weights by confirming Prout's law of the whole multiples of hydrogen. Pythagoras had won out in every field: atoms were made up of various arrangements of a small number of elementary particles, the proton and the electron, which were joined fifteen years later by the neutron. Further, the structure of these atoms was governed by an extraordinarily simple arithmetic. Even the transmission of energy took place between these geometric constructions by means of the discontinuous exchange of these new elements of the physical world represented by quantum rays. Soon molecules—the smallest, at least—were to join the category of "quantified" structures, that is, structures regulated by simple and discontinuous laws, and were given corresponding geometric forms.

Since the atomic nuclei contain but a limited number of particles, the explanation of a long period of life in certain unstable (radioactive) elements on the basis of the mechanics of the relative motions of these various particles became very difficult. Who could believe that it might be ten thousand million years before the decisive configuration necessary for the breaking apart of an ensemble composed of a few dozen particles in rapid motion would occur? The collapse of all conceptions as to the universe of continuous laws—and the corresponding Newtonian determinism—became evident. Since it was necessary to connect these phenomena to some notion of causality, physicists found themselves reduced, as it were, to adding to the two kinds of causality invoked by the ancient philosophers—that is, efficient causes and final causes —a probable causality: a system placed in conditions such that it is capable of undergoing various spontaneous transformations is affected or governed by coefficients representing the probabilities of these transformations in time units. No sufficiently precise description of the makeup of the system can be given that will permit a certain prediction as to whether it will undergo such and such a change. One can say that its interior structure eludes fine analysis, and that thus it has no real existence; what it presents as reality are its coefficients of probability. However, these can have a continuous or discontinuous distribution, according to whether the modes of transformation are infinite or finite in number.

In the field of chemistry, quantum laws finally made it possible to understand the reasons for the stability of molecular structures and to penetrate their complex architecture. The chemical molecule, and particularly the large molecule of organic compounds, has become a being, an absolute object, all of whose exterior reactions are measured and calculated as though a living creature were being dealt with. This knowledge stops, however, as soon as an attempt is made to go beyond general behavior and predict the precise, individual reactions of such and such a molecule: at this point the fundamental indetermination of the system is revealed, and we must be content—as in the case of living things—with predictions of probability.

If we pass from the large molecules to consider the most elementary forms of life, the real universe takes us—by a transition the exact characteristics of which are not yet known —to the smallest distinguishable creatures: the viruses. Are these actually alive in the full sense of the term? Are they rather very large molecules that possess only one of the characteristics of life, the ability to reproduce, but not that of creating and maintaining an interior milieu by means of a constant metabolism? Their stability seems to be based directly on the stability of chemical species and to present, as a result, a quantum origin, whereas the stability of a living cell is based on a continual struggle, a continual construction that is constantly in opposition to destructive forces and the invasion of disorder—this thanks to the utilization of free energy derived from without in the form of solar radiation or exothermic chemical reactions. Perhaps the possibility of separating the two principal aspects of life—reproduction and metabolism (the condition necessary for development)—will be proved and found to be the origin of a deeper understanding of the nature of the living organism.

In any case, quantum discontinuities have come into play even with regard to large-scale beings, if only in the field of genetics. The genes, carriers of hereditary characteristics, are macromolecular in nature, and it seems certain that the sudden changes they can undergo during ionic radiation, for example, are quantum changes. As a result, when we observe blue or black eyes in the people around us, we should put this difference down to the existence of molecules and to the discontinuous nature of the energy they contain. Furthermore, this is not the only branch of biology where interpretations based on fundamental discontinuities come to the fore. For example, neurophysiology, and in particular that of the sense organs, deals with effects and interactions—such as that of light on the cells of the retina—the quantum character of which would seem to be essential.

However, though the quantum theory allows us to posit the stability of the characteristics of living beings in a logically acceptable manner, and to interpret the sudden changes they sometimes undergo, it does not directly provide a means of understanding how, in what causal way, discontinuous changes occurring on the molecular level—and therefore rather simple —in principle, can bring about results that are as complex as those observed in heredity as well as in neurophysiology. In fact, here again, enlarged but unchanged in substance, is the question put by chemistry: how can all the variety of properties in a compound substance be reduced to the combinations of a few elementary particles made up according to numerical rules that are, in the end, rather simple?

Thus we come to a new phase in the evolution of the conceptions about the structure of the universe. The first was, in a way, naïvely numerical; the second was governed by the introduction of physical sizes the continual variations of which are more in conformity with the varied and changing spectacle of nature; the third brought us to the rediscovery of the numbers, dear to Pythagoras, at the root of everything and the importance of which now appears clearly. In this perspective, the definition of the connections between the fundamental simplicity based on numbers, the continuous scale of physical sizes, and the extreme complexity of the real phenomena surrounding us was still lacking. Two principal paths were followed: that of statistics and that of structure, the former permitting the linking of certain continuous physical sizes to groups of events in the discontinuous infrastructure, the existence of which we have recognized (atoms and molecules, quanta, living things), and the latter allowing us to discern a precise and numerical link between certain of the events that occur at the level of this infrastructure and certain phenomena on our own level, among which are those that condition our daily life and our control over nature.

We will now attempt to show, using an important example, how these two methods can be applied, in what fields they are valid, and what are their interactions. As an example, let us take the distribution of energy among the molecules of a body—of a gas, for example—that is brought to a certain temperature. If the only thing known about these molecules is the fact that they are able to move in the three dimensions of space and revolve about themselves on three rectangular axes, it should be clear that the available energy will be divided indifferently according to these six possibilities and that we must apply to them the statistical calculations based on our ignorance of any structural details. Simple formulas are thus obtained that have been found perfectly applicable to gases in many respects, and in particular in the calculation of the rise in temperature resulting from the addition and distribution of a new source of energy to the molecules contained in a given volume of gas (specific heat). But certain studies carried out in different directions, bearing, for example, on low-temperature gases or on electromagnetic rays (visible light, for example) enclosed in equilibrium within a body brought to a certain temperature, showed that the statistical method alone, based on ignorance of mechanical details, by no means sufficed to account for the observable phenomena. Simple hypotheses then had to be put forward concerning on the one hand the somewhat geometric structure of the molecules and on the other the structure of the energy and the changes it brings about. Thus it became necessary to establish a distinction between the different possibilities of the rotary movement of molecules according to their form (without taking into consideration the three spatial dimensions). Dumb-bell-shaped diatomic molecules, such as the hydrogen molecule, can revolve about their symmetrical axis only in accordance with a discontinuous series of speeds corresponding to the possession of a series of rotating energy levels, in such a way that numerous collisions can occur without any alteration in speed until such a collision that the speed suddenly augments or diminishes, passing to another level in the series. We can see that such structures bring about great changes in statistical calculations, since they correspond to a "knowledge" that comes to limit the general "ignorance" that was originally posited. The equal division of energy no longer takes place between the six different possibilities of motion, and the specific heat is greatly changed. Hypotheses of the same type should be developed concerning the intervention of the internal structure of complex molecules, certain parts of which may move in rapport with the remainder. It is remarkable that the observed energy discontinuities always correspond to completely locally defined motions: rotations, vibrations, that is, periodic motions. They do not appear in motions that can be defined only by rapport with another system, like translations, which are known to be of only relative value. This is in accordance with the theory of relativity, for a discontinuous series of possibilities in such motions would provide a basis for an absolute definition of speed.

The applications of the statistical method, ordered, as one might say, by structural conditions, have been extremely wide and have given rise to outstanding successes. It is clear that this method may well be an excellent means of bringing about further discoveries. The scientific process may be as follows: a structure is unknown and is supposed in the beginning to be of either type. If statistical calculations give a result in conformity with the experiment, our ignorance remains—either because the structure does not exist or because it has no place in the phenomena under consideration; if the experiment does not conform to the statistics, structural hypotheses must be made, at first simple and later more complicated, until the statistics bearing on the supposed knowledge account for the experiment. In physics and biology it has frequently happened that structures thus posited and proved by this indirect method have later been confirmed by more direct methods, such as microscopic observation.

To give an example of the inverse method, in which a structure previously thought to be proved has been demonstrated to have no influence over all the observable phenomena and must thus be considered to be nonexistent, we can come back to atomic nuclei. It was legitimate to suppose, *a priori*, that these nuclei, made up of a small number of fundamental particles, formed a stable mechanical system— similar to the solar system. Thus the elements—very small and possessing great energy—are animated by extremely rapid movements, vibrations, or rotations. If such a geometrical structure exists, it can be defined at any given instant, and stability or possible instability may result. With such speeds, the various possible configurations must appear very frequently, a great many times per second, and it is conceivable that certain unstable nuclei have a very short life-span. However, it also happens that nuclei with a makeup very similar to the short-lived nuclei and at the same time equally unstable have an extraordinarily long life-span. One might suppose that the number of its particles would be extremely high, but this would run counter to all other experiments, which tend to show that this number is at most several hundred. Thus it must be granted that the unstable configuration is made up with an extreme precision that is revealed only after this long period of waiting. However, the calculated precision becomes unimaginable: for example, it would be necessary to represent the number of rotations by a number followed by forty zeros in order to symbolize this situation. Lastly, conditions outside the nucleus (temperature, pressure) have no discernible effect on the life-span; this leads us to believe that they have *no* effect on the geometrical dispositions of the nucleus with an equally unimaginable precision. Under these conditions, it is wise to admit that no spatial structure determines the moment of disintegration. Statistics show that our ignorance will persist, that every spatial structure possible will probably remain inaccessible, and that we should be wise to admit its nonexistence.

In this paper there can be no question of dealing with fundamental particles, which now constitute a new field of physics, comparable in importance to the molecular, atomic, and nuclear fields. For our purpose it will suffice to point out that the two universes come into this field in the same manner as into the others: what we have called the duality between waves and corpuscles is a form of the duality between the continuity of fields of force and the quantum discontinuities subject to them. In this area are also to be found the principles governing the incarnations of energy and matter within their structures and their complexities—for example, the principle of symmetry. Certain great minds, such as Einstein, have been strongly attracted by the continuous universe, and they have tried to tie the whole of physics up with it; for the time being, it would seem that this duality is fundamental and that one must await the discovery of new principles in order for us to be able one day to arrive at a unity in the universe, a unity even more profound than that provided by the modern quantum theory.

V

Up to this point, we have considered the case of relatively simple structures, such as the molecules of mineral chemistry and atomic nuclei, those structures in which a rather limited number of elementary parts are to be found and in which statistics are controlled by the discontinuous structure of local energy and the exchanges for which it provides. The successes of the theories and calculations based on such structures have been extremely numerous when they have been, so to speak, let loose in the continuous universe of motion and relative positions. These successes have covered the theories of atomic nuclei as well as those concerning the stars, and it would appear that in the area that was at one time called "the mineral kingdom," science can rely on them with confidence. On the other hand, where other classical kingdoms, such as the living kingdom, are concerned, the structures have been found to be infinitely more complex, and new notions, still based on fundamental discontinuities, have had to be elaborated in order to allow for a more exact interpretation of observed phenomena.

This time the point of departure was not found in the phenomena surrounding man but in man himself; this is easy enough to understand, since man is a part of the living kingdom and one of its most complex representatives. It would be impossible at present to analyze the complexity of a human state of mind, but the analysis of the exterior product of these states of mind, that is, voluntary actions, would appear to be more accessible. The attempts at analysis have been brought to bear in particular on those actions that have as an end result some influence on other human states of mind, that is, on the "messages," the well-established physical character of which—during their passage from the sender to the receiver—allows for the employment of the normal methods of the so-called exact sciences. This analysis has shown that the complexity of a message can be reduced to a series of choices, like the dots and dashes of the Morse code, for example, where the series of successive choices between the dash and the dot creates groups that stand for letters that, in turn, form the words and phrases of the message. When the unit of choice has been decided by a choice between the two sides of an alternative, it is possible to calculate how many such units stand for a letter of the alphabet, a word, a decimal number, indeed any message. The complex of a particular type that has been defined and measured in this way is called information. It has the advantage of being numerical and is capable of being converted into a mathematic operation. It has been generalized in such an extraordinarily wide manner that it is possible to evaluate the complexity of a molecule of nuclear acid or of a Rembrandt engraving by means of units of information. In the former case, it is a question of defining the chain of basic chemical functions that take place along the molecular chain, and in the latter it takes the form of defining by means of a line-by-line scanning, as in television, with a choice between white or black for each small section of the scanning. Of course, the case of a naturally discontinuous complexity, such as that of molecules, gives rise to a simpler and more rigorous analysis than that of the lines of an engraving: indeed, in this latter case, the passage from continuous to discontinuous necessitates the use of a screen or bead, of a preliminary network of arbitrary size.

Where the various manifestations of life are concerned, it might be said that the complexity is generally discontinuous, and that it is consequently possible to make out a real elementary structure in such manifestations. To return to the problem of motion: an object seen determines a retinal image. The sensory effect of this continuous image is transmitted by means of the screen created by the sensitive elements of the retina. When the object moves, new sensory elements are successively affected by the image, while others are abandoned. This fundamental discontinuity in the sensation of displacement disappears in the overall perception we call movement.

The natural screen is very fine, and the reconstitution of the perception of continued movement may be effected by means of much larger artificial screens, like those used in film-making. It is known that the most continuous perceptions, such as those of temperature or pressure, can in reality be reduced to elementary nerve impulses that are repeated at very brief intervals.

These physical discontinuities are linked to the cellular structure of living beings. Discontinuities having a chemical origin come into effect at a much more rarefied level, that of molecules. It is interesting to note that gas molecules were discovered by means of the statistical method posited for them. In fact, if one examines an animal or vegetable grouping made up of individuals of the same species, and if statistics based on some of the measurable characteristics of these individuals are established (size, color, form, etc.), one generally arrives at a bell-shaped graph, so-called because it shows the existence of a "normal" value for the characteristics in question with the arranging around this value of a number of objects that diminish with distance. In this case, the statistics can be conceived as statistics of probability, the greater distances indicating the least probable. That is to say, there is a continuity in the variation under consideration, but there is no underlying structure—or that, if the structures exist, they have no effect. However, it frequently happens that the graphs are more complex and show several "maxima"—that is, several "normal" character values, with arrangements around them. It may then be said that the species breaks up into subspecies, sometimes called Jordanian—after the botanist who first described them in the four-leafed Draba Verna. A discontinuous structure should therefore be found at the basis of these statistics. Thanks to the studies undertaken in hybridization, Mendel and, later, Morgan and his followers were able to indicate this discontinuous structure of hereditary characteristics and show, particularly, that it was linear: in modern language, we would say that it corresponds to information that can be symbolized by a series of numbers, for example a linear series of lines and points or of the numbers 0 and 1. Since then, it has been found that such linear series exist materially in the basic chemical functions characterized by the molecular chains of those nuclear acids contained in the chromosomes. The information cannot be written out in a binary fashion, which would have been possible had there been but one alternative for the successive choices, whereas there are four basic chemical functions represented: in heredity, therefore, the information is derived from a fourfold basis. The reasons for this variety, greater than the possible minimum, are probably stereochemical and are at present barely understood. The progress in recent years of microscope work, optical as well as electronic, has made possible a closer perception of the details of this interior structural complexity of the cell. The chromosomes appear to us as being almost like the long spools of a speech describing the characteristics of the being whose heredity they transmit, a speech written in chemical language and a four-letter alphabet. Protoplasm, which was long considered a relatively homogenous mixture of many dissolved substances and "colloids," was seen to be made up of precisely constructed organites, sacs, and tiny canals bounded by layers of molecules, and these various structures held together by microscopic fibers. One of the most important of these organites, the centriole, which seems to be the guiding center of cell division, resembles a six-cylinder motor, so mechanically precise is its structure, formed as it is by six spiral tubes joined by longitudinal supports. We have here architecture on the molecular level, an architecture that has the marvelous ability to reproduce itself in its different parts without the offspring losing any of their properties. Thus, the whole living world is constructed on the scale of large molecules, possessing a complexity of a discontinuous nature, containing information of a linear character.

Structure and complexities are based on the fundamental discontinuities in the cell nucleus, in the cell, in the nervous system. Consequences of these structures with regard to life, heredity, and neurophysiology: might it not be possible to extend the possibilities of these structures even further to include mental processes, or the human relations to which they give rise? It would seem that *Gestalt* psychology—to use the classic German word—contains an implicit acceptance of such a construction, a more or less distant repercussion of those of the living organism itself. The synthetic character of the *Gestalt* is similar to that which is linked with the complex, individualized groups found in the study of heredity. If it is possible to discern the characteristics of an adult individual through certain structural elements in his chromosomes, by means of a chain of events not yet completely known but of whose existence we are convinced, would it not be possible to suppose a similar connection between the *Gestalt* and some material structure within the central nervous system? Further, family, tribal, and social structures are based on mental representations having a precise structure, and might not these, too, in principle, be connected to the individual complexities present in each of the individuals making up the structure, similar to the way in which the same chromosomes are present within all the cells in our body?

Furthermore, one might perhaps find such a fundamental quantified structure in other types of mental processes. Thus memory, whether based on sight, hearing, or smell, is seen by means of analysis to be composed of a limited number of synthetic signs, and not of continuous, overall perceptions. The scenes or landscapes that one remembers do not exist in the memory as photographs having continuous nuances from which new details may be recaptured through greater effort, but as pictures made up of a certain number of colors or stereotyped forms that give an illusion of being complete and detailed thanks to our imagination's faculty of embellishment. This is doubtless the reason for the complete satisfaction that is given by fine works of art, which are often extremely incomplete and rudimentary: they contain a certain number of universal synthetic characteristics to which the spectator contributes an automatic embellishment that fills in the missing details. From this point of view, the work of art and memory have a similar structure, which may explain their close relationship. If such a structural analysis of the work of art is justified, it would doubtless help account for the success of abstract art.

Memories being acquired characteristics, the biological structures that permit their development are not to be found in the chromosomes or, in general, the germens. Perhaps it is again a case of large molecules containing in their complexity a recorded fact. Perhaps, on the other hand, and on a larger scale, the information given by the memory is to be found recorded in the system of interconnection of the neurones, by means of the opening or closing of the synapses: in any case, the fundamental discontinuities that are basic to all recording of this sort must be looked for on the molecular scale.

This very brief survey of the possible position of the mental faculties in the structure of the universe would not be complete without some allusion to modern mathematics. Mathematics has for a long time attacked the problems of the relationships of the continuous and discontinuous, and has established very shrewd theories in this field. It is interesting to note that the modern tendency is to direct mathematics toward questions of structure. From the structure of ensembles and groups it has proceeded to the structure of veritable abstract universes within which many heretofore isolated theories have been joined together to form increasingly general systems. In a certain sense, mathematics is investigating more and more profoundly the very structure of human thought.

VI

Thus we have covered the final stage in our journey through science, from antiquity to the first decades of the twentieth century, following the guiding thread provided by the eternally present duality between continuous and discontinuous, law and structure, size and complexity, quantity and quality. After varied adventures, it would seem that the two notions have arrived at a sort of equilibrium, for there cannot be any question of a complete description of the universe based on one of them alone. The surprising thing is that it is quantity that seems most affected by relativity, whereas quality has a more absolute aspect. It might be said, perhaps more clearly, that the discontinuous structures are the stable elements of our universe, the relationships they form among themselves, regarded as a whole, making up the continuous and variable element. Finally, to distinguish these two elements once more in a different way, the continuous part of the universe is that which gives rise to exact predictions, to causal laws, to determinism, whereas the structural elements—discontinuous and complex—are the basis for the undetermined, the unpredictable. Continuity, variability, relativity, and determinism go together. Discontinuity, stability, absolutism, and indeterminism are inseparable. Truly, we live in a strange universe.

TRANSLATED FROM THE FRENCH
BY DAPHNE WOODWARD

PHILOSOPHY OF PHYSICAL SCIENCE
IN THE TWENTIETH CENTURY *

H. Margenau and J. E. Smith

I

Historical survey

The main drift of philosophical thought at a given time has invariably been determined by that aspect of experience taken most seriously during the given period. Thus, for example, the course of philosophy in the ancient world was determined by interest in the cycle of nature and the political life of man, and in the medieval world by the concern for God and the religious life. In the modern period since the Renaissance, knowledge and control of nature through natural science have been the dominant force influencing our deepest thought about the universe and our place in it. The impact of natural and mathematical science upon philosophy together with philosophy's own response all but exhausts the story of philosophy in the past half century. The impact has shown itself in several ways—through philosophical analysis of the method and principal concepts of the sciences themselves; through the philosophical analysis of mathematics and the

* Journal of World History, IV, 3.

attempt to find a logical basis for its structure; through the construction of empiricist philosophies claiming to admit as evidence for a view only the sort of evidence acceptable to the special sciences; and not least through the revision of the cosmological world picture as required by developments in physics modifying the meaning of such basic notions as matter, time, space, causation, and physical object. In short, the situation is a complex one in which the influence of science is manifest both in the analysis of science by philosophy and in the construction of philosophies after the pattern of experimental science. In addition to this reciprocal influence there is the more general result that attention has come to be directed to the nature of language and communication, leading in turn to various types of analytic philosophy purporting to identify philosophy with questions of meaning and linguistic usage. This more general result of the influence of science upon philosophy has made itself felt to some degree in virtually all of the philosophical positions of the twentieth century and it may be seen as the direct consequence of the challenge laid down by science to some of the traditional claims of philosophy. The history of thought has shown that whenever there is fundamental criticism of accepted beliefs and modes of thought, communication becomes an issue and language a focal point of discussion.

The aim of this first part of the present article is to provide a brief but accurate historical sketch of philosophical positions revealing the impact of science in one way or another within roughly the past seventy-five years. It must be understood that while certain main tendencies can be clearly distinguished, there are lines of influence to be drawn between them and a not inconsiderable overlapping of problems. To obviate a confusion not otherwise avoidable in a brief account the main emphasis will be placed upon the tendencies themselves and upon their principal representatives; cross currents will be omitted and only brief attention will be paid to restatements and revisions.

A. *Pragmatism and instrumentalism*

Despite the considerable mystery surrounding the birth of the philosophical position now known as pragmatism, it is still legitimate to think of Charles Peirce's paper, "How to Make

Our Ideas Clear" (*Popular Science Monthly*, 1878) as being the earliest printed formulation of the main ideas behind the movement. As the title implies, Peirce's paper was concerned chiefly with the meaning of concepts, and he construed meaning as a function of *action* and of *future sensible effects* or *consequences*. The nerve of Peirce's original theory is that clarity means distinctness and that a difference in meaning, the difference, for example, between hard and soft, must consist in specifiable differences in sensible effects and in the behavior of both the thing tested and the investigator carrying out the test. Moreover, meaning is closely related to the actual testing, and Peirce more than once implied that it is unmeaning to assert that something is hard or smooth unless it has actually been put to the test. Thus if we assert that something is "hard" as distinct from being "soft" we mean that, when a test is actually made, the thing *will* behave in a specified way and the investigator *will* identify this behavior or effects with the thing itself and *will* come to expect them when he is in the presence of that thing. Meaning is reflected in our expectations, our behavior, and habits; according to this view it is precisely at this point that we find the essential connection between thought and the purposes and interests of the thinker, for thought is viewed as a means of settling belief and of providing the self with an intelligent basis for action. It soon became evident, however, that to talk of meaning as the expected consequences of an idea or belief might mean either the logical consequences of the belief itself or it might mean the full set of consequences to the life of the self holding that belief and acting upon it. This ambiguity revealed the inner tension within pragmatism between its *empiricism* or the aim of following the experimental and futuristic outlook of science and its *humanism* or the belief that human purposes and action have rights and that theoretical thought ignores these rights at the risk of becoming irrelevant to man's deepest concerns.

Pragmatism began as a theory of meaning, but it soon developed into a theory of truth and ultimately into a full-scale interpretation of the nature and function of science in the modern world. Whereas Peirce still retained a conception of truth very close to that of objective idealism and realism in the medieval sense, his followers were more inclined to talk of truth as a value to be achieved or as something that was somehow made in the course of investigation. For both William James and John Dewey, truth was conceived as something that happened to a proposition and as a relation between a claim made upon reality by an idea or an assertion and the success with which the claim could be fulfilled. Thus James set forth his well-known analysis of the relation between percept and concept by means of the figure of cash and banknotes. Despite the simple-minded misunderstanding to which this figure has given rise, it is exact and it reflects what he took to be the view of a scientific empiricism on the matter. Percepts he likened to cash and concepts to banknotes; the former represent the realities given to observation and the latter are claims made by us upon this observable world. To be clear and valid concepts must refer to their proper percepts and, like banknotes, they must be capable of exhibiting their validity by the success with which they can be "cashed," i.e., the success with which they can lead us, like a map, to the percepts themselves and can be exchanged for them. Banknotes or concepts are claims upon reality and their validity is dependent upon an actual test: do they yield the demanded percepts or not? James's chief complaint was against those who, as he believed, traded with "mere" banknotes or concepts for which no perceptual cash could be found.

James placed great stress upon human life and conduct particularly in regard to moral, religious, and metaphysical beliefs, and he advocated an experimental approach to these problems in analogy to natural science. In his well-known essay, "What Pragmatism Means" (*Pragmatism,* 1907), he proposed approaching such formidable issues as that between determinists and defenders of free will and that between pluralists and monists by asking what differences in consequence would result for the life of the individual believer if he were to follow this line of belief and conduct rather than that. For James a difference in thought had to *make* a difference in fact, but for him such differences were to be estimated by paying attention in the first instance neither to science nor society but to the purpose of the individual self, a fact that serves to distinguish his thought from that of both Peirce and Dewey.

Whereas Peirce had placed most emphasis upon logical, methodological, and metaphysical problems and James upon psychological, moral, and religious issues, Dewey was to bring pragmatism to its most systematic form by the placing of biological, social, and political problems in the foreground. With Dewey the doctrine of evolution became decisive for philosophy in that he sought to lay bare the biological basis of man and his thought, and his instrumentalism (as he preferred to name his doctrine) was dedicated to the thesis that in the struggle for survival man's intelligence is his principal weapon, making it possible for him to sustain himself in a precarious world. In an important essay, "The Influence of Darwinism on Philosophy" (1910), Dewey attacked classical philosophy and eschewed what he called absolute origins and finalities, declared the priority of change over permanence, and called attention to the importance of chance and accident in the processes of the natural world. Dewey's entire philosophy may be described as a comprehensive attempt to show how human intelligence, brought to its most accurate and effective form in the method of science, can overcome the doubt, uncertainty, and contingency of life through scientific knowledge and control of the natural environment. In his *Logic, The Theory of Inquiry* (1938), *The Quest for Certainty* (1929), and in his systematic metaphysic *Experience and Nature* (1925), Dewey consistently maintained the theory of thought as an instrument or method whereby man attacks the environment and seeks to transform it in a manner that continues to make life not only possible but progressively better. In this regard it is difficult to find any modern philosopher whose thought was more completely and decisively determined by the outlook, the aims, and especially the method of natural science.

The close connection here emphasized between action, behavior, and meaning, coupled with the positivist verifiability principle (see below), was later to suggest to P. W. Bridgman his "operationalist" theory of meaning. In a book, *The Logic of Modern Physics* (1927), he advanced the thesis that the meaning of scientific concepts is identical with a set of operations actually performed by the investigator. Bridgman's position has an initial plausibility if attention is confined to concepts clearly involving measurements, but it must face great difficulties when used to interpret concepts necessary for the most comprehensive physical theory.

B. *Logical positivism or empiricism*

Without claiming that he is in any sense the historical founder of the movement, no consideration of the positivist program is complete without mention at least of Ernst Mach, professor of physics and later of philosophy at the University of Vienna at the end of the last century.[1] Mach's view of explanation as the description of a class of phenomena instead of the reduction of cases to previously held principles and his consistent sensationalism requiring that all concepts and assertions in science be reducible to discrete sensations had a marked influence upon later positivism. Mach, however, differs from later views in that he placed primary emphasis upon the world of phenomena and not, as was to be the case with Carnap and others, upon the *language* of science. Mach's proposal was to eliminate from mechanics all concepts but those that stand for observables, and his chief aim was, as he expressed it, to "get rid of metaphysical obscurities." This latter aim was, and still is, one of the foremost planks in the platform of logical empiricism.

From the same Vienna where Mach propounded his sensationalistic empiricism came the group of philosophers, logicians, and mathematicians who were to form the famous "Vienna Circle" of logical empiricists. The history of this group counting among its members, M. Schlick, O. Neurath, R. Carnap, F. Waismann, H. Hahn, and others, together with the development of the movement in England and America, is the history of modern positivism. The details of this development stretching from the 1930's to the present are too intricate and extensive to be set forth here, but fortunately they have been recorded and interpreted by several participants in the program and activities of the Circle. Positivism or logical empiricism is, as the name implies, an empiricist viewpoint aiming at the reduction of all knowledge to foundations in experience construed as the domain of the given or presented. The goal envisaged is a purely sensationalist construction of the world by means of concepts all of which are reducible to presented data; concepts not so reducible are to be branded as meaningless and eliminated from serious thought. Although the radical character of the original pro-

---

[1] According to the account given by Philipp Frank *(Modern Science and Its Philosophy* [Cambridge: Harvard University Press, 1949], pp. 6 ff.; 17-19), of the development of the Vienna Circle, Mach's sensationalism and his "antimetaphysical tendencies" had considerable influence upon those later working within the Circle. The accounts given by Feigl and Kraft also support this view.

Also of importance was the work of Karl Pearson *(The Grammar of Science,* 2nd ed., London, 1900), especially his view of the unobservables in physical theory and his idea that concepts represent a "shorthand" for the description of phenomena.

gram has since been modified, the narrowly empirical character of the movement remains. The chief consequence of this outlook for philosophy was the desire to eliminate all metaphysics (conceived as discourse about "unverifiable entities") and to replace the so-called traditional problems of philosophy with purely epistemological questions—syntactical, semantic, and pragmatic—raised by the language and formulations of the natural sciences. In more recent years a further development, the ideal of replacing all constructive philosophy by the *unity of science,* has assumed a place of the highest importance in the movement. The original weapon of logical empiricism, the verifiability theory of meaning according to which the clear meaning of a sentence is to be determined by a specification of the manner in which its truth might be tested, remains the chief instrument of attack upon all problems. It is, however, important to note that the criterion in question has been subject to significant modifications since its original formulation. The article by Hempel, "Problems and Changes in the Empiricist Criterion of Meaning"[2] sets forth the development of the verifiability criterion and shows the changes that have been necessary in order to avoid the embarrassing consequence that earlier formulations, if consistently applied, entailed the meaninglessness of many obviously significant assertions in the sciences themselves.[3]

Whereas positivists have frequently written as though their own position represented the whole story of the relations between science and philosophy, this is in fact very far from the truth. Other equally clear tendencies and lines of development may be discriminated which have actually been closer in their import to the progress of science itself than has the programmatic analysis of logical empiricism. These are: studies in the foundations of mathematics and the construction of logics of relations expressed in symbolism aimed at achieving the utmost in clarity and rigor; new discoveries and theories in physics and allied natural sciences by such men as Einstein, Planck, Bohr, Heisenberg, and others, leading to far-reaching changes in the scientific world picture inherited from classical mechanics; the development of a behavioristic psychology seeking to transform psychology into a branch of physiology

---

[2] *Revue internationale de philosophie,* Jan. 1950, pp. 41-63.
[3] It is important to note that some philosophers have refused to accept the thesis that empiricism requires the verifiability criterion and thus that logical positivism is the only genuine empiricism: see W. T. Stace, "Positivism," *Mind,* Vol. 53, 1944.

by stressing overt behavior and virtually identifying mind with physical movements; the development of linguistic or analytic philosophies focussing attention upon the nature and function of language and upon the concept of truth required for semantic and logical purposes. In briefly sketching these enterprises the broad picture of the mutual relations between science and philosophy will be further filled in. Consideration of new discoveries in physics will be omitted from this section in view of the fact that they are central to the discussion in Part II.

C. Studies in the foundation of mathematics and the development of mathematical logic

One of the most remarkable intellectual phenomena in the past three quarters of a century has been the critical and constructive interplay that has taken place between mathematics and formal logic. The seventeenth and eighteenth centuries witnessed enormous progress in the field of mathematics and in that time more mathematical territory was conquered than in any comparable period since the time of the ancient Greeks. Nor was the nineteenth century to be outdone in the matter of discovery, as is demonstrated by the theory of transfinite numbers (Canto) and the development of non-Euclidean geometry (Lobatschewski, Riemann), to mention but two discoveries taking place within that time, but these developments and others were possible only as a result of another phenomenon that was to prove decisive for both mathematics and logic. Whereas the two preceding centuries were those of conquest, the mathematicians of the nineteenth century first began to question the security of the victories allegedly won. Mathematicians began analysis into the foundations and logical structure of their subject in order to clarify the assumptions involved in mathematical demonstration and to bring proof up to the most rigorous standards. Accordingly attention was directed to the nature of definition and of axioms, to the logical status and function of postulates, and especially to the theory of deduction itself. This drive toward critical reconstruction of the basis of both arithmetic and geometry led logicians in turn to reflect upon their own discipline and especially upon the part to be played in logic by the concept of relation. The charge was made that traditional logic had paid too much attention to subject-predicate attribution and it began to be asked whether the theorems of arithmetic could be treated in this fashion or not. Upon the assumption that they could not, relational logics and logical algebras (George Boole) began to appear and not only did the concept of relation assume a place of fundamental importance in logic, but, as Whitehead was later to emphasize, mathematics began once again to be regarded as the science of relation and not simply as that of quantity.

In the period falling roughly between 1870 and 1895 the work of three men, Richard Dedekind, Gottlob Frege, and Georg Cantor may be singled out as aiming at a most significant goal—the reduction of mathematics to the theory of sets and the subsequent derivation of number theory from purely logical conceptions. The goal, as made explicit by later thinkers such as Russell, was to make mathematics a part of logic by replacing all "mathematical" elements with logical definitions. The enterprise was to be carried out by means of devices such as a purely logical analysis of a *sequence* of numbers and the derivation of the *real numbers* themselves through analysis of continuity. These researches (especially those of Frege) and discussion resulting from the efforts of Peano and others to axiomatize arithmetic led Russell at the turn of the century to take up the problems involved and to make the most sustained effort of all to develop what later became known as the *logicistic* thesis concerning the foundations of mathematics. In his own *Principles of Mathematics* and *Introduction to Mathematical Philosophy* and in the monumental work done in collaboration with A. N. Whitehead and basic to all modern logic and metamathematics, *Principia Mathematica,* Russell sought to carry out the program of founding mathematics upon logic alone. Central to the Russell-Whitehead thesis is the definition of the real numbers as classes of classes so that sets and their relations become the ultimate logical elements out of which mathematics is to be built. Discussion of difficulties encountered in the execution of the plan plus those that arose as a result of the solutions—the axioms of infinity and reducibility and the theory of types—proposed to deal with them is beyond the scope of the present account, but it is noteworthy that these problems have continued to remain in the center of discussion despite the fact that many no longer believe in the feasibility of the reduction that Russell and others sought to accomplish.

A bold program is always likely to produce equally bold criticism, and the proposal of other alternatives was not long in coming. Hermann Weyl's comment upon the character of the mathematical situation in the first half of the present century may serve as the introduction to the other two schools of thought that developed, the so-called formalist and intuitionist positions. Weyl wrote:[4]

> The nineteenth century had witnessed the critical analysis of all mathematical notions including that of natural numbers to the point where they got reduced to pure logic and the ideas "set" and "mapping." At the end of the century it became clear that the unrestricted formation of sets, subsets of sets, sets of sets, etc., together with an unimpeded application to them as to the original elements of the logical quantifiers "there exists" and "all" (cf. the sentences: the [natural] number n is even if there exists a number x such that $n = 2x$; it is odd if n is different from $2 \ x$ for all x) inexorably leads to antinomies. The three most characteristic contributions of the twentieth century to the solution of this Gordian knot are connected with the names of L. E. J. Brouwer, David Hilbert and Kurt Gödel.

The name of Hilbert is at once to be associated with formalism or the thesis that symbols, their relations, and the operations to be performed upon them constitute the essential nature of mathematics and of all purely deductive systems. The ultimate aim of Hilbert was to achieve a mathematics free of contradiction by means of an axiomatic method making use of "meaningless" elements (or of elements said to be "implicitly defined" by the axioms themselves) as the ultimate constituents of the formulas chosen as axioms. Consistency and the absence of contradiction became the ultimate criteria; a given system is consistent on Hilbert's view if and only if there is no formula F of the system such that both F and not-F are provable. The later logical work of Hilbert concerned with his "proof theory" represented an attempt to show from a logical standpoint how such consistency might be achieved. As is well known, however, this line of approach to the difficulties encountered by other methods was dealt a serious and, in a sense, mortal blow by the publication in 1931 of the incompleteness theorems, as they are commonly known, discovered by Kurt Gödel. The principal result relevant at this point is that Gödel showed the impossibility in principle

---

[4] See "A Half Century of Mathematics," *The American Mathematical Monthly*, Vol. 58 (1951), pp. 523-553.

of demonstrating the consistency of a system *broad enough to contain all the formulas of elementary number theory* within that system itself. The demonstration rests upon the contention that in any such system there will always be at least one formula that is "undecidable," i.e., that can neither be proved nor disproved within the system. This result has led to a long series of investigations into what have come to be known as "decision problems" or the specification of an exact recipe for determining whether a given formula is or is not among a given set of formulas in a finite number of steps. It has been possible to axiomatize special regions of mathematics and to demonstrate their completeness, but viewing the formalist program as a whole, particularly as regards the impact of Gödel's incompleteness theorem upon it, the judgment of Weyl is both clear and just: "What Gödel showed was this: if the game of mathematics is actually consistent, then the formula of consistency cannot be proved within the game."[5] The only alternative has been to abandon the original program and settle for as much completeness as can be achieved.

Another and totally different approach to the problems initially tackled by Hilbert and others was that of the intuitionist or finitist mathematical theory. In the twentieth century we associate principally with this view the name of L. E. J. Brouwer. As early as 1908 Brouwer had attacked the classical logical laws and raised doubts about their validity apart from consideration of the subject matter to which they are applied. This line of thought was pursued by him later in his denial of the validity of the law of excluded middle when applied to infinite sets after the fashion of Cantor and others. It is well known that there are difficulties surrounding the exact understanding of the intuitionist thesis (for example, the precise meaning of the intuitive iteration), but despite this fact the main line of approach can be stated in a manner adequate for present purposes. Brouwer not only attacked the idea of constructing the natural numbers or of defining them in terms of logical primitives alone, but he also directed attention to the range of the quantifiers, "all," "any," "there is." Essential to his interpretation is the contention that we must never conclude that "there is" a natural number possessing a certain property solely from the demonstration that "all"

---

[5] The reference to mathematics as a "game" is intended as a description of the formalist thesis of the nature of mathematics.

members of the set to which it belongs do *not* have the property in question. Instead, Brouwer demanded that every assertion of the form, "there is an *x* such that *x* has the property *p*" where *x* refers to a natural number, must be demonstrated by the actual construction of the number (or recipe for such construction) in a finite number of steps. The principal difference between this position and "classical" or nonintuitionistic mathematics is that while classical mathematics treated the infinite as actual or existential, intuitionism views it as potential and thus in need of construction; for neither Brouwer nor Weyl is the "totality of all natural numbers" allowable as a given complete set. Intuitionism thus set itself in opposition to the program of the logicists as well as the formalists; against the former it demanded construction and against the latter the intuitional derivation of the numbers. Each of the interpretations has identifiable representatives at present and it would be an error to maintain that any of these programs has been abandoned.

D. *Development of behavioristic psychology*

The application of experimental techniques to the study of living organisms, first in animal and later in human psychology, led to the development of the thesis that consciousness is a fiction and that its contents are translatable without remainder into overt movements or behavior. Dissatisfied with the results of the so-called introspective psychology, I. Pavlov, the famous Russian psychologist and physiologist, in the years following 1905 turned to what he regarded as more empirical techniques, confining attention to observable phenomena and seeking to explain patterned responses in physiological and behavioral rather than in mental terms. Later the work of John Watson in America gave a tremendous impetus to this new approach and in his book, *Behavior: An Introduction to Comparative Psychology* (1914), he came as close as anyone has ever come to asserting the *complete identity* between mind and thought on the one hand and behavioral response on the other. Behavioral psychology had an enormous influence upon pragmatism because it put itself forward as an experimental science and it met the need of these thinkers for "public" as distinct from "private" verification in a domain notoriously inaccessible to controlled research. Moreover, the close connection between meaning and action maintained by pragmatists now received support from an experimental science. Logical empiricists and empiricists of other schools also welcomed the new science because it not only provided them with a weapon for attacking existent idealisms, but it also fitted in harmoniously with their own criteria of meaning and their avowed purpose of explaining all occurrences through observed phenomena and their relations. To many it appeared that the older dualism between mind and matter might be overcome by means of a universal phenomenalism, in which differences between "mental" and "physical" would become differences in the context in which phenomena occurred instead of an unbridgeable gap between two fundamentally different types of reality.

E. *The development of linguistic or analytic philosophies—semantics*

As has already been pointed out, a great deal of modern philosophy has been concerned with questions of meaning and consequently with techniques of logical analysis aimed at attaining the utmost clarity of assertion and rigor in argument. The pursuit of these aims led, in turn, to the development of semantics and to the construction of formalized languages designed to express the results of scientific and philosophical research. Within the broad category of analytic philosophy we may conveniently distinguish the following types or trends: the atomistic empiricism of Russell; the common-sense analysis of G. E. Moore and the Cambridge School; the linguistic philosophy of Wittgenstein, which exercised such influence on Russell, Moore, and many members of the Vienna Circle; the later development within logical positivism, chiefly through the work of Carnap, of syntactics or science of the formal properties of languages; the semantical theory of A. Tarski, the foremost representative of the Polish School of logic and metamathematics; and the positivism of A. J. Ayer in England. A vast literature representing several decades of discussion has grown up around these positions and the reader is urged to consult the principal works of the philosophers mentioned. In what follows it is possible to give no more than a brief description of the aims envisaged and the most significant ideas developed in the attempt to realize them.

Russell, who has not inaptly been described as a "logician

among philosophers," has stood as the foremost recent representative of classical British empiricism extending from the
epistemological thought of Locke and Hume to the present
time. His thought differs from that of his predecessors in the
fundamental feature that logic and mathematics play a larger
part in his empiricism than had ever before been the case.
Central to his thought (*Mysticism and Logic*, 1918; *Our
Knowledge of the External World*, 1914) is the concept of
analysis or the logical resolution of given complexes into their
identifiable constituents with the result expressed in the
form of a definition. Despite changes in his conception of the
nature of the ultimate constituents of reality, the concept of
analysis remains as that which provides a unity running
through a long series of developments. Closely related to his
logical method (illustrated in such works as *The Analysis of
Matter*, 1927, and *The Analysis of Mind*, 1921) is his theory
of constructions or process whereby the world of ordinary
objects is built up out of more elementary entities. Russell,
like many other philosophers sensitive to the seeming discrepancies between the world of ordinary experience and the
world as described by contemporary physics, was anxious to
reconcile the two and to this end he proposed the thesis that
the perceptual world is a "logical construction" out of "sense
data." Physics, however, takes another view and resolves the
world into particles in motion, but the object of which physics
speaks is also a construction out of those ultimate constituents
that physics holds to be real. Through the theory that the
entities of which the world is composed are "neutral" in their
character, i.e., correctly described neither as "mental" nor
"physical," Russell hoped to show that what had been called
"mind events" and "physical events" are not two fundamentally different kinds of events since both are now to be
understood as constructions out of this "neutral stuff." Despite his neutralist theory, the classical empirical view continued to make itself felt; in later versions Russell reverted
to the position that the facts of sense (i.e., *our own* sense
data) are the "hardest" data, or data least open to dissolution by critical doubt, and that the most adequate picture of
the world is one in which these data are carefully described
and expressed by means of the laws of logic, in their external
relations to each other (cf. *An Inquiry into Meaning and
Truth*, 1940). Russell thus emerges as a "piecemeal" as distinct from a systematic philosopher, as a pluralist rather than
a monist, and, above all, as primarily a mathematician and

logician seeking to apply to the persistent problems of philosophy concepts and doctrines better adapted to the theory of deduction and the foundations of mathematics.

Much less directly influenced by natural science than either Russell or Carnap but nevertheless dedicated to a type of analytic philosophy was G. E. Moore of Cambridge University.[6] He maintained that the proper business of philosophy is analysis and his early activity was directed against what he regarded as the hopelessly muddled writings of the absolute idealists and the paradoxical doctrines they held. The peculiar trait of Moore's type of analysis is that he believed it to be rooted in both common sense and ordinary usage. There are statements, he held, such as "there are material objects," that are known to be true when the terms are understood in the sense in which they are intended by people who are not philosophers; the task of the philosopher is not to establish the truth or falsity of such statements but to pay attention to what they mean. Philosophy is essentially an activity and the goal of philosophy is clarity.

In 1922 there appeared a most unusual and cryptic book written by a no less cryptic and elusive thinker, Ludwig Wittgenstein, who was later to become the successor of Moore at Cambridge. The *Tractatus Logico-Philosophicus*, as it was called, presents, among other things, an interesting puzzle: how is it possible that such a strange book, consisting as it does of a collection of propositions often aphoristically expressed, of staccatolike sentences ("The world is everything that is the case"; "Substance is what exists independently of what is the case"; "Logical operation signs are punctuations") expressing both novel ideas and ancient ones in a curious combination of precision and vagueness, should have had such a profound influence upon thinkers like Russell, Moore, and Carnap, all of whom had extraordinarily high standards of clarity? It is most likely that these thinkers were more fascinated by the manner and interests of the man himself than by his writings, since, until the appearance of his *Logical Investigations* in 1953, he published no book but the *Tractatus*.

---

[6]*Principia Ethica*, 1903, is an important book both for its ethical conclusions and as an example in which the sort of analysis Moore advocated is applied to a concrete and traditionally philosophical subject matter. Of great significance is the article, "The Refutation of Idealism," which appeared in *Mind* in 1903, reprinted in *Philosophical Studies*, 1922.

It is, nevertheless, impossible to overestimate the influence he exercised on modern linguistic and analytic philosophy.[7]

Wittgenstein's main concern was with the nature of languages and the conditions under which they may be significantly employed. Science, he believed, is concerned with questions of empirical truth and falsity in relation to the facts themselves, but philosophy has essentially nothing to do with the discovery of such truths since it is not a theory "but an activity" (4.112), and its main concern is the discovery of the structure and properties of the language used to state the facts (cf. 4.112: "The result of philosophy is not a number of 'philosophical propositions,' but to make propositions clear"). A thoroughgoing logical atomist, Wittgenstein viewed the world as a vast collection of atomic facts and knowledge as an affair of "picturing" these facts in "logical space" (cf. 2.1: "We make pictures to ourselves of facts"; 2.11: "The picture presents the facts in logical space, the existence and nonexistence of atomic facts"). The problem for the theory of symbolism is to discover how language must be structured in order to picture the facts adequately. Wittgenstein's answer to this problem is that if language is to perform its function there must be a point of identity between it and what it pictures (cf. 2.16: "In order to be a picture a fact must have something in common with what it pictures".[8] Essential to his thesis is the idea that it is impossible to express in language what is common to both the linguistic expression and the fact (2.172); this can only be *shown* because no fact which is a picture is self-representative.

The development of later logical empiricism after the dissolution of the Vienna Circle in Europe has been dominated by the logical work of Rudolf Carnap. His thought is distinguished from that of many other analytic philosophers be-

---

[7] F. Copleston, *Contemporary Philosophy* (London: Burns, Oates, 1956), pp. 6 ff. As Copleston has reminded us, the influence was reciprocal since Wittgenstein attended the lectures of Moore and acknowledged his own indebtedness to Russell. Hence, while Wittgenstein did much to establish the thesis that philosophy is essentially analysis of language and the "logical clarification of thought," the fact remains that this cardinal principle of analytic philosophy was well established at Cambridge by the turn of the century and that means long before the work of either Wittgenstein or the Vienna Circle.

[8] To avoid confusion it must be borne in mind that Wittgenstein called the pictures of facts themselves facts so that both the picture and the fact pictured are said to be facts. A more thorough treatment of Wittgenstein's thought would take us well beyond the *Tractatus* and the theory of picturing facts stated in that work.

cause it has been concerned so specifically with problems arising out of the *language of science*. Moreover, Carnap proposed to replace all classical philosophy with what he called "syntactics" and set forth the view that philosophy should become the "logical syntax of the language of science." This means that Carnap, as in the case of so many other contemporary philosophers, regards most if not all of the so-called classical problems of philosophy as "inextricable tangles" and that he is ready to abandon them. Instead, philosophy must be conceived primarily as logic and it must direct its attention to questions arising out of the analysis of statements occurring in the natural sciences. Accordingly most of his work has been centered upon the discussion and modification of such topics as the positivist meaning criterion, the relation between truth and confirmation, the nature of induction and probability, and the formal structure of languages to be used in mathematics and physics. It is important to notice that his earlier program of syntactical philosophy was later enlarged to include semantical questions when he realized that logical questions implicit in scientific discourse could not be confined to the syntactical approach originally adopted. His later development of "semiotic" or theory of signs contained the threefold distinction between syntactics, semantics, and pragmatics, that has now become standard.

A. Tarski of the Polish school should be mentioned in this connection because of his attempt to analyze the concept of truth and because of the influence of the semantic theory of truth that results. This theory is actually a correspondence theory (Tarski even describes it as doing justice to "the classical Aristotelian conception of truth") formulated as a semantic theory, i.e., as a theory that is concerned with "certain relations between expressions of a language and the objects [or "states of affairs"] 'referred to' by those expressions." Tarski's work in the theory of deductive systems and more recently in connection with specific decision problems has been of much significance.

Logical positivism would be little known except to professional philosophers were it not for a remarkable little book that expressed in simple and straightforward language the main contentions of the position. *Language, Truth and Logic* by A. J. Ayer has been in recent years the standard text of positivism, although it contains little that had not already been expressed by others in a less accessible form. Ayer began with the positivist program of eliminating metaphysics and of establishing philosophy as analysis and he tried to show how the new approach might be able to deal with problems in ethics and even in theology. Like most positivists, Ayer later toned down his original position particularly because of some of the consequences it proved to have for ethical theory.

F. *Other tendencies in the philosophy of science*

No account of the relations between science and philosophy in recent years would be complete without mention of the thought of two British scientists, Sir Arthur Eddington and Sir James Jeans. Both were interested in the philosophical and cosmological implications of such topics as the theory of relativity, the development of quantum mechanics, and the discussions of the principle of causality that followed on the heels of Heisenberg's famous "uncertainty principle" (see below). Eddington paid considerable attention to what he called "scientific epistemology" and maintained that an understanding of the type of knowledge sought in science is actually an aid in the attainment of that knowledge. How seriously he took his own principle can be discovered in his book, *The Philosophy of Physical Science* (1939), where he maintained that, since no science at all is possible without observational techniques and procedures, a great deal can be ascertained about the world observed from a careful study of the observer. This means that what we know is not a wholly "objective" world, but one that is "selectively subjective," and Eddington believed that "generalizations that can be reached epistemologically have a security which is denied to those that can only be reached empirically" (i.e., generalizations that include epistemological considerations and do not purport to refer to the world totally apart from the conditions of the observer). Eddington was also a staunch supporter of the thesis that human freedom can ultimately be supported by considerations drawn from indeterminacy theory in modern physics.[9]

[9] Jeans is less important for the philosophy of science than Eddington; he was more interested in cosmological description as his popular books, *The Mysterious Universe* (1930-31), *The Universe Around Us* (1931), and *Physics and Philosophy* (1943), will testify. He did much to bring to the attention of the intelligent layman the changes in the conception of the universe that he believed were required by the modern developments in astronomy, physics, and astrophysics.

Work of considerable importance for the philosophy of science was carried out by Ernst Cassirer, representing the so-called Marburg School of Neo-Kantianism, which developed in the later nineteenth century. In many historically oriented books and articles Cassirer outlined his "functional" theory of scientific concepts and theories. He was concerned mainly to show that the epistemological theory of Kant is not inextricably tied to Newtonian mechanics or to Euclidean geometry and that his general interpretation of science is capable of application to new developments and especially to the discoveries expressed in relativity theory. He interpreted science as a system aiming at the *unification of experience* at many levels and to the basic Kantian epistemology he added his own vast knowledge in the history of language and of science, in order to show how scientific theories performed this function of unification. Extending Kant, he maintained that science is not so much an unalterable knowledge of a world of substances as "a point of view" from which the world is viewed and ordered. Thus, for example, the principle of causality is regarded by him not as a law governing a closed domain, but as a conceptual formulation of a principle defining the *kind* of order that is discovered through scientific research. He sought to show that all the concepts of physics and mathematics must be interpreted as expressing certain types of order in human experience. Science, he believed, is not the extension or refinement of the common-sense view of the world, but represents a new, theoretical point of view speaking or expressing itself in a specially developed symbolism, especially that of mathematics. A great deal of Cassirer's work dealt with the nature and function of symbolism and he carried his analysis into all domains, treating the myths and symbols of religion no less than the numerical language of science. There is an affinity between his view and that of Dewey regarding science, with the difference that whereas the latter stressed pragmatic control, Cassirer viewed science more as rational comprehension after the manner of the philosophers of the seventeenth and eighteenth centuries.

Notable success in synthesizing natural science with the concerns of the humanities was achieved by F. S. C. Northrop, whose stimulating volume, *The Meeting of East and West*, sought to interpret the impact of Western science upon the Oriental cultures in terms of the native habitat and the history of each. His analysis of scientific methodology involves features reminiscent of Kant's *Critique* as well as the sober appraisals of positivism, and has had a distinct appeal to workers in modern science.

In concluding this historical survey of the subject we must be reminded that much has had to be omitted. Multiplication of details, however, would not suffice to make clear the full depth of the mutual involvement of science and philosophy at the present time; this can be done only through an understanding of several basic notions in recent physical theory together with a grasp of the extent to which they have led us to modify older conceptions of the surrounding universe. To these matters the succeeding section is addressed.

II

The scientific background

The second part of this paper, which has the purpose of exhibiting the often subtle connections between philosophic thought in this century on the one hand and the scientific discoveries supporting it on the other, is afflicted by a clearly discernible obliquity. For it is restricted to physical science. This restriction is made necessary both by the authors' range of competence and by the limited space at their disposal. It does not imply a prejudgment ascribing superior significance to physical science as a motivator of philosophic reflection, even though it has been argued that physics, being the most exact natural science and having achieved the greatest power of prediction, is by these tokens also endowed with maximum philosophic fertility.

On the other hand it is true that the mood of science in a given era is to some extent a common feature of all sciences, and therefore the description of it in one area exhibits what goes on in others. We mention in support of this statement the vogue enjoyed by empiricism and operationism, modes of analysis that arose in physics, throughout the domain of the social sciences and psychology; the reverberations of such specific discoveries as uncertainty (see below) and complementarity in biology and psychology.

Three things have happened in this century which, more than any other, succeeded in exerting profound effects on philosophy of science, and we shall deal with them in sequence. One is the progressive revelation that matter, the good old stuff of ancient Greece or the impenetrable atom of the nineteenth century, is much less solid, uniform, and simple than was originally supposed. At the risk of seeming paradoxical, we shall term the series of events and interpretations documenting this assertion the dematerialization of matter. Next on our list of significant discoveries is a group of facts indicating a failure of the continuity of motion in the atomic world, the failure of a deep-seated postulate whose disavowal threw philosophy of science into peculiar gyrations that have not completely subsided even today. And thirdly, we must recall certain developments that draw into question a principle ordinarily called causality, a principle whose rejection is sometimes said to entail freedom. Finally, as a sort of unconventional excursion, it will be shown how, in this seemingly uncoordinated *mélée* of scientific facts, there may be found the elements that account for the tenacity of so "unscientific" a philosophy as the existentialism of our day.

Dematerialization of matter

If any label serves to characterize the scientific philosophy of the Western world at the beginning of the present century, it is probably materialism, the doctrine that regards all the facts of the universe as explainable in terms of matter and motion, and in particular explains all psychical processes as material changes in the nervous system. Its basis lay in the belief that science has shown matter to be ultimate, not reducible to anything else and yet exceedingly versatile as a carrier of phenomena. Coupled with these qualities was its visual familiarity, an ease of comprehension and a pictorial obviousness which beguiled the scientists into thinking that matter was as simple and devoid of problems as it was versatile.

Actually, matter was present in two forms: continuous in the all-pervasive, luminiferous ether that filled the universe, and discrete in the atoms that moved through the ether. To trace the changes in these conceptions is to lay the groundwork for an understanding of the philosophies of science which have dominated the last five decades.

Nature and meaning of the ether constituted a challenge to scientific imagination in 1900. The two obvious questions, (1) what are its intrinsic properties and (2) how does it move, had already been asked; but the answers received had been unsatisfactory. Let us review these answers.

Normal matter has definite density as well as definite compressibility. When waves pass through a fluid, their speed depends upon density and compressibility in a well-known way: the product of density times compressibility equals the reciprocal of the square of the wave velocity. Hence, if the speed of the waves is known, inferences can be drawn with respect to these two parameters that are apparently not open to direct experimentation, presumably because the ether is too tenuous. But the waves transmitted by the ether are light waves, and their velocity is known to be enormous. Density and compressibility must therefore both be extremely small quantities. This result, however, is hard to accept since our intuition suggests that a very light substance should possess a large compressibility.

Another intrinsic property is the state of aggregation of the ether. One would expect it to be a fluid, preferably a gas. This conjecture can be tested by observing the kind of waves transmitted by it, for a fluid can support only longitudinal waves. Unfortunately, light waves are transverse.—Is the ether then a solid? If so, it must transmit *both* longitudinal *and* transverse waves, but alas, light waves are incorrigibly transverse. The ether seemed to be neither gaseous nor liquid nor solid in the light of such conflicting observations.

These infelicities were known in 1900. They raised difficulties in connection with the ether idea, to be sure. Scientific ingenuity, however, was able to overcome them, for it succeeded in devising most unusual models for a luminiferous ether and thereby was able to account for its pathologies. There are on record serious conjectures as to structure which "ether molecules" must possess in order that the bulk substance shall transmit only transverse waves. One of these pictures an ether molecule as composed of three mutually perpendicular flywheels, spinning at a fast rate and geared together in unusual ways. But naturally, such proposals were accepted with reluctance, and many philosophers felt the need of treating these speculations by Occam's razor. What started out as continuous matter became exceedingly complex, indeed so complex that it began to tax the credulity of scientists.

Even more serious difficulties arose, however, in connection with the ether's state of motion. Did it repose in majestic splendor like the Parmenidean sphere? Or did it move along with the celestial bodies, being entrained by them perhaps in the manner of the earth's atmosphere? The second alternative was dominated by the fact, fully recognized for centuries, that light travels in straight-line motion from one heavenly body to another and shows none of the aberrations that would accompany its passage through an ether in a state of streaming tortuously through space as it clings to variously moving bodies. The presumption therefore was that the ether must be stagnant, permitting all objects to move through it.

This hypothesis was put to an experimental test by Michelson and Morley[10] in 1887, and the result was perplexing. For it indicated that there is no way of telling, by optical or any other means, whether motion relative to a stationary ether occurs. This was the first great insight clearly established in our present era, intimated in 1900 and announced in 1904 by Poincaré as the *principle of relativity* and described as a disposition of nature to render impossible all knowledge of the state of motion of the luminiferous ether. Then came the work of Lorentz, who developed his famous transformation formulas and thereby explained in mathematical detail why the ether failed to be discoverable. The work of FitzGerald, Einstein, and Minkowski drew the ultimate conclusion, namely, that a material ether is unnecessary, useless, and therefore to be rejected. Thus a favorite of earlier ages, continuous, space-filling stuff, was banished from the scientific scene.

Discrete matter, the hard, impenetrable pellet of stuff called the atom, has not suffered quite so severe a fate. For it is still with us, though in a greatly modified and chastened form. Vague knowledge of its electrical nature was a legacy of the nineteenth century. J. J. Thompson had begun to picture the atom as a sphere of positive electricity containing smaller negative charges. Rutherford and Soddy discovered its instability by observing that in radioactive emission, a transformation occurs from one element to another. And to make things worse, these transformations happen randomly, in ac-

---

[10] The series of experiments by Michelson and Morley and its repetitions by others extended well into the twentieth century. For full historical account see D. C. Miller, "The Etherdrift Experiment and the Determination of the Absolute Motion of the Earth," *Review of Modern Physics*, 5 (1933), p. 203.

cordance with no namable scientific principle but the laws of chance. The whole development culminated in the ingenious conception of Rutherford, who demonstrated beyond doubt that the atom has essentially the structure that is now common knowledge. Its core, or nucleus, is positively charged and heavy; around it move, in planetary fashion, enough negative electrons to make the entire atom electrically neutral. And as to its size the following description may be revealing. If our bodies were enlarged until they extended from the earth to the North Star, a hydrogen atom within them would have a nucleus the size of a tennis ball, its electrons would be 300-foot spheres and revolve about the tennis ball in orbits some ten miles in diameter. The hard and solid atom has become mostly empty space.

This picture is still too simple. The nucleus is not a uniform sphere but has its own structure and is subject to change. The electrons are not simple objects but possess a spinning motion and other more baffling and poorly understood properties. Science is no longer sure that they have size: they may indeed be points, mathematical singularities haunting space. The riddle has not been solved, but one conclusion stands out above all uncertainties: the concept of the atom, too, has undergone changes which are hardly misrepresented by the term dematerialization.

In principle, of course, this development does not argue against the philosophic doctrine of materialism, least of all in its dialectical form, for matter can be the last instance of explanatory appeal even if its structure is highly complicated. Nevertheless, the philosophic mind wonders whether anything so far from simple, so mysterious and impermanent can provide the ultimate resolution of all problems, and indeed whether there is such an ultimate resolution at all. It is for this methodological reason that materialism has largely lost its point.

Discontinuity of motion

As man observes the visible universe about him, he cannot help but conclude that motions proceed in continuous fashion. The flight of a bird, the fall of a stone, the motion of a star in the sky, indeed, the movement of man himself are obvious examples of a progression from point to point. Despite the convincing power of these examples, modern science has begun to question the continuity hypothesis. The problem confronted here is ordinarily discussed in rather forbidding mathematical terms, and these often becloud the issue. The details, it is true, cannot be treated without analysis. But the details are perhaps not of maximum philosophical importance; what has happened can be seen in connection with a simple and homely problem, familiar to everyone. The considerations that follow have been used by one of the authors in another publication in which the problem of continuity is treated more fully and in the context of very recent thought.[11]

Consider the appearance of a firefly in a dark summer night. To the eye, the motion of this insect is not continuous; what it presents is a succession of bright spots or streaks at different places in our field of view. The judgment that this phenomenon represents the uninterrupted passage of an object from one point of space to another is based, strictly speaking, on an interpolation between the bursts of luminosity that are actually perceived. Yet common sense, and indeed scientific description, regard themselves fully justified in performing that ideal supplementation of immediate perception that the interpretation of these sporadic darts as continuous motion demands. The chief reasons for this attitude are the following.

First, the hypothesis of continuous motion is testable through other experience. It is possible to watch the firefly in the daytime, when its progression from point to point becomes visible. This settles the issue in large part, although it may not convince the inveterate skeptic who feels that, when unilluminated, the firefly behaves like the angels to whom St. Thomas attributed the ability of emerging at separate points without having to traverse the intervening distances. To answer the skeptic, we must demonstrate the simplicity and convenience of the continuity hypothesis. Thus we add to the fact of testability a second item of evidence of a more rational sort, namely, the simplicity of the geometric curve on which the luminous dots are situated. If the interpolated path were very irregular, showing unlikely curvatures and strange convolutions, doubts as to continuity might arise; the smoothness of the plotted trajectory goes a long way toward removing them.

[11] Henry Margenau, "Advantages and Disadvantages of Various Interpretations of the Quantum Theory," *Journal of the Washington Academy of Sciences*, 44, 1954, p. 265.

In the last analysis, the validity of every scientific theory rests on two kinds of evidence: (1) empirical verifiability of some of its consequences, and (2) rational coherence, or economy of thought, or simplicity conveyed by the ideas composing the theory. It is because the hypothesis of continuity in reference to the motion of the firefly satisfies both of these criteria that common sense accepts it.

As we now transfer the discussion to the electron in an atom, we pass across a decade or two in which the modern theory of quanta was developed. This need not detain us here, for the recent history of quantum mechanics is found in every modern text on atomic physics, and some of its philosophical problems have been widely discussed. We therefore state the facts as they are demanded by, and appear against the background of, this modern theory without interrupting the discourse by an explanation of the detailed evidence that corroborates them.

Atomic entities, like electrons, present phenomena that, on the purely empirical side, are not unlike the sporadic emergence of a firefly at night. To be sure, the electron in an atom cannot be seen. Nevertheless if the results of experiments and observations using the refined techniques of modern physics can be trusted, an electron in what is called a Bohr orbit reveals its position as a random set of points located throughout a region of space in the neighborhood of the so-called classical orbit. More precisely, if a series of position measurements were made while the electron is in the unvarying state known as the ground state of the hydrogen atom, the results would form a probability aggregate of known spatial distribution; the individual positions thus established will dot this region in a curious manner, offering no immediate suggestion as to continuity of motion.

Hence the question naturally arises: Can we regularize these emergences by the same principles that were employed in concluding that the path of the lightning bug was continuous? Or do we confront here a situation calling for an entirely different treatment? It is at this point that the strangeness of modern physics reveals itself, that its heresy to past philosophic conceptions becomes evident.

Unfortunately, the road leading to empirical verification of the continuity hypothesis in the case of the electron is blocked, not merely by incidental obstacles arising from imperfections of measurement or observation, but also by misfortunes of a more fundamental kind. For the electron is intrinsically too small to be seen; the act of vision, even if it were possible, requires a time far too long for a clear ascertainment of instantaneous positions. Last but not least important is the fact that elementary particles are promiscuous entities, with a perversity that prevents us from ever being sure that we see the same individual in different observations.

Hope might arise at this point that such conclusions bespeak merely the imperfection of our present knowledge, that when the full story is told the apparent inconsistencies will disappear. No one can say whether it be true; but the tenor of modern physics is to believe the story as it now appears, the reason being that their contradictions would violate the most fundamental principles of the theory of quanta, the only theory capable of explaining what can in fact be observed about electrons. The conclusion is thus inescapable: there is no daytime in which the electron's path could be watched. Empirical evidence for a substantiation of the continuity hypothesis is not at hand.

Let us therefore examine the continuity interpretation from the point of view of simplicity or economy of thought. Here we encounter another failure. A curve drawn through the measured points at which the electron appeared becomes complicated and aimless, wandering in erratic fashion, with no preference for connecting neighbors, a curve intertwining and crossing itself in obvious labor to accommodate the observed positions of the electron. Certainly nothing is gained in ease of conception, in plausibility, or in power of prediction by this artifact, even though it be familiar and recommended by all past experience.

Thus it is seen that the atomic realm confronts the physicist with a novel kind of problem in interpretation, with a challenge to explain or rationalize perhaps in ways to which he is not accustomed. And nature is not generous in providing hints for the solution of this methodological puzzle; the difficulties of direct verification we have already noted are so great that theories cannot readily be exposed to tests. The sphinx is noncommittal. The physicist has an embarrassing amount of freedom in making his interpretations.

And how happily would he welcome the logical experts on "theory construction," the men who have put scientific procedure on blueprints, to whom the facts suggest inductively a hypothesis with computable probability. Here is a place where the principles of theory construction could be tried with profit for the benefit of both science and philosophy. But nothing seems to be happening to relieve the suspicion that there are no recipes for constructing successful theories, that the creative act in factual discovery as well as in the theoretical interpretation refuses to be codified. This point may be converted into a significant comment on modern philosophy of science. Largely because of the impossibility of making road maps for scientific research, because of the growing realization that the constructions of science are not merely inductive generalizations of numerous facts, recent philosophy seems to be moving away from the extreme forms of positivism (e.g., of the Vienna Circle type) that inspired the earlier decades of this century.

It is now accepted that atomic motions are not necessarily continuous that the microcosm need not satisfy those propensities for visual intuition of all happenings with which experience in the molar realm has endowed man. Things intrinsically too small to be seen may be quite unlike the visual, factual, and intuitable models that seem so clear to us; the denizens of the microcosm may be subject only to more subtle and more abstract human considerations, perhaps considerations of purely mathematical or logical sort. Scientists have begun to speak of mathematical and logical models!

Perhaps a bolder simile might help to clarify this situation. Scientific method explains phenomena by attributing properties, now often called observables, to physical systems like stars, stones, and electrons. In the science of the last century these observables are continuously present and meaningful; they are "possessed" by objects. A stone has size, mass, weight, color at all times—it cannot be thought without them. But does an electron have color? Clearly, this must be denied because it is much smaller than a wave length of visible light. Hence somewhere on the scale of things this observable becomes assignable. The question has thus arisen whether similar discontinuities may not occur in the assignability of other observables, for instance position.

In the human sciences, there occurs a class of observables that, although useful, do not exhibit the unvarying attachment to systems that characterizes the possessed observables of classical physics. Anger, happiness, composure are psychological qualities of man, often used in the same way for the purpose of describing his mental state as the physicist uses position, velocity, and mass of an electron, for example. But there is this important difference: anger, happiness, and composure may be present or not; man is *sometimes* angry, happy, or composed, but there are states in which the attribution of these qualities is meaningless. Anger, happiness, composure are sometimes present and sometimes not. They might be called "latent" observables, which come into being and then disappear, and no one would be disposed to claim continuity of anger, happiness, and so forth.

Could it be that the observables of atomic particles are of this latent variety? Could it be that an electron in certain states simply has no position but manifests this quality upon measurement, the observable being elicited as it were by the act of human interference? Anger, happiness, composure can be called into being by human intervention, indeed by acts of inquiry. This interpretation of atomic observables, which amounts to a radical denial of continuity as that phrase is usually understood, is by no means generally accepted, but it presents itself for discussion and study in the face of the facts.

There is another way of stating the salient features of the recent discoveries in quantum mechanics. We have seen that the electron in the hydrogen atom, when its position is measured, gives widely divergent and apparently inconsistent answers to the experimental query of its whereabouts. We noted that its "path," when interpreted continuously, is erratic and complicated. There is no simplicity and no great significance in the result of a single measurement. Nor are there laws that connect the individual observations. But the average of a multitude of observations does obey a simple principle embodied in the equations of quantum mechanics. Individual observations are lawless and chaotic, yet there resides within the totality a measure of regularity on which analysis and mathematics can seize. This is where probabilities enter the scene. Single, unique events in the atomic domain are unpredictable, but the probabilities are determined by mathematical laws.

Thus it is seen that a surrender of continuity of motion does not require a renunciation of lawful description. It still leaves possible the rigorous analysis of the probabilities that rule the event. And so it has come about that the equations of quantum mechanics no longer talk about individual happenings in the atomic world but about the average behavior of a multitude of events. In a sense, then, the use of probabilities in atomic physics is enforced by the lack of coherence of the story relating individual events, that is to say by the recurrence of discontinuities of a very general and basic kind in the domain of external observations that relate to atomic entities. This emphasis on probabilities, however, raises problems with respect to the meaning of the causal sequence containing the individual events. To these problems we now direct our attention.

Causality

The meaning of causality that will here be considered is the one that stands in the center of the quantum controversy. There are others, and confusion has arisen because writers are not always clear in stating what they conceive causality to be. The conception under review is the classical one found in the works of Kant, Laplace, and Cassirer, and is the one employed by most physicists.

To explain it we first note that every physical system is described in terms of *states* that change in time. For example the state of a body undergoing thermal changes may involve its temperature, its volume, and its pressure; these variables along with others serving in the description are said to be variables of state, or variables defining a state. Another physical system, e.g., one called an elastic body undergoing deformations, has states that are defined in terms of stresses and strains. Common to these two instances is the supposition that the variables of state, however defined, change in time in a manner conforming to certain equations which are called laws of nature. In the first instance they are the laws of thermodynamics, in the second the laws of elasticity. Future states are therefore predictable if a complete present state is known. A prior state of a given system is then called the cause of a later state, the later state the effect of a former.

The principle of causality, in this sense, asserts for every physical system the existence of a determinate temporal continuum of evolving states, all referrable to the same physical system.

The simplest physical system, indeed the one for which a causal theory was first developed, is the moving particle. Its states are pairs of variables: positions and momenta; the laws of nature governing their evolution is Newton's second law. The latter is a differential equation of the second order requiring two constants of integration in its complete solution. Position and momentum of the particle at a fixed time can serve as constants of integration and therefore determine the solution at all times.

In symbols, if x is the position of a particle moving along a straight line and p (= mass times velocity) is its corresponding momentum, then Newton's law prescribes that $\frac{d^2x}{dt^2} = F$ (x). Its general solution has the form $x = f(t)$, and it contains two arbitrary constants because the differential equation is of the second order. These constants may be taken to be the position x_1 at some time t_1 and the momentum p_1 at the same time. When these are inserted in $f(t)$ the solution becomes definite, we know x and hence $\frac{dx}{dt}$ (and therefore the momentum p) at all times and can therefore *predict* x and p for any t when x_1 and p_1 are given. This is a typical example of causal analysis or causal prediction. A "state" is simply an assignment of x and p.

States and laws of the causal theory must always have this internal affinity. The states must be so chosen that they provide the information demanded by the initial conditions that make the solution of the law complete. It follows from this circumstance that the definition of states in a causal theory cannot be altered at will without requiring corresponding changes in the laws of nature, and a change in a law will generally necessitate a redefinition of the state of a system.

Newton's theory of the motion of particles is the prototype of all causal description. Understandably, though perhaps regrettably, the particular laws and states entailed by Newton's theory have come to be regarded as the essential elements of causality, and *it is often forgotten that causality can hold with respect to different laws and different states.* This misunderstanding has led to the belief that quantum mechanics is no longer a causal discipline.

The reason is contained in the previous section, where it was shown that the *position x* of small entities, if measured, is an inconsistent variable in terms of which a causal theory cannot be built. Heisenberg's uncertainty principle affirms a similar status for the momentum p of an atomic entity and shows furthermore how the indeterminacies of position and momentum are related, in particular that they cannot both be known with precision. (If Δx and Δp are the standard deviations of position and momentum measurements, then the product $\Delta x. \Delta p$ cannot be smaller than a certain universal constant, $\frac{h}{2}$). This spells the doom of Newtonian causality, because the states it involves are now neither theoretically significant nor available by observation; x and p have become inappropriate as variables of state.

It is not idle, however, to ask the question whether the new law of quantum mechanics (Schrödinger's equation) selects, or is compatible with, states in terms of other variables, and whether these variables permit a causal description in the more formal sense of our principles. That is in fact the case; only it happens to be the misfortune of these new variables, and of the states they define, to be somewhat strange and elusive when judged from Newton's familiar standpoint. As we have seen, they turn out to be probabilities.

Here then is the situation with respect to causality today. Those who insist on retaining the old "classical" definition of states, which ties state variables to single observations, in particular to an assignment of x and $p,$ are forced to relinquish the causal principle. If, however, one is willing to modify the meaning of state, is willing to accept a statistical definition of state that sees significance (perhaps exclusively) in probabilities, then there is no need to reject causality. For, as a formal relation between states at different times, it continues to hold.

Regardless of this choice it is true that individual events are no longer subject to rigid determination by natural laws. Prediction of a single future event on the basis of a single present or past event is often impossible. This means, of course, that something philosophically noteworthy slips through the net of scientific determination. And if the lawful states, which satisfy differential equations but are related to events through probabilities only, are called essences, while the unique contingencies of our experience are regarded as existences, then the existentialist is right in claiming that essences have lost control of the world of existences.

SELECTED BIBLIOGRAPHY

I

G. Bergmann, "Logical Positivism" and "Semantics," *A History of Philosophical Systems,* ed. V. Fermi. New York: Philosophical Library, 1950.

P. W. Bridgman, *The Nature of Physical Theory.* Princeton: Princeton University Press; London: Oxford University Press, 1936.

L. E. J. Brouwer, "Intuitionism and Formalism," Bulletin of the American Mathematical Society, XX (1913-1914), pp. 81-96.

G. Cantor, *Gesammelte Abhandlungen*. 1932.

R. Carnap, *The Continuum of Inductive Methods*. Chicago: University of Chicago Press; London: Cambridge University Press, 1952.

————, *Logical Foundations of Probability*. Chicago: University of Chicago Press; London: Routledge, Kegan Paul, 1950.

————, *The Logical Syntax of Language*. New York: Harcourt, Brace; London: Geo. Routledge, 1937.

A. Church, "Bibliography of Symbolic Logic," *Journal of Symbolic Logic*, I (1936), pp. 178-212.

————, *Introduction to Mathematical Logic*. Princeton: Princeton University Press; London: Oxford University Press; 1956.

R. Courant and H. Robbins, *What Is Mathematics?* New York: Oxford University Press, 1941.

R. Dedekind, *Was Sind und was Sollen die Zahlen?* 1887.

G. Frege, *The Foundations of Arithmetic*. London and New York: Oxford University Press, 1950.

K. Gödel, "Über formale unentscheidbare Sätze der Principia Mathematica und verwandter Systeme I," *Monatshefte für Mathematik und Physik*, XXXVIII, pp. 173-198.

D. Hilbert, *The Foundations of Geometry*. Chicago: University of Chicago Press, 1902.

S. C. Kleene, *Introduction to Mathematics*. Amsterdam: 1952.

A. Kolmogoroff, "Zur Deutung der intuitionistischen Logik," *Mathematische Zeitschrift*, XXXV (1932), pp. 58-65.

V. Kraft, *The Vienna Circle*. New York: Philosophical Library, 1953.

C. I. Lewis, *A Survey of Symbolic Logic*. Berkeley: University of California Press, 1918.

E. Nagel, "The Formation of Modern Conceptions of Formal Logic in the Development of Geometry," *Osiris,* VIII (1939), pp. 142-222.

O. Neurath, *Le développement du Cercle de Vienne*. Paris: 1935.

F. S. C. Northrop, *The Logic of the Sciences and the Humanities*. London and New York: Macmillan, 1946.

————, *The Meeting of East and West*. London and New York: Macmillan, 1947.

A. Pap, *Analytische Erkenntnistheorie; Kritische Übersicht über die neueste Entwicklung in England und U.S.A*. Vienna: 1955.

E. Post, "Formal Reductions of the General Combinatorial Decision Problem," *American Journal of Mathematics*, LXV (1943), pp. 197-215.

H. Reichenbach, *The Rise of Scientific Philosophy*. Berkeley: University of California Press; London: Cambridge University Press, 1951.

D. D. Runes, ed., *Twentieth Century Philosophy*. New York: Philosophical Library, 1943.

M. Schlick, "On the Relation Between Psychological and Physical Concepts," Feigl and Sellars, eds., *Readings in Philosophical Analysis*. New York: Appleton-Century-Crofts, 1949.

A. Tarski, *A Decision Method for Elementary Algebra and Geometry*. Santa Monica: Project Rand, 1948.

———, *Logic, Semantics, Metamathematics*. London and New York: Oxford University Press, 1956.

A. N. Whitehead, *The Concept of Nature*. London and New York: Macmillan, 1920.

———, *Science and the Modern World*. London and New York: Macmillan, 1925.

P. Wiener, *Evolution and the Founders of Pragmatism*. Cambridge: Harvard University Press; London: Oxford University Press, 1949.

R. L. Wilder, *Introduction to the Foundations of Mathematics*. New York: John Wiley; London: Chapman & Hall, 1952.

II

O. Cassirer, *Determinism and Indeterminism in Modern Physics*. New Haven: Yale University Press, 1956.

A. Einstein, *Ann. der Physics,* XVII (1905), p. 891.

W. Hensenberg, *The Physical Principles Theory of the Quantum Theory*. Chicago: University of Chicago Press, 1930.

Henry Margenau, "Advantages and Disadvantages of Various Interpretations of the Quantum Theory," *Journal of the Washington Academy of Sciences,* XLIV (1954), p. 265.

———, *The Nature of Physical Reality*. New York: McGraw-Hill, 1950.

H. Poincaré, "Address on the Principle of Relativity," *Bulletin des Sciences Mathématiques,* XXVIII (1904), 302.

E. Rutherford and F. Soddy—their article in *Philosophical Magazine* (6), iv (1902), p. 370.

E. Schroedinger, *Wave Mechanics*. Glasgow: Blackie Sons Ltd., 1928.

R. S. Shankland, *Atomic and Nuclear Physics*. London and New York: Macmillan, 1955.

ANTHROPOLOGY IN THE
TWENTIETH CENTURY*

Clyde Kluckhohn

Anthropology is the study of the constants and variations in human physique and human behavior. It deals both with raw human nature and with human nature as modified by the historical process and as varyingly expressed in different environmental situations. In its approaches and in its subject matter anthropology ranges from the areas traditionally assigned to the natural sciences through those often classified as "social sciences" to the humanities. In many countries anthropology today is largely a natural science in intent and, in part, in content. If one looks at the total anthropological enterprise in the world, the bulk of the effort now employs methods that belong to the social or behavioral sciences. Nevertheless an approach that would ordinarily be considered humanistic remains prominent in linguistics, archaeology, and studies of primitive music, literature, art, and other topics.

These diverse traditions and the widespread and ramified nature of anthropological inquiry mean inevitably that any discussion within the limits of these pages must be intensely selective. It is not possible to do more than state and briefly discuss what, in the opinion of one anthropologist, are some

* Journal of World History, III, 3.

major trends and their implication. No attention can be given
to the summary of factual findings, however important, except
insofar as these bear immediately upon main intellectual currents.

I. Some Outstanding Developments by Language-group and Country

France. Whether Durkheim and Mauss, to name only the
two most illustrious, were "anthropologists" or "sociologists"
is a meaningless question, given the organization of French
academic life. Certainly they both used ethnographic materials, and certainly they both had a profound influence upon
anthropological theory alike in France and abroad. They and
other great figures—Hubert, Lévy-Bruhl, Granet—made their
most significant contribution in developing a method of comparative analysis of field data collected by others. To the
task of analysis they brought characteristically French qualities: logical subtlety, thorough training in philosophy and the
other humanities, universalism. Deriving much from Comte
and yet also modifying his doctrine in many ways, they all
maintained that anthropology is "a science of the same type
as the other sciences, and that its ultimate end lies in the discovery of general relations between phenomena."[1] Durkheim
and Mauss recognized the psychic nature of social and cultural
phenomena but insisted that these phenomena were not reducible to individual psychology. Mauss argued that psychological life could be explained on only two levels: that of
language and other forms of social symbolism; that of physiology and biological necessity. The result of this position of
"the French school" was that anthropology remained relatively
isolated from both academic and medical psychology, while
cooperating vigorously with geography, history, comparative
religion, and, to some extent, linguistics.

Archaeology in France has been outstanding, but with some
exceptions such as Hubert its significance has been substantive
rather than theoretical. Biological anthropology has on the

[1] Claude Lévi-Strauss, "French Sociology," pp. 503-37 in *Twentieth
Century Sociology* (G. Gurvitch, ed.; New York: Philosophical Library,
1946), p. 504.

whole languished during this century save for the scrupulous descriptions of fossil men by Vallois and others. Recent innovating work by French students of population is influencing the research of British and American physical anthropologists.

The "armchair" tradition of French cultural anthropology has been for some decades a matter of past history. Alfred Métraux, Rivet, and Lévi-Strauss, for example, in South America; Griaule and many others in Africa; Leenhardt and others in French Oceania—all have carried out first-rate field work. In theory, *Les structures elémentaires de la parenté* [2] can hold its own with the classic works of Durkheim and Mauss.

British Anthropology. During roughly the first quarter of this century anthropology in the British world was characterized by eclecticism in theory, with evolutionary tendency still predominating in the work of Frazer, Marett, Lang, and others; by the production of much sound tribal ethnography; by insistence upon the unity of archaeology, ethnology, social anthropology, and physical anthropology as a single subject. In 1922 Radcliffe-Brown published *The Andaman Islanders* and Malinowski *Argonauts of the Western Pacific*. To state the matter oversimply, these two books symbolized the discovery by British anthropologists of Durkheim and Mauss. Thenceforth social anthropology has developed as a kind of sociology of "primitive" peoples, preoccupied with workmanship and highly technical investigations of kinship and other aspects of social organization [3] and increasingly isolated from the other branches of general anthropology. The traditional concern of ethnology has been widely rejected as "conjectural history." In a well-known paper Radcliffe-Brown [4] wrote:

> The newer social anthropology . . . differs from the older in several vital respects. It rejects as being no part of its task the hypothetical reconstruction of the unknown past. It therefore avoids all discussion of hypotheses as to historical origins. It rejects all attempts to provide psychological explanations of particular social or cultural phenomena in

[2] Paris: Presses Universitaires de France, 1950.

[3] In fairness, it should be added that there have been contributions of fine quality in ritual, law, politics, economics, and, to a lesser extent, esthetics.

[4] A. R. Radcliffe-Brown, "The Present Position of Anthropological Studies," *British Association for the Advancement of Science, Centenary Meeting* (London: Spottiswoode, Ballantine, and Co., 1931), Section H, Anthropology, p. 15.

favour of an ultimate psychological explanation of general sociological laws when these have been demonstrated by purely sociological inquiries . . . It applies to human life in society the generalizing method of natural sciences, seeking to formulate the general laws that underlie it, and to explain any given phenomena in any culture as a special example of a general or universal principle. The newer anthropology is therefore functional, generalizing and sociological.[5]

Most of this reads almost like a translation from the French! During the past generation British archaeology and physical anthropology have led or moved firmly in step with world-wide movements in these fields. Archaeology has not only been descriptively sound but also, as exemplified in the writings of V. G. Childe, Grahame Clark, and K. P. Oakley, theoretically vigorous. Physical anthropology has contributed signally to studies of human evolution (e.g., Sir Arthur Keith and Le Gros Clark) on the one hand and, under the influence of Karl Pearson and R. A. Fisher, to problems of statistical analysis on the other. More recently, younger students such as J. M. Tanner have been advancing the investigation of constitutional anthropology. British linguistics, though producing descriptions and analyses (especially of African languages) of a high order, has been generally philological rather than anthropological.

British social anthropology, following the directions indicated by Radcliffe-Brown in 1931, has developed in a nationally distinctive manner. In 1951 an American anthropologist, G. P. Murdock, wrote as follows:[6]

[5] Cf. Evans-Pritchard in his inaugural lecture at Oxford seventeen years later:
". . . social anthropology . . . studies societies rather than peoples and cultures and uses the methods of the natural, besides those of the historical sciences, seeking to formulate sociological laws of a general kind. . . . Use of the methods of the natural sciences implies that societies must be conceived of as systems analogous to the systems postulated by these sciences, and that the explanation of an institution or custom must be in terms of its function in the maintenance of the whole system of which it forms a part. If we are to eschew conjectural reconstructions of the past there is, in the absence of historical records about most of the societies we investigate, no logical model on which we can make abstractions and build them into a coherent account other than that provided by the concept of a social system."—*Social Anthropology* (New York: Oxford University Press, 1948), pp. 5, 8-9.

[6] "British Social Anthropology", *American Anthropologist*, LIII (1951), 465, 467-71. See also: Meyer Fortes, "The Structure of Unilineal Descent Groups," *American Anthropologist*, LV (1953), pp. 17-41; and R. H. Lowie, "Ethnography, Cultural and Social Anthropology," *American Anthropologist*, LV (1953), pp. 527-34.

For a decade or more, anthropologists in other countries have privately expressed an increasingly ambivalent attitude toward recent trends in British anthropology—a curious blend of respect and dissatisfaction . . . the descriptive and analytical writing of the British social anthropologists attains an average level of ethnographic competence and theoretical suggestiveness probably unequalled by any comparable group elsewhere in the world. This explains and justifies the respect so widely accorded them. Offsetting these merits, however, are a number of special limitations which many professional colleagues abroad find difficult to understand and impossible to defend.

The British social anthropologists, in the first place, do not concern themselves with the entire range of cultural phenomena but concentrate exclusively on kinship and subjects directly related thereto, e.g. marriage, property, and government. To be sure, some of them . . . have dealt with economics and others . . . with religion. Nevertheless it is an incontrovertible fact that such major aspects of culture as technology, folklore, art, child training, and even language are almost completely neglected.

A second limitation is geographical. For a generation hardly a single professional British ethnographer has worked with any society not located in a British colonial dependency . . . .

A third limitation . . . is an almost complete disinterest in general ethnography—difficult to account for in a country which has produced a Tylor and a Frazer. Of the two or three thousand primitive societies in the world whose cultures have been recorded, the British social anthropologists as a group reveal a concern with and knowledge of not more than thirty . . .

The British social anthropologists, in the fourth place, are as indifferent to the theoretical as to the descriptive writings of their colleagues in other lands . . .

A fifth blind spot is the almost complete disinterest in history . . . .

From the neglect of history is directly derived a sixth limitation, namely, a lack of interest in the processes by which culture changes over time, such as invention, acculturation, secondary reinterpretation, selective elimination, integrative modification, and drift . . . .

A seventh limitation is a widespread indifference to psychology. . . .

The special province of anthropology in relation to its sister disciplines is the study of culture. Alone among the anthropologists of the world the British make no use of the culture concept . . . .[7]

. . . the anthropologists of continental Europe, the United States, Latin America . . . meet on common ground. With the English, however, they can find no overlapping interest unless they happen to be concerned on a world-wide scale with a restricted range of cultural phenomena impinging directly upon kinship. With this exception the only claim of the British school to the name of anthropology rests on the fact that they conduct much of their field research in nonliterate societies.

In their fundamental objectives and theoretical orientation they are affiliated rather with the sociologists . . . .

To these strictures Raymond Firth[8] has replied (in part) as follows:

. . . much of what Murdock has said is just and calls more for reflection than reply . . . Yet the professional British society . . . comprises very varied interests . . . To emphasize differences only would be a mistake. But to ignore them—as Murdock has tended to do—would be to distort the present picture . . .

British social anthropology has got its character by isolating its sphere of inquiry. It has developed at an early stage both a tradition of field research among relatively self-sufficient integral cultures, and a coherent body of theory to explain them. The categories used have been largely conventional. But in ritual, kinship, economics, law, language, politics, British social anthropologists have helped to provide a more precise framework of ideas and sub-

[7] E. E. Evans-Pritchard makes the following comments on this point: "Tylor . . . and others who leant towards ethnology conceived its aim [that of social anthropology] to be the classification and analysis of cultures, and this has been the dominant viewpoint in American anthropology for a long time, partly, I think, because the fractioned and disintegrated Indian societies on which their research has been concentrated lend themselves more easily to studies of culture than of social structure; partly because the absence of a tradition of intensive field work through the native languages and for long periods of time, such as we have in England, also tends towards studies of custom or culture rather than of social relations: and partly for other reasons."—*Social Anthropology* (London: Cohen and West Ltd., 1951), p. 17.

[8] Contemporary British Social Anthropology," *American Anthropologist*, LIII (1951), pp. 474, 477. See also Raymond Firth, "Social Organization and Social Change," *Journal of the Royal Anthropological Institute*, LXXXIV (1954), pp. 1-20.

stantial propositions. Recently, the combinations of structural concepts and comparative interest have led to more definite concern with typology and social correlates of types on a wider scale than before.

In a very recent paper Fortes reaffirms the autonomy of social anthropology as an "inductive science" to be contrasted with "the historical character and methods of ethnology on the one hand and the interest in the thoughts, feelings, and actions of individuals which is the province, strictly speaking, of psychology, on the other." Fortes concludes with a succinct statement in which the central elements of the British position are either expressed or implied:

At the beginning of this article I referred to the so-called British school of "structuralist" anthropology and its debt to Radcliffe-Brown's teaching. The tendency thus labeled is most effectively represented in Professor E. E. Evans-Pritchard's distinguished book *The Nuer* . . . . What is significant about this book is not only what it accomplishes but what it leaves out. It is an example of applying strict rules of relevance in the selection and presentation of field data in accordance with a clearly defined frame of analysis. It is ethnography based on a theoretical discipline, the discipline of structural analysis as first given shape by Radcliffe-Brown. An American student at the University of Chicago found the right word when he contrasted this kind of ethnography with what he called the "grab-all" ethnography that is the conventional practice. This, in a nutshell, is our chief debt to Radcliffe-Brown. By following principles well proven in the natural sciences he has created the framework of a unified and rigorous discipline within the many-sided field of interests covered by the anthropological sciences. Like all scientific disciplines, it is limited to its proper range of data and works within the boundaries of its specific conceptual system. We can already see that the development of a science of social structure is bringing about rapid growth in such closely related disciplines as comparative jurisprudence and comparative politics. It will also make possible the much more rapid growth of the twin science of culture, whose main outlines have changed little since Tylor first set them down.

It would take much space to argue with Fortes the question as to whether the "main outlines" of the study of culture have changed but little in ninety-odd years. It is, however,

necessary in a treatment of intellectual history to query
whether the "discipline of structural analysis" was first given
shape by Radcliffe-Brown (and Malinowski) or by Durkheim, Mauss, and their associates.

The German-Speaking Area. British "functionalism" and
"structuralism" have had some influence as in the work of
Ploetz, F. Krause, and W. Mühlmann. Indeed both Krause in
his *Strukturlehre* and R. Thurnwald stated explicitly some of
the principal "functional" tenets in advance of Malinowski
and Radcliffe-Brown. But in the main German cultural
anthropology has been ethnological in the strict sense: historically oriented, descriptive, concerned with the problems of
material culture and environment, museum-centered. The
"school" that has had the most explicit theory and the greatest influence abroad has been the *Kulturkreislehre*.

This doctrine derives from work in human geography by
Ratzel and others and from the antievolutionistic theories of
Ankermann and Graebner. Graebner drew much of his method
from Bernheim's *Lehrbuch der historischen Methode*. As re-
formulated by two professors at the University of Vienna,
Fathers Wilhelm Schmidt and Wilhelm Koppers, the *Kulturkreislehre* attempts to provide a schematization for the ethnological facts of the whole world. The first and basic problem
of ethnology is that of working out cultural connections. Its
proper aim, as a branch of history in the widest sense, is to
reveal to the greatest possible extent the spatial and chronological antecedents of the known presence of a given cultural
fact at a particular time in a particular place. Only after
we know—roughly, at least—the cultural and environmental
context in which a given custom or artifact evolved can we
properly bring psychological and environmental interpretation into play. A cultural phenomenon can be fully understood
only in the framework of the concepts and premises of the
cultural groups in which it evolved, not simply in the light of
its present-day setting.

The *Kreise* are held to date back to prehistoric times in their
essence and to have been diffused by migration over the
world. Their precise number and characteristics are delineated
variously at different points in the development of the theory,
for the schema has not remained static. But the classification
tends to rest upon the distinction between food gatherers,
food producers, and secondary (or mixed) cultures that
evolved in the Neolithic. Each of these ethnological types
has three or more subdivisions. Thus one of the mixed cul-

tures has been characterized as a fusion of "mother-right" and "totemism." Both the theory and the historical accuracy of the various *Kreise* have been subject to endless critical discussion into which we cannot enter here. In addition to their theory, however, the members of this group have contributed with enormous energy and learning to the analysis and synthesis of archaeological and ethnological data. One may instance Father Schmidt's monumental *Der Ursprung der Gottesidee*.

Today there are few ethnologists who accept the *Kreise* as formulated by F. Graebner and W. Schmidt. Indeed it would be more correct to speak of "The Vienna School of Ethnology" rather than of the "Kulturkreislehre group." The "Vienna School" (as represented by Koppers, Haekel, Heine-Geldern, Jettmar, and others) continues to maintain strong emphasis upon diffusion and other historical phenomena but admits the validity of functionalist and structuralist approaches and does not follow a rigid schema of *Kreise*.

Physical anthropology in the German-speaking world and, to a lesser extent, prehistory have not yet recovered from the considerable affiliation they had with the Nazi regime. In any case German physical anthropology was largely tradition-bound at a pre-Mendelian level with the exception of limited collaboration with geneticists such as Eugen Fischer.

United States. In this century, prior to about 1930, the history of American anthropology was very largely the history of Franz Boas and his associates and students. Boas himself in a thousand books, monographs, and articles dealt with linguistics, folklore, archaeology, statistics, physical anthropology, art, social organization, material culture, and almost every other subdivision of cultural anthropology. His students (notably Robert Lowie, Ruth Benedict, and Margaret Mead) pioneered the exploration of the relation of the individual to culture. No aspect of anthropology was the same after Boas. In physical anthropology he made evident the importance of variability and of environmental liability—within limits. He created almost singlehanded the subject of anthropological linguistics, foreshadowing, among other things, the investigation of the interdependence of language and other aspects of culture that was later carried much further by such people as Edward Sapir, Dorothy Lee, and B. L. Whorf. In archaeology he had much to do with the introduction of stratigraphic methods into the New World. In cultural anthropology he relentlessly documented the historical viewpoint, the fact that the processes that determine events are imbedded in time as well as in situation. It is impossible to "summarize" Boas briefly: *nihil tetigit quod non ornavit—et multa tetigit.* Leslie Spier[9] rightly says:

> The life of Franz Boas coincided with the establishment of anthropology as a discipline of definite scope and method. He, more than any other individual, can be credited with determining the nature of its field and giving to it the scientific approaches of objective empiricism, carefully controlled analysis, firmness of aims, and scrupulous self-discipline in defining the axioms of one's thoughts. For all that he insisted that he was merely analyzing fundamental views of his predecessors; so far as anthropology is a science, he made it one.

During the past twenty-five years American anthropology has developed in many different directions. Physical anthropology has moved toward experiment and toward genetics. Archaeology has greatly enlarged its explicit theory. Linguistics has flowered, attaining elegance and sophistication to the degree that it is considered by many to constitute a model for other behavioral sciences. In cultural anthropology there have been notable advances in the study of social organization, cultural change, culture and personality, values, "modern" communities, and applied anthropology. But only Alfred Kroeber and Edward Sapir have attained to a towering eminence comparable to that of Boas.

Other countries. Outstanding anthropological work has been done by nationals of many countries, but it is probably fair to say that major theoretical innovations have come in this century primarily from the French, German, and English-speaking areas. Here comments on other regions must be limited to a few by way of illustration. In China (until recently) and India the leading anthropologists have usually been trained in the "British school," though the *Kulturkreislehre* has had some influence in India. In Japan, on the other hand, German and French influence dominated until 1945.

The Dutch have produced many first-rate ethnographies and studies of folklore in Indonesia and some impressive work in linguistics, primitive religion, and physical anthropology. Anthropological work in Belgium during this century has been

---

[9] "Frank Boas and Some of His Views," *Acta Americana,* I (1943), pp. 108-27.

limited. Jacques Maquet and others are now carrying on interesting investigations in the Congo. Switzerland has had some distinction in physical anthropology, particularly through the groups clustering around Eugène Pittard at Geneva and Otto Schlaginhaufen at Zürich. There has also been considerable sound production in cultural anthropology. Since 1938 the Anthropos Institute (of Father Schmidt's group) has been located at Fribourg. To the Danes we owe exceptionally thorough studies of Eskimo archaeology and ethnology. The Scandinavians generally (and the Finns) have been leaders in precise investigations and analyses of folklore. Pre-Soviet Russia was distinguished by ethnographers of exceptional quality such as Bogoras, Shirokogoroff, and Jochelson. Not many scholars in the Western world are familiar in other than a general way with Soviet anthropology, though some useful surveys have appeared in English. In Italy there has been little exciting in this century, though work by Sergi and other physical anthropologists was of importance the first few decades. Today the research of some Italian population geneticists has assumed great significance for biological anthropologists in other countries. There are also a few signs that Italian cultural anthropology is stirring.

Anthropology has languished, on the whole, in the Iberian peninsula, though some good work is now appearing from Portugal. In Latin America, however, anthropology has been vigorous. Work in Mexico in archaeology, linguistics, and most especially in applied anthropology is in the forefront of world anthropology. In Manuel Gamio and Alfonso Caso, Mexico may claim two of the most eminent of living anthropologists. Brazil has likewise been a center of important theoretical and substantive endeavor in cultural anthropology.

General. There are various histories of anthropology or portions of anthropology, but none is both up to date and of high quality. The best overall picture of the subject, both as regards fact and concept, appears in two volumes reporting upon an international conference held in 1952. Consultation of these volumes and especially the accompanying bibliographies will make evident what is only possible to state here: namely, that twentieth-century anthropology in the world has accomplished much in the fields of human and primate evolution, anthropometry and "racial" description, local and regional archaeology, historical and descriptive linguistics, folklore, ethnography, and distributional studies.

Another cross-national trend in the twentieth century that

should be noted explicitly is the anthropological study of other than "primitive" peoples. In the preceding century, though many leading anthropologists emphatically rejected identifications of anthropology with "barbarology," there was in fact little investigation of the "higher civilizations" except for the research of Sir James Frazer and others upon data from classical antiquity. This century, and particularly during the past twenty-five years, there has been significant anthropological writing upon France, Britain, Japan, the U.S.S.R., the United States, China, Germany, India, Norway, Guatemala, and a number of other European and Latin American nations. In part, these enterprises have been in the nature of "self-studies"; in part, the descriptions have been written by foreign anthropologists.

National differences in emphasis, interest, and skill persist. Genetical anthropology has developed mainly in the English-speaking world. Archaeology and ethnology are most firmly united in the German-speaking world, as fits the strong German emphasis upon the historical approach. The French continue to show great analytical power and scientific imagination. The British social anthropologists are the most skilled workmen in their specialized field. The study of culture and personality has been almost exclusively an American phenomenon, though it is beginning to receive some attention in France, Germany, Japan, and some of the British Dominions. The anthropological study of values (at least under that name) was initiated in the United States, but Raymond Firth, Audrey Richards, and others in the British world are beginning to give their attention to this subject. Applied anthropology has developed most strongly in Mexico and the English-speaking world, though previous work in the Netherlands and ongoing international work within the United Nations should not be overlooked.

II. General Developments: Theory and Method

Theory. From present perspective the most noteworthy development in twentieth-century anthropology appears to be the steady growth of theory. Apart from excellent descriptive works, nineteenth-century anthropology was dominantly speculative or adapted anthropological fact into molds derived from Darwinian evolutionary biology. In the first quarter of this century anthropologists in many parts of the world reacted by retreating to data-collecting with minimal interpretation. Gradually, under the influence of Boas on one side and the French and British schools on the other, there developed a strong movement in the scientific direction. Assumptions were scrutinized and concepts examined and defined with some care. Attempts have been made increasingly in all branches of anthropology to give mathematical expressions to data. While anthropology today has little theory that a physicist would recognize as such, the contrast with 1900 is striking. At that time explicit theory of other than a historical or vaguely evolutionary sort was virtually absent. Today some aspects of linguistics possess theory of some elegance, and from Boas on anthropologists have used linguistics as a theoretical model for the examination of culture generally. Theory in physical anthropology emerges as a formulation in terms of comparative human biology of broader biological principles of population genetics, ecology, paleontology, and experimental biology. Archaeology is somewhat torn between history and science but is making strides toward bridging that famous gap. Theory in cultural anthropology (apart from linguistics) is still rudimentary, except in the field of social organization. Culture, the central concept, is still somewhat amorphous.

Many of the principal theoretical trends have already been noted. But explicit mention should be made of renaissance of evolutionary theory in cultural anthropology in somewhat new guises. There are two principal forms. That of V. G. Childe and Leslie White has a somewhat Marxian cast. On the other hand, the approaches of Daryll Forde and Julian Steward are concerned in a nondoctrinaire way with the interrelations between ecology,[10] technology, and social organization in the development of fairly regular sequences of cultural forms. W. Mühlmann has also reopened the subject in Germany and Sinha in India.

Methods. From techniques of interviewing and use of personal documents to archaeological and linguistic dating and the techniques of experimental physical anthropology, the

[10] Some of the American archaeologists have also been following the ecology-population approach very fruitfully—e.g., Gordon Willey. [*Prehistoric Settlement Patterns in the Virú Valley, Perú*, Bulletin 155, Bureau of American Ethnology (Washington, D. C.: Government Printing Office, 1953.)]

present period contrasts with that of 1900 as sharply as in the
realm of theory. But since the methods involved are so various
and so specialized, it is not possible to detail them here. It is,
however, important to note one issue. Anthropological bor-
rowings of natural science methods (e.g., those of geology,
chemistry, paleobotany, and the like in archaeology; those of
immunology and population genetics in biological anthropology, etc.) have, in general, evoked discussion only as to
refinements and as to their proper application. The use of
statistics in physical anthropology, certain aspects of archaeology, and some aspects of linguistics and cultural anthropology
has received widespread acceptance. But the demands of
psychologists and other behavioral scientists that cultural
anthropology become completely quantitative and otherwise
conform to certain patterns set by the physical sciences have
met with considerable resistance and the assertion that anthropological method must remain in some essentials of a different order. Some cultural anthropologists do not disagree
with the striving toward mathematicization in principle but
feel that the mathematics involved must come from topology
or some new mathematical specialty rather than from any
mathematic based upon the logic of probability. This controversy arises inevitably from the nature of anthropology as
in part history and humanity, in part "social science," and in
part natural science. The methods of anthropological linguistics are the most distinctive as well as the best defined in cultural anthropology—or in the behavioral sciences generally.
Yet measurement and statistics are used only for certain
special purposes.

III. INTERDISCIPLINARY INFLUENCES

History and Anthropology. There is an enormous literature
on this subject. I shall cite only some of the newer references
because their bibliographies contain most of what is of permanent interest in the older publications. In my own view,
history is a method and an approach as well as a discipline.
Anthropology, like astronomy, geology, biology, and economics has a historical side—inescapably. The course of human
evolution, the dispersal of mankind over the face of the earth,

and the development of human cultures are historical problems. The methods of one branch of anthropology, archaeology, are essentially those of history, with modifications
appropriate to the data. "Archaeology is the history of peoples
who have no history." That phase of physical anthropology
that is concerned with evolution is substantially a historical
inquiry, as is a considerable aspect of anthropological linguistics. Within cultural anthropology, it is increasingly customary
to distinguish cultural history or ethnology from social
anthropology. The former is diachronic and deals with diffusion, migrations, and culture change. The latter is primarily
synchronic and concentrates upon processes thought to be
resultant upon specific types of situation and of social structure. Most anthropologists would agree with E. B. Tylor's
statement long ago: "Much learned nonsense is due to attempting to explain by the light of reason what must be
understood in the light of history." On the other hand, Ortega
y Gasset's "Man has not nature; he has only history" is an
overstatement. Cultures are the products of history, yes; but
they are the result of history as conditioned by man's biological
nature and environing situations.

Some influence has gone from anthropology back to history. This may be seen to a slight extent in the work of
Toynbee, more clearly in the writings of Ralph Turner.
Harold A. Innis' *The Bias of Communication* is in a sense a
companion piece to the greatest work on history by an anthropologist. Rushton Coulborn is another historian who shows
great anthropological sophistication.

Philosophy and Anthropology. This interrelationship has
been far less thoroughly discussed. There is a rather slight
paper by Paul Honigsheim, "The Philosophical Background
of European Anthropology." Abraham Edel has published
a good paper on some aspects of the implications philosophy
and anthropology have for each other. Herman Wein has
surveyed some problems in the light of "philosophical anthropology," a movement of some dimensions in Germany and
German-speaking Switzerland at present. But the only really
thorough study thus far is Bidney's on Cassirer.

Nevertheless there is evidence that philosophers are interested in anthropology at present. One, David Bidney, has
turned to anthropology professionally. Within five years three
major books by philosophers have appeared that draw heavily
on anthropological data. Two other philosophers have actually
written books on the basis of their own field work. The

philosophic interest tends to center, naturally enough, on the problems of cultural relativity and values. But in reading recent philosophic writing one is struck by the degree of penetration of anthropology, even including technical matters of physical anthropology, into philosophic thought.

Other Humanities. Edward Sapir's relation to the humanities was unusual and yet very anthropological. Dorothy Lee[11] writes:

> It was probably this constant preoccupation with the concrete, with the raw datum of experience, the unlabelled, not-abstracted, not-classified, which first made him realize the importance of the field as defining its constituent parts. Certainly later, when he became aware of the anthropological implications of all this, he insisted always on the actual; and his famous precision and rigorousness of method was, in fact, an insistence on the significance of the field, since only the actual, the concrete, is still part of the preanalytic field which defines it. Sapir's apprehension of the whole was expressed simultaneously in poetry and scientific writing. . . . Language itself was an aspect of culture for Sapir, an entrance point which led to meaning and conceptualization of experienced reality; so that his interest in language was eventually an interest in social science, psychology, philosophy, art.

The inevitable interconnections between anthropological studies of music, art, and "literature" and the corresponding humanistic disciplines have already been mentioned. The details of this reciprocal influence would in themselves require a long essay. Some case histories are well worked out. I can here note only one additional point: some rebirth of the interest of classicists in anthropological materials. The best example is the remarkable book by E. R. Dodds, *The Greeks and the Irrational.*

A. L. Kroeber[12] beautifully delineates the essentials in the connections, historical and present, between the humanities and anthropology:

> The "social sciences" developed definitely later than the humanities . . . . In the past . . . the phenomena of man's

---

[11] "Shapers of the Modern Outlook. Edward Sapir: Social Scientist," *The Canadian Forum* (March, 1953), pp. 273-74.

[12] Sol Tax *et al.* (eds.), *An Appraisal of Anthropology Today* (Chicago: University of Chicago Press, 1952), pp. 358-61.

culture, his products and values, or at least certain of them, have, by general consent, been left to . . . the humanities. Now humanists unquestionably operate evidentially. They not only cite evidence; it was they who invented the footnote. They are also empirical in procedure in starting from a given point, although this may be mainly what others have written before them . . . . What, however, the humanities failed in was systematic conceptualization . . . they exact evidence; they do not exact its broadest possible intellectual organization.

. . . The social sciences do not work in depth . . . the humanities do agree with the natural sciences in operating in depth . . . . Just what does "depth" mean in this connection? I should say that "depth" means intensity of search. In proportion as inquiry is ready to go far and long, to go deep, to take into consideration everything relevant instead of quickly setting off some enclave, we have depth. Depth is a quality that scholars in the humanities have generally sought for to the best of their abilities, as physicists and biologists have also sought for it. But I agree with Lévi-Strauss's challenge of depth in the social sciences. How can there be depth when fundamentals are not seriously inquired into?

. . . Anthropology largely represents an unconscious effort of total natural science to extend itself over the area traditionally held by the humanities . . . . It is in this extension of scientific method to the field and material of the humanities that I see the future of anthropology largely lying . . . linguistics has long ago shown us the road. Scientific linguistics grew out of philology—in other words, out of a humanity interested in certain endless particulars of letters considered valuable in themselves and recognizing a hierarchy of languages, of forms, and of better and worse values. From this, linguistics gradually disengaged itself as a genuinely pure science and has had extraordinary development, which no natural scientist who realized what the development had been would ever deny as true science.

Natural Sciences. In many countries following the German model of university organization, physical anthropology and, in some cases, archaeology are assigned to the natural science faculty. In Britain and the United States anthropology is represented in the Royal Society and the National Academy of Sciences. Even in countries where formal affiliation with the natural sciences is minimal, anthropologists and natural scientists cooperate in overlapping fields ranging from ethnobotany to the mineralogy of pottery. Since physical anthropology is part of general biology and since archaeology cannot but depend upon several earth sciences, collaboration in these subjects is particularly marked. However, it should not be forgotten that anthropological linguists work more and more closely with physicists of acoustics, communication engineers, and biologists specializing in the anatomy and physiology of the speech organs.

Sociology and Anthropology. In some countries, such as Italy and France, the line between sociology and cultural anthropology is not very sharply drawn. In Britain, as we have seen, social anthropology has become, in effect, the sociology of primitive peoples. Throughout the world there is probably a general tendency for the lines between sociology and cultural anthropology to become somewhat blurred. In the United States, there are now many joint departments, and many of the younger professionals have received substantial training in the second field. Not that this is an altogether equable "marriage." Some American sociologists feel that their subject is being "corrupted" by anthropology, others appear to resent anthropologists as "poachers." Nor is an antagonistic trend absent on the other side of the fence. Many anthropologists fear that too close an affiliation with sociology will weaken the tradition that all anthropologists should have some training and competence in biological anthropology, archaeology, and linguistics. They value the historical and biological outlook more characteristic of anthropology than of American sociology. The dominant American viewpoint is probably that cultural anthropology must maintain its autonomy from sociology and its unity as a subject embracing natural science and humanistic elements as well as some from "social science." Not only in the United States but generally, the separation of two fields that are in so many respects concerned with the same object of inquiry is very puzzling to the layman. Yet, whatever the logic of the matter may be, the differences in outlook in the two fields remain. This is a product of training, emphasis upon "primitives" and the comparative point of view in anthropology, and the selection process for the two disciplines.[13] The simple fact that anthropologists are accustomed to handle concrete objects whereas, as Kroeber

---

[13] It is sometimes said in the United States that sociologists become so because they dislike their society and want to reform it; anthropologists dislike their culture so they leave it. There is just a grain of truth in this quip.

says, the sociologists have no museums counts for something.

Psychology and Anthropology. In spite of a sizable amount of collaboration in research and some in teaching, the anthropologists and academic psychologists of the English-speaking world maintain, on the whole, an attitude of cautious reserve toward one another. In other countries (except recent Japan—under American influence) they appear to live pretty much in relative ignorance of each other's work.

Academic psychology weighs heavily experimental or "behavioristic" approaches. From this outlook the methods of cultural anthropology appear too rough and ready, lacking in "controls." On their side, the experience of anthropologists has so deeply underlined the significance of the ramified context that they are cautious about accepting the universal applicability of various psychological "laws" (e.g., those of learning). Anthropologists prefer completeness of context to dismembered precision. Anthropology distrusts "similarities" that are taken from the investigator's point of view as independent, self-contained elements. Anthropologists believe that "elements" must be seen in the first instance without labeling in terms of another culture and defined and classified by their position in the total field of which they are a part.

Anthropologists are ordinarily more comfortable with students of personality and "clinical" psychologists. These latter try to get a picture of the whole of a culture. In both cases this entails, for the time being at least, some deficiency in workmanship as well as loss of rigor. Yet holistic, controlled impressionism has certain merits, at any rate for the time being, in this particular stage of the development of the human sciences.

The "laws" of social psychology must be, in the anthropological view, transformed into generalizations that take account, where necessary, of cultural variability. For several reasons anthropologists are skeptical of attempts, overt or disguised, to "reduce" culture to psychology. But there is no doubt that psychology is indispensably relevant to the understanding both of universal culture and of distinctive cultures. The broad ground plan of all cultures arises out of prerequisites determined by human needs as well as by the human situation. Nothing could be more evident than that psychology must help explicate the universal categories of culture both in their generality and in their multitudinous, culturally patterned modifications. It is equally certain that anthropologists can help psychologists understand the cultural dimensions of motivation, learning perception, cognition, and the rest.

Psychiatry and Anthropology. For better or for worse, anthropology has absorbed much more from medical psychology, and especially psychoanalysis, than from academic psychology. For all of the extravagant dogmatism and *mystique* of much psychoanalytic writing, the anthropologist sensed that here at least was what he had long been demanding in vain from academic psychology: a theory of raw human nature. Moreover, there were experiential factors that drew the psychoanalysts and anthropologists together. Psychiatrists of all persuasions, in fact, were showing that there was meaning in the most apparently chaotic and nonadaptive acts of the mentally ill. This struck an answering chord for the anthropologist because he was engaged in demonstrating the fact that the seemingly bizarre patterns of non-Western cultures performed the same basic functions as did our familiar customs. The amnesty that the psychoanalyst grants to incestuous dreams the anthropologist has learned to accede to strange customs. That is, both insisted that even "weird" behavior had significance in the economy of the individual or of the culture. There is also the circumstance that psychoanalysis developed and used a series of concepts (phantasy, libido, the unconscious, identification, projection) that applied specifically to human beings and that anthropologists found useful toward a better understanding of religion, art, and other symbolic behavior.

Other Fields. There are good surveys of present relationships between anthropology and education, law, medicine, geography, and economics. Nothing comparable exists for the study of government, but the British anthropologists, in particular, have worked in the area of political behavior.

IV. GENERAL IMPACT OF ANTHROPOLOGY UPON TWEN-TIETH-CENTURY THOUGHT[14]

The hybrid monster, anthropology, is lusty these days. In a world where educated men and women now recognize that the ways of other tribes and nations cannot remain matters of indifference or antiquarian curiosity, anthropology suddenly finds itself fashionable. Anthropologists have returned from the natives and are thinking and talking about the wide contemporary world. In the present situation the constances and variations between peoples, and the reasons for them, are a matter of the most intense practical as well as intellectual concern.

The panorama of peoples and their ways constructed by recent anthropology has made a number of significant contributions to the modern temper. The most specific is perhaps the demonstration, alike by physical and cultural anthropologists, that, while there may be meaningful biological differences between populations, "race," as judged by observation of a few outwardly visible features, is not a trustworthy guide. This conclusion rests, in part, on what is probably anthropology's broadest generalization: the necessity of taking into account the cultural dimension in all understanding of human behavior. In generality and in explanatory power "culture" is on a level with the categories of gravity in physics, disease in medicine, and gene in biology. Any particular culture of given locus in space or time is merely a specific manifestation of a greater phenomenon of which any one variant is only a temporary phase. This notion replaces a static conception of human social life with a dynamic one.

But anthropological knowledge and the anthropological viewpoint are disturbing to many. In the first place, they challenge "common sense" and threaten the stability of familiar, cherished values. They make enormously complex the question "What is human nature?"—to which the "practical"

[14] For an informal but well-pointed discussion that brings out at least main contemporary currents in the United States see Crane Brinton *et al.*, "The Application of Scientific Method to the Study of Human Behavior," *American Scholar*, XXI (1952), pp. 208-26.

man and the traditional intellectual find it convenient to have
a pat answer. In the second place, anthropology seems to
some to open the way to a complete and chaotic relativism.
The empirical data of anthropology do not warrant this fear.
Yet it must be admited that only recently have anthropologists
begun to give the order and similarity in human cultures
equal weight with the contrast and variability that are also
there. In spite of this, anthropology has, directly and indirectly, made an important, if not the leading, contribution to the
rebirth of a conception that was taken for granted by, say,
Pascal and Burke—and perhaps Goethe—but that for a
hundred years was obscured: namely that the things all men
hold a common bulk at least as large as those that separate
them. Anthropology, as well as technology—especially in the
realm of communication—has made physical appearance,
language, and custom seem less relevant than humanity. The
creation myths of the Polynesians take their place with those
of the Hebrews. When T. S. Eliot juxtaposes Dante, Heraclitus, and a Sanscrit epic or James Joyce draws words from a
dozen languages and folklore from fifty cultures or when Igor
Stravinsky and Karl Orff write music that is at once "primitive" and Greek and Oriental, then we are living in an an-
thropologically sensitive world.

There are some, also, who are not happy that anthropologists are now working in international relations and industry
and studying contemporary civilizations generally. Anthropologists feel that a science that sees institutions and values
in cross-cultural perspective has its necessary place in all investigations of mid-twentieth-century problems. But those
who are troubled by anthropology's new look doubt the applicability of anthropological methods to complex, dynamic
cultures. It is true that some anthropologists have been too
hasty and far-reaching in entering the "modern" arena. And
one can point to a few irresponsible pronouncements suggesting that anthropology has *the* answer rather than a useful
but partial and limited contribution to make to *some* contemporary problems. There are anthropologists who are undoubtedly a bit intoxicated by the heady wine of a little power
over the here and now, for until recently they had drunk only
the austere nectar of detached contemplation of the long ago
and far away. On the other hand, it is only factual to point
out that the great bulk of anthropological publication remains
descriptive, detailed, rigorous within the limits of the theoretical framework. Against the few messianically tinged books of

too facile generalization that have caught the public eye, one can name hundreds of solid monographs produced in the same time period.

Finally, some theologians and philosophers reproach anthropology with exalting the irrational and nonrational aspects of human behavior. Actually, anthropology has very seldom been "vitalist" in tone, urging a surrender to the forces of chaos and unreason. Rather, anthropology has been steadily committed to the search for discoverable regularities. Anthropology seeks to extend the areas that reason can understand and perhaps to some extent control. This may help a little to halt the flight to the irrational, the terrified retreat to the older orthodoxies that we have seen on a mass scale in this century. The hallmark of the good anthropologist must be a curious mixture of passion and reserve. In our world, where varied peoples and cultures now find themselves in uncomfortably close contact, it is the primary intellectual function of anthropology to supply, on a smaller scale and in a scientific manner, the perspective that philosophy has traditionally attempted in a global and unscientific manner.

SELECTED BIBLIOGRAPHY

I

E. H. Ackerknecht, "Trends in European Anthropology," *Transactions of the New York Academy of Sciences*, XIII (1951), pp. 181-184.

H. G. Barnett, *Innovation, The Basis of Cultural Change*. New York: McGraw-Hill, 1953.

E. Bernheim, *Lehrbuch der historischen Methode: Mit Nachweis der wichtigsten Quellen und Hilfsmittel zum Studium der Geschichte*. Leipzig: Dunker & Humblot, 1889.

J. Dias, *Rio de Onor*. Porto: Instituto de Alta Cultura, 1953.

F. Eggan, "Social Anthropology and the Method of Controlled Comparison," *American Anthropologist*, LVI (1954), pp. 743-764.

———, *Social Organization of the Western Pueblos*. Chicago: University of Chicago Press; London: Cambridge University Press; 1950.

C. Erasmus, *Las dimensiones de la cultura*. Bogota: Editorial Igueima, 1953.

H. Field, "Anthropology in the Soviet Union, 1945," *American Anthropologist*, XLVIII (1946), pp. 375-397.

M. Fortes, "Radcliffe-Brown's Contributions to the Study of Social Organization," *British Journal of Sociology*, VI (1955), pp. 16-30.

W. Goldschmidt, "Social Class in America: A Critical Review," *American Anthropologist*, LII (1950), pp. 468-483.

M. J. Herskovits, *Franz Boas*. New York: Scribner's, 1953.

H. Hoijer (ed.), *Language and Culture*. Chicago: University of Chicago Press; London: Cambridge University Press; 1955.

W. Howells, "The Study of Anthropology," *American Anthropologist*, LIV (1952), pp. 1-8.

F. Keesing, *Culture Change: An Analysis and Bibliography of Anthropological Sources to 1952*. Stanford: Stanford University Press; London: Oxford University Press; 1953.

C. Kluckhohn, "Some Reflections of the Method and Theory of the *Kulturkreislehre*," *American Anthropologist*, XXXVIII, 1936.

W. Koppers, "International Symposium of Anthropology," *Mitteilungender Anthropologischen Gesellschaft in Wien*, LXXXIII (1953-1954), pp. 40-60.

A. L. Kroeber (ed.), *Anthropology Today*. Chicago: University of Chicago Press; London: Cambridge University Press; 1953.

———, and others, "Franz Boas 1858-1942," Memoir 61, American Anthropological Association, 1943.

———, *The Nature of Culture*. Chicago: University of Chicago Press; London: Cambridge University Press; 1952.

C. Lévi-Strauss, "Language and the Analysis of Social Laws," *American Anthropologist*, LIII (1951), pp. 153-164.

———, and others (eds.), "Results of the Conference of Anthropologists and Linguists," Memoir 8, *International Journal of American Linguistics*, 1953.

R. H. Lowie, "Gegenwartsströmungen in der amerikanischen Völkerkunde," *Mitteilungen aus dem Museum für Völkerkunde in Hamburg*, XXIII, 1951, pp. 7-27.

R. MacIver, article in *Encyclopedia of the Social Sciences*. London and New York: Macmillan, 1931. Vol. I, pp. 199-203.

D. Mandelbaum (ed.), *Selected Writings of Edward Sapir*. Berkeley: University of California Press; London: Cambridge University Press; 1949.

M. Mead and R. Metraux, *The Study of Culture at a Distance*. Chicago: University of Chicago Press; London: Cambridge University Press; 1954.

W. Mühlmann, "*Anthropolgie*," Handwörterbuch der Sozialwissenschaften. Stuttgart: Gustav Fischer, 1954.

G. P. Murdock, *Social Structure*. New York: Macmillan, 1949.

K. Odaka, "Japanese Sociology: Past and Present," *Social Forces*, XXVIII (1950), pp. 400-419.

C. Osgood and T. Sebeok, (eds.), "Psycholinguistics," Memoir 10, *International Journal of American Linguistics*, 1954.

J. Pelzel, "Japanese Ethnological and Sociological Research," *American Anthropologist*, L(1948), pp. 54-72.

T. Penniman, *A Hundred Years of Anthropology*, rev. ed. London: G. Duckworth; New York: Macmillan; 1952.

P. Phillips and G. Willey, "Archaeological Method and Theory," *American Anthropologist*, LV (1953), pp. 615-633.

W. Schmidt, *Der Ursprung der Gottesidee*. Fribourg, Switzerland: Paulus Verlag, 1926-1954. 11 vols.

L. Spier, "Franz Boas and Some of His Views," *Acta Americana*, I (1943), pp. 108-127.

M. N. Srinvas, *Religion and Society Among the Coorgs of South India*. London and New York: Oxford University Press, 1952.

W. Taylor, "A Study of Archaeology," Memoir 69, American Anthropological Association, 1946.

T. Tentori, "Precendenti Italiani agli Studi di Etnologia della Civilita Occidentale," *Scritti di Sociologie e Politica in Onore di Luigi Sturzo*. Bologna: N. Zanichelli, 1953.

W. Thomas (ed.), *Yearbook of Anthropology—1955*. Baltimore: Lord Baltimore Press, 1955.

P. Tolstoy, "Morgan and Soviet Anthropological Thought," *American Anthropologist*, LIV (1952), pp. 8-18.

E. Z. Vogt, *Modern Homesteaders*. Cambridge: Harvard University Press, 1955.

L. White (ed.), *The State of the Social Sciences*. Chicago: University of Chicago Press; London: Cambridge University Press; 1956.

II

E. Albert, "The Classification of Values: A Method and Illustrations," *American Anthropologist*, LVIII, pp. 221-248.

M. Bakan, "Current Issues of Importance in American Sociology and Related Disciplines," *The Review of Metaphysics*, VI (1952), pp. 141-153.

R. Benedict, "Anthropology and the Humanities," *American Anthropologist*, L (1948), pp. 585-593.

D. Bidney, *Theoretical Anthropology*. New York: Columbia University Press; London: Oxford University Press; 1953.

R. Bierstedt, "The Limitations of Anthropological Methods in Sociology," *American Journal of Sociology,* LIV (1948), pp. 22-30.

J. Birdsell, "On Various Levels of Objectivity in Genetical Anthropology," *American Journal of Physical Anthropology,* X, n.s. (1952), pp. 1-8.

F. Bourricaud, "Indétermination de la Sociologie," *Critique,* X (1954), pp. 973-982.

R. Brandt, *Hopi Ethics.* Chicago: University of Chicago Press; London: Cambridge University Press; 1954.

V. G. Childe, *Social Evolution.* London: Watts, 1951.

R. Coulborn, "Causes in Culture," *American Anthropologist,* LIV (1952), pp. 112-116.

M. Demerc (ed.), *Origin and Evolution of Man.* Vol. XVI of *Cold Spring Harbor Symposia on Quantitative Biology.* Cold Spring Harbor, N. Y.: The Biological Laborator, 1951.

H. E. Driver, "Statistics in Anthropology," *American Anthropologist,* LV (1953), pp. 42-60.

A. Edel, *Ethical Judgments.* Glencoe, Ill.: The Free Press, 1955.

——, "Some Relations of Philosophy and Anthropology," *American Anthropologist,* LV (1953), pp. 649-660.

D. Forde, "The Integration of Anthropological Studies," *Journal of the Royal Anthropological Institute,* LXXVIII (1951), pp. 1-10.

H. K. Fry, "Anthropology and Psychology," *Medical Journal of Australia,* April 18, 1953, pp. 538-543.

S. Gillin (ed.), *For a Science of Social Man.* New York: Macmillan, 1954.

L. Gottschalk, C. Kluckhohn, and R. Angell, *The Use of Personal Documents in History, Anthropology and Sociology.* Bulletin 53 (1945), Social Science Research Council, New York.

Z. S. Harris, *Methods in Structural Linguistics.* Chicago: University of Chicago Press; London: Cambridge University Press; 1951.

C. Hempel, "Fundamentals of Concept Formation in Empirical Science," *International Encyclopaedia of Unified Science.* Chicago: University of Chicago Press.

M. J. Herskovits, *Economic Anthropology.* New York: Alfred A. Knopf; 1952.

P. Honigsheim, "This Philosophical Background of European Anthropology," *American Anthropologist,* XLIV (1942), pp. 376-387.

H. A. Innis, *The Bias of Communication.* Toronto: University of Toronto Press; London: Oxford University Press; 1951.

C. Kluckhohn, "An Anthropologist Looks at Psychology," *American Psychologist,* X (1948), pp. 439-442.

W. Kohler, "Psychological Remarks on Some Questions of Anthropology," *American Journal of Psychology,* L (1937), pp. 271-288.

A. L. Kroeber, *Configurations of Culture Growth.* Berkeley: University of California Press, 1944.

———, "The Place of Anthropology in Universities," *American Anthropologist,* LVI (1954), pp. 764-767.

———, and C. Kluckhohn, "Culture: A Critical Review of Definitions and Concepts," *Papers of the Peabody Museum of Harvard University,* XLVII, 1, 1952.

L. Leary (ed.), *Motive and Method in the Cantos of Ezra Pound.* New York: Columbia University Press; London: Oxford University Press; 1954.

C. Lévi-Strauss, "Histoire et Ethnologie," *Revue de Metaphysique et de Morale,* LIV (1949), pp. 363-391.

———, "Place de l'anthrologie dans les sciences sociales et problèmes posès par son enseignement," *Les Sciences sociales dans l'enseignement superieur.* Paris: UNESCO, 1954.

G. Lindsey (ed.), *Handbook of Social Psychology.* Cambridge, Mass.: Addison-Wesley 1954.

W. Muhlmann, "Entwicklung und Geschichte," *Archiv fur Kulturgeschichte,* XXXIV (1952), pp. 107-129.

———, "Ethnologie und Geschichte," *Studium Generale,* VII (1954), pp. 165-177.

M. T. Newman, "The Application of Ecological Rites to the Racial Anthropology of the Aboriginal New World," *American Anthropologist,* LV (1953), pp. 311-328.

D. Riesman, "Toward an Anthropological Science of Law and the Legal Profession," *American Journal of Sociology,* LVII (1951), pp. 121-135.

S. Sinha, "Evolutionism Reconsidered," *Man in India,* XXXV (1955), pp. 1-18.

R. F. Spencer (ed.), *Method and Perspective in Anthropology.* Minneapolis: University of Minnesota Press; London: Oxford University Press; 1954.

G. Spindler (ed.), *Anthropology and Education.* Stanford: Stanford University Press; London: Oxford University Press; 1955.

R. Turner, *The Great Cultural Traditions.* New York: McGraw-Hill, 1941.

H. Wein, "Von Descartes zur heutigen Anthropologie," *Zeitschrift fur philosophische Forschung,* II (1948), pp. 296-314.

L. White, "Evolutionism and Anti-Evolutionism in American Anthropology," *Calcutta Review,* CV (1947), pp. 30-40.

———, *The Science of Culture.* New York: Farrar and Straus, 1949.

INDEX

Abbagnano, N., 238
Abbassids, 132
Abbey of Fontenay, France, 199
Abbey of Royaumont, France, 199
Abd-al-Karun ibn al-Mutannà, 153
Abd-al-Rahmän al-Sufi, 161
Abderrahman III, 136
Abraham, Don, 161
Abū Bakr, 165
Abu-l-Qāsim al-Zahrāwi, 160, 163
Abū-l-Qāsim Maslama al-Mayriti, 137
Abū Mas'ar, 155
Abu-Salt Umaya, 164
Accadian treatise, 99, 100
Accademia dei Lincei, 313
Accademia del Cimento, 310, 314
Acapuncture, Method of Chinese
    treatment, 113
Achaemenian Persians, 89
Achard, 198
Acosta, Father (Historia natural y
    moral de las Indios), 299
d'Acquapendente, F., 316
Adaptation, 338
Adelard of Bath, 147, 149, 153, 227,
    228, 230, 236
Age of Illumination, 78
Agricultura Nabatea, 197
Ahmad ibn al-Yazzär, 147
Ai Shēng, 126
Alamani, 173
d'Alverny, M. T., 155, 157
Al-Batalyusi, 159
Alain de Lille (De planctu Naturae),
    231, 232, 234, 236
Albert the Great, 234
Albert of Saxony, 254
Albigenses, 204
Alcohol, first appearance in Salerno,
    185
Aldrovandi, 315
Alençon, siege of, 180
Alexander, King, 101, 102, 103, 104
Alexandrian culture, 130
Al-Fārābī, 56, 157, 159, 160, 165
Al-Fargānī, 164
Alfonso, P., 147, 148, 149, 162, 163,
    164
Alfonso the Wise, 160-61, 178, 180,
    203
Alfred of Sareshel, 157
'Ali abi-l-Rihal, 161
Alī ben Abbās, 147
'Alī ben Ahmad al-Imrämī, 150
'Alī ben Jalaf, 161
Al-Jwārizmī, 145, 153, 157
Al-Kindi, 145, 157, 163
Allevard, Dauphiné, 217
Alloying, where carried on, 69-70
Alonso, Father M., 155
al Mamûn, 133
al-Mansûr, Caliph, 132, 133
Alpetragius, 159
Alpujarra, 177 n
Al-Qābīsī, 155
Al-Razī, 160, 165
Ambelikoú B., 68
Amerinds, 48
Anabaptists, 283
Anatole of Berito, 197
Anatolia, 65
    copper in, 69

Anaxagoras, 79
Andrés, Jewish interpreter, 164
de Angulo, L., 152
Ankermann, 403
Anthropology, Brazil center of cultu-
    ral, 406
    impact of, on twentieth-century
        thought, 414
    and philosophy, 410-11
    and psychology, 414
    and psychiatry, 415
    in twentieth century, 396-418
Apollonius, 157, 296
Applied physical sciences, 316-17
Aquinas, T., 233, 234, 260, 277
Arab culture, 130
Arabs, and chemistry, 184
    use of Greek fire, 179
Archaemenian Empire, 103
Archaeological periods, 36
Archaeological record, list of material
    embodiments, 56, 57, 60, 61
    neolithic section of, 62
Archaeology, 35, 405, 408
    Eskimo, 406
Archimedes, 254, 296
Architecture, study of, 192, 202
Argabhata, 82, 85, 104
'Arīb ibn Sa'id, 138
Aristippus, 243
Aristobulus, 102
Aristotelianism, 240, 255, 302
Aristotelians, 249, 252
Aristotle, 131, 159, 160, 165, 249, 260,
    264, 277
Aristoxenes of Taranto, 103
d'Aspa, G., 161
Aston, isotopes by, 350
Astrolabe, 190
Astronomic Tables, 137
Astronomy and mechanics, 313
Aterian, 47, 54
Atkinson, G. (Les Nouveaux horizons
    de la Renaissance française),
    307 n
Atton, Bishop, 142, 143
Aubert, M., 196 n
Auctores, 227
Auger, Prof., xv
Auger, P., 340
Augustine, St., 228
Augustus, Emperor, xxiii
Aurignacion, I, 46, 53
Averroes, 159, 160, 165
Avicenna, 277
Ayer, A. J. (Language, Truth and
    Logic), 374, 378
Azarquiel, 137, 157, 161
Al Zazari, 181

Bacon, F., xxiii, 164, 265, 267
Bacon, R., xxii, 158, 212
Bacon, T., 269
Bainbridge, J., 285-86
Balandier, G., 332
Ballista, use of, 177
    value of, 210
Banu Musa brothers, 181
Barchinonensi, L., 143
Bar-cochba, 132
el-Battanyi, 94

bar Hiyya, A., of Barcelona, 149, 150, 156, 158
Barlowe, W., 280
du Bartus, 288
Bauhin, J., 260, 261, 315
Bavarians, 173
Beda, N., 297
Bede, 135
Beeckman, I., 265, 266, 269, 270, 280, 281, 288
Behavior, instinctive, 36-37
   learned, 37
Behavioristic psychology, development of, 373
Believers, priesthood of, 265
Belon, 316
ben Anatoli, Y., 164
ben Astruc Bonsenior, 163
ben David, A., 155
Benedict, R., 404
ben Ishaq, S. T., of Tortosa, 160
ben Luqa, Q., 161
ben Mose, I., 161
ben Saul ibn Tibbon, J., 158
ben Sémuel ibn Hasday, A., 159
ben Sēlemo al-Harizi, J., 159
ben Sid, Ishaq, 161
ben Mose ha-Kohen, J., 161
ben Yosef ibn Ayyub, S., 160
Bernard of Chartres, 227
Bernard, St., 230, 233, 236
Bernard, S., 331 n
Bernouilli, J., 312
Bertet, Father, 303
Bestiaries, 231
Beza, 275
Bibliothèque nationale, Paris, 145, 182, 189
Bidney, D., 410
Biggs, N., 277, 278
Bile, concept of, 96
Biot, J. (Études sur l'astronomie indienne et sur l'astronomie chinoise), 92
Blaeu, W., 282
Blagrave, J., 282
Blasi, A., 165
Bloch, M., 199, 225
Boas, F., 404, 405
Bock, J., 260, 315
Bohr, 350, 368
Bolas, 46
Bonaventura, St., 234
Bonfil, M., Bishop of Gerona, 143
Bonis de Montauban, 211
Bon signori (Sienese bankers), 211
Bookkeeping, method of, 210-11
Borelli, 313, 316
Borough, W., 282
Borrell II, Count of Barcelona, 142
Bostocke, R., 277, 278, 285
Boucher, G., 195
Bouillant, 313
Boulton, M., xxi, xxviii
Boyle, R., 270, 273, 284, 307
Bracciolini, P., 244
Brahé, T., 285
Brahmi, Indian script, 98
Brahmanism, 89, 94
von Braunmühl, A., 129
Brezzi, P. (Classical Civilizations and the Orient), xi n
Bridgman, P. (The Logic of Modern Physics), 366

Brinton, C., 416 n
British Museum, 145
Bronze Age, 68
Bronze, production of, 69
Brouwer, L., 371, 372, 373
Browne, T., 263
de Brujas, R., 153, 156
de Brune, J., 279, 288
Brunner, E. (Christianity and Civilization), 223, 324
Brunelleschi, 209, 210
Brunfels, O., 260, 315
Bruni, L. (Isogagicon Moralis Disciplinae), 244, 245, 251
Bruno, G., 305
Brussels, ban on carding at, 200
Buddhism, 109
   in T'ang period, 116
Buddhists, 109
Building projects, 203
Bullinger, 261
Burckhardt, J., 222
Buridan, 213, 254
Busson, M. (La pensée religieuse de Charron à Pascal), 306 n
Byzantines, use of Greek fire by, 179

Cabeo, Father, 314
Calder, R., xvi, xvii
Calvin, J., 263, 276, 278, 279, 289
Calvinism, 259
   and Copernicanism, 286
Calvius, 312
Cambridge School, 374
Campanella, 246
Campo, E., 331, 333
Cana, Miracle of, 229
de Candolle, A., 294, 300, 309, 310
Cantor, G., 370
Capello, M., 135
Cardan, 305
Carding, first mechanized, 184
Carnap, A., 367
Carnap, R., 376, 377
Carpenter, N., 276, 285
Carpini, P., 195
da Carrara, F., 187
Case, 73
Caso, A., 406
Cassiodorus, 129
Cassirer, E., 380, 391
Castril Museum, Granada, 177 n
Catapult, use of, 177
Catholicism, 291, 292, 293, 300, 301, 306
Catholics and Protestants, contribution to progress of science, 309-19
Cats, J., 288
Causality, 391
Celestin III, 176
Cesalpino, A. (De Plantis), 315
Chabot, H., 330, 333
Chalcidius, 226
Chang-Chung-ching, 113
Chang Chi, 113, 125
Chang Su-hsün, 124
Chang Ting of Wu-tai, 120
Chang ts'ung-chêng, 125
Chang Tzū-hsin, discovers irregularity of sun's motion, 111, 116
Chang Yü-hsi, 126
Chao Fei, 111
Ch'ao Yüan-fang, 118
Chaplin, C., xxvii

Charles of Anjou, 165
Charles the Bald, 135
Charles I, 277
Charles V, 205
Chartres Cathedral, 181, 227
  pillars of, 208
Chartrians, 224, 226, 228, 231, 234, 235
Charts, first, 189-90
Chasles, M., 129
de Chelles, P., 208
Chen Ch'êng, 126
Chên Luan, 110
Ch'ên Fu of Sung, 115
Chenu, R. F., 222
Chen-to-Wang (Ssu-nan Chih-nan-chen yü Lo-ching-p'an), 127 n
Chên Yen, 125
Chia Ssū-hsieh, 114
Chia Tan, 124
Chih-nan-ch'ê, contrivance, 127
Chih-nan-yü, 127
Childe, V. G., xii, xiii, 34, 399, 408
China, agricultural techniques in, 114
  astronomy, cartography, and mathematics in, 122-24
  gunpowder and magnetism in, 126
  introduction of astronomy in, 313
  medical science and pharmacology in, 118
  printing and paper-making in, 120
  sciences in, 108-27
  tin found in, 69
  spinning wheel in, 193
  use of pit-coal in, 195
Chinese, invention of gunpowder by, 195
  use of magnet, 126
Ching Chin-shao, 124
Ch'ing-li, 120
Chiu-chang-suan-shu (Arithmetic of Nine Sections), 109, 110
Chou-kou-tien, cave of, 38, 55
Chu Chên-hêng of Southern Sung, 125
Chu Hsi-chieh, 124
Ch'ü-t'an-hsi-ta, 117
Church of San Isidro, Madrid, 174
Cicero, M., 227
Cistercians, 198
Civilizations, developments in, 171
Clair, R., xxvii
Clark, G., 399
Clark, Le Gros, 399
Clavius, Father, quoted, 299, 313
Clocks, in England, 182
  in France, 182
  in Germany, 182
  in Italy, 182
Clusius, 260, 261
Coiter, V., 261
Collective migrations, 199
College of La Flèche, 297
Collège de Montaigu, 297
Collegium Mechanicum, 266
Colombo, R., 316
Columella, L., 197
Company of Jesus, 297, 298, 311
Constantine III, 136, 227
Constantino ("Africano"), 146
Continuity, 388
Copernican theory, 285
Copernicus, N., 239, 268, 275 n, 276, 302, 308, 313

Copleston, F. (Contemporary Philosophy), 377
Copper, alloy of, 69
Copper Age, 69
Cotes, 284
de Cornaut, J., 204
Council of Lateran, 226
Council of Trent, 300, 304
Counting, when first used, 49
Cranmer, T., 261
Crescenti, P., 207
Creswellian culture, 55
Crombie, A. (Augustin to Galileo. The History of Science A.D. 400-500), 292
Cromwell, O., 273
Crossbow, use of, 177
Crusaders, the, 197
Ctesibius, xxii
Culpeper, T., 277
Cypriotes, 65

Daneau, L., 284, 288
Dante, 417
Darius, King, 102
Darwin, C., xxviii, xxix, xxx, 345
Datini, F., 211
Daud al Banakati, 194
Davy, H., xxiii
DDT., xviii
Dedekind, R., 370
Dee, J., 281
Deist, H., 327
Delhaye, Ph., 236
Delisle, 176
Dell, W., 278
Dematerialization of matter, 382-83
Demiurge, the, 230
Democritos, 260
Desargues, 312
Descartes, R., 297, 302, 303, 312
Dessauer, F., 325
Dewey, J., 380
Diaba Verna, 358
Diderot, D., 185
Diepgen, P., 97
Digges, L., 266
Digges, T., 263, 266, 281, 285
Dionysus, the Areopagite, 131
Dioscorides, 132
Discontinuity of Motion, 385-90
DNA (deoxyribonucleic acid), xviii, xx
Dodds, E. (The Greeks and the Irrational), 411
Dog, domestication of, 57, 58
Domesday Book, 173
Donat, 227
Donne, J., 289
Dry cultivation in Syria, the Levant, Greece, and the Balkans, 63
Durkheim, E. (Elementary Forms of Religious Life), 52, 397, 403
Dyeing, 184
Dynasties
  Ch'ên, 109
  Chì, 108
  Chin, 108, 121
  Liao, 121, 122
  Liang, 109
  North Wei, 11
  Northern, 112, 114
  Northern Wei, 109
  Southern, 111, 112

Sui, 115
Sung, 108, 121

Early Bronze Age, 63
École de Chartres, xiv
Eddington, Sir A. (*The Mysterious Universe*), 379
Edison, T. A., xxv
Eighty Years' War, 265
Einstein, A., 368, 384
Elbing seal, 187
Electron, 387
Eliot, T., 417
Elisséeff, V. (*The World; 400 A.D.-1300 A.D.*), xi n
Ellul, J., xxix
Emir of Cordova, 136
Emir al-Hakam II, 139
Empiricism, 267
Engels, F. (*Anti-Duhring*), 324, 333, 335 n
English Civil War, 273
Enthusiasm and science, 273
Entropy, 350
Erasmus, 297
Erigena, J., 135
Escurial Library, 178
Esteban of Zaragoza, 162
Euclid, 157
Eudoxus, xxi
Evans-Pritchard E. (*The Nuer*), 399
Events, historical dimension of, 248
Experimental science, origins of, 252

Fabri, Father, 303, 312
Fabriano, Italy, 175
de la Faille, Father, 312
Fallope, 316
Faraday, M., xxiii, xxvi
Faral, E., 227
Faray, translator, 165
Farrar, D., 289
Febvre, M., 203
Feigl, 367 n
Ferguson, W. K. (*The Renaissance in Historical Thought: Five Centuries of Interpretation*), 223 n
Fermat, P., 312, 314
Feurwerksbücher, 204
Fibonacci, L., 210
Ficino, M. (*De Christiana Religione*), 241, 243, 246, 251, 384
Filippo of Tripoli (Fenicia), 165
Filliozat, J., xiii, 88
Firth, R., 334, 407
Fisher, F., 334
Fisher, R., 399
Fitzgerald, 384
La Flèche, 303
Fleming, J. A., xxv
Florence, Italy, 241
Fludd, R., 283
Folsom points, 54
Forde, D., 408
de Forest, Lee, xxv
Fortes, M., 399
Foster, S., 282
Fourastie, J. (*Le grand-espoir de XXᵉ siècle*), quoted, 325
Fournier, Father, 298
Francesco of Carrara, 170
del Bene, Francesco, 211
Franco-Cantabrian portrayal, 50

Frank, P. (*Modern Science and Its Philosophy*), 367 n
Franklin, B., xxviii
Frazer, Sir J., 407
Frederick II, King of Sicily, 164
Frege, G., 370
French Gravettian, 54
Freud, S., xxx
Fuchs, L., 260, 263, 315
Fulling, when mechanized, 184
Fustat, saltpeter used at siege of, 180

Galen, 227, 260, 264, 277
Galileo, G., xxii, 239, 253, 254
   case of, 301-6, 313, 317, 318
   condemnation of, 302
Gallego, P., 162
de Gama, V., 103
Gandhara, 89
Gaon Saadi, 158
de Garlande, J., 173, 177
Garrico, M., 406
Garton, G., 179
y Gasset, O., 410
Gellibrand, H., 269, 282, 286
Geology, palentology, mineralogy, 314
Geometrical theorems, application of, 72-73
Geometry, applications of, 72
Geon, H., 131
Geoponic knowledge, 197
Gerbert, 142
Germans, arts of mining and metallurgy of, 201
Gerona Cathedral, 173 n
Gesner, K., 261, 315
Gestalt psychology, 359
Gilbert, H., 267
Gilbert, Master, 227
Gilbert, W. (*De Magnete*), 285, 287, 307, 314
Gille, B. (*Les problèmes techniques au XVIIᵉ siècle*), xiv, 316
Giraldus of Aurilloc, 143
Girard, A., 312
Glanvill, J., 273
Glasbergen, 73
God, glory of, 262
Goddard, 274
Gödel, K., 371, 372
Godwin, Fr., 285
Godwin, W., xxviii
González, J., 163
Gotmar, Bishop of Gerona, 139
Gottschalk, L. (*The World, A.D. 1300 to the End of the Eighteenth Century*), xi n
De Gouvea, A., 297
Graebner, 403
Graecus, Marcus, 180
Grand Khan, 195
Gravettian phase, 47
Gravettians, 48
Great Wall of China, 115
Greek fire, 179
Gregorius XIII, 110
Gregory, J., 312
Gregory of Nyssa, 235
Gresham College, 282
Grienberger, Father, 302
Grimaldi, 314
Grimaldi, caves of, 53
Gudiel, G. G., Archbishop, 163
Von Guericke, O., 314

Guilds, 199-200
Gundisalvo, D., Archbishop, 155, 156

Haeckel, 404
Hahn, H., 367
ha-Levi, Y., 159, 161
Hall, J., 271, 272, 277, 284
Hammond, B., xxviii
Hammond, J. L., xxviii
Han Dynasty, 109
el-Hariri, 159
Harun al-Rashid, Caliph, 133
Harriot, 312
Harrison, G. (*What Man Can Be: The Human Side of Sciences*), 329, 330 *n*
Harvey, W., 307, 316
Hasday ibn Saprut, 136
Hauser, H., 305
Havedic, Armenian engineer, 203
Hawkes, J. (*Prehistory and the Beginnings of Civilization*), xi *n*
Heinsius, D., 288
Heraclitus, 96, 97, 100, 417
Hildebert of Lavardin, 227
Hindus discover decimal system of notation, 84
Hippocrates, 260
Hippocratic Collection, 100, 102
Hippolytus, St. (*Refutation of All Heresies*), 105
d'Hirson, T., 207
Hispanus, J., 153, 155
Hither Asia, refining of silver in, 70
Helm, 72
Hempel, 368
Heine-Geldern, 404
Henry I of England, 147
Henry, J., xxvi
Hermann Contractus, Monk of Reichenau, case of, 145-46
Hermann of Corinthia (*Planisphere*), 228
Hermann, the Dalmatian, 153
Hero of Alexander, xxii, 175, 187
Heracleitus, 81
Herrade of Landsberg, 181
Hipparchus, 94
Hippocrates, 98, 160
Ho Ch'êng-t'ien, 110, 111, 112, 116
Holland, 265
  Calvinism in, 288
  Mennonites in, 273
  sciences and technology in, 259
Holmes, V. T., Jr., 223
Holzschuler family of Nuremberg, 210
Honigsheim, P., 410
Honnecourt, V., 175, 178, 179, 180, 182, 183, 185, 202, 204, 208, 209, 214
Hood, T., 266
Hooke, R., 314
Hooykaas, R., xiv, 258, 292, 293, 294, 295, 296, 300, 304, 307, 308, 311, 312, 315
Hopkins, G., xxvi
Hoppers, 304
Hoste, Father (*Théorie de la construction des vaisseaux*), 317
"Hsing-li-shuo," 125
Hsü Ang, 116
Hsuan-shi-shu, astronomical table, 111
Hsüang-tsung of T'ang, 117, 121

Huan-ti, 112
Huang-fu Mi, 113
Huang Shang, 123
Hubert, Master, 204
Huet, Archbishop of Avranches, 298
Hugo, V., 226
Hui-tsung, 125
Hui of Wei of the Three Kingdoms, 110
Hroswitha, nun, 139
Humanism, 296, 297, 299
  and scientific development, 295
  Catholic attitude toward, 296
  and Catholic Church, 297
  problem of, 230-41, 248, 249
Humanists, 239, 242, 245, 247, 251, 298 *n*
  attitude toward religious toleration, 251
  hostility toward Aristotle, 252
Humbert, P., 298 *n*
Hume, D., 375
Hunayn ben Ishaq, 136, 157
Hundred Years' War, 205
"Hungary," 67
"Hun-i," armillary sphere, 111
Huygens, C., 307, 312, 313, 314

I Hsing, 116, 117, 118, 123
ibn Aflah, Y., 159
Ibn al Baitar, 179
Ibn al-Saffār, 156
Ibn al-Yazzār, 162
Ibn Bajtya-su family, 133
Ibn Bassāl, 138, 162, 197
Ibn Daud (Johannes David), 156
ibn Ezra, R. A. of Tudela, 151, 152, 158
Ibn Gabirol, S., 156, 158, 163
Ibn Khaldun, 223
Ibn Paquda, 158, 159
ibn Ridwān, 'A., 159
Ibn Sab'in of Murcia, 164
Ibn Sā'id, 137
Ibn Tibbon family, 158-59
ibn Tibbon, M., 159
ibn Tibbon, S., 159
Ibn Tumort, 157
Ibn Wāfid, 138, 197
Ibn Yanāh, 158, 159
Ignatius, St., 298
Ile de France, 196
India,
  Greek astronomy in, 93
  Greek occupation of, 101
  and scientific exchanges in antiquity, 88-96
  zoology in, 85
Indus, 59
Industrial Revolution, xxi, xxviii
Innis, H. (*The Bias of Communication*), 410
Inventions, secret of many, 202
Ipswich seal, 187
Isidore, St., of Seville, 129, 135
Italian Humanism, 241
Italian Quattrocento, 223

Jaime II, King, 163, 165
James, W., 364, 365
Janne, H., 331 *n*
Jansenists, 298 *n*
Jarmo, 62
Jaspers, K., quoted, 330, 332

Jeans, Sir James, 379
Jefferson, T., xxviii
Jesuits, in France, 303
    at Grenoble, 303
Jivaka, 83
Jochelson, 406
John of Hollywood, 182
John of Salisbury, 224, 226, 234, 236, 237
Joinville, J., 196
Jordan, P., quoted, 329
Jourdain, A., 154
Joyce, J., 417
Juan of Toledo, Archbishop, 155
Juan of Segovia, Bishop, 155
Justinian, 131

Kao Hsien-chih, 121
Kapila, 81
Kapitza, P. L., xxvi, xxx
Keith, Sir A., 399
Kepler, J., 262, 263, 265, 268, 276, 306, 307
Ketensis, R., 153
Kharosthi, script, 98
Khmers, 95
Kircher, Father, 315
Kircher, A., 298
Kluckholn, C., xv, 396
K'o-chü, 115
"Ko-wu-chih-chih," 122
Koppers, W., 403
Kossinna, 36
Kostienki, 54
K'ou Tzung-shih, 126
Koyré, A., 308, 309
Kraft, 367 *n*
Krause, F., 403
Krober, A., 405
Kulturkreislehre, 403, 404
Kurdistan, 65
Kyeser, C., 204

Labat, M., 99
La Ferrassie, 51
Lalouvère, Father, 312
Lamarck, P., 345
Langmuir, I., xxvi
Langiulli, N. F., 255
Lana-Terzi, Father, 317
van Lansbergen, J., 287
van Lansbergen, P., 263, 266, 287
Lapidaries, 231
à Lasco, J., 261
Last Glaciation, 45
Late Bronze Age, 68
Late Glacial period, 47
Lateran Council, 177
Lateran Museum, 192 *n*
Lathes, 181
Latimer, H., 261
Latitudinarians, 277
Laud, W., 277
Lee, D., 404
    quoted, 411
Leewenhoek, 307, 316
LeFèvre of Etaples, 297
Leibniz, G., 312
de Loyola, I., 297
Leo, Byzantine philosopher, 181
Leurechon, Father (*Récréations Mathématiques*), 312
Lévi-Strauss, C., 397 *n*, 398
Levy-Bruhl, 49

Lewitzky, B., 327
Lia Kao of Yüan, 125
Liao Ling-tsan, 123
Li Chi, 119, 124
Li Ch'un-fêng, 117, 118
Liege, mills at, 214
Liege, water supply of, 217
Lilley, L. (*Automation and Social Progress*), quoted, 328
Linnaeus, 345
Lister, M., 315
Liu Ch'ao, 116
Liu Hui, 110
Liu Hsi-sou, 122
Liu Wan-su, 125
Lobatschewski, 369
Locke, A., 374
Lombard, P., 236
Lot, F., 129, 179
Louis, St., 204
Lovel, Sir B., xix
Lower Paleolithic Clactonian, 44
Lower Paleolithic period, 41, 46, 49
    tools, 41-42, 43
Lowie, R., 399, 404
Luka, Costa Ben, 197
Lull, R., 190
Lunar Society, xxv
de Lunis, G., 165
Luther, M., 276, 278
Lutheranism, 259
Luttrel psalters, 192

McNeill, J. (*The History and Character of Calvinism*), 287 *n*
MacRae, D., 334
Mach, E., 366
Machiavelli, N., 245
Magdalenian IV, 53, 54
Magdalenian period, 47
Magdalenian phase, 47
Magdalenians, 48
Magnetism and electricity, 314
Maimonides, 160
Majumdar, R. C., xiii, 77
Malebranche, N., 314
Malpighi, M., 316
Malthus, T., xxviii, xxx
Malvern Abbey, 147
Man, discovery of, 240
    in nature, 242-44
    in society, 244-46
Manetti, G. (*De Dignitate et Excellentia Hominis*), 241, 244
Manfred, son of Frederick II, 165
Manichee, 117
Maquet, J., 406
Mansura, 180, 196
Marburg School of Neo-Kantianism, 380
Marco, Canon of Toledo, 157
Margenau, H., 362, 386 *n*
Mariotte, Abbé, 307, 314
Maritime Matters, progress in, 191
Martini, 314
Mary, Queen, 192
Mā-sā-Al-lāh, 141
Marx, K. (*Capital*), xxix, 324, 332, 333, 334
Marxism, 332, 334
Masā-al-lāh, 155
Maslama of Cordova, 148, 153, 156
Massif Central, France, 202
Mästlin, M., 285

Mathematics, 311-12
Mauro, R., 129
Mead, M., 404
Measurement, 73
Mechanization of industry, 214
Mecklenburg, Duke of, 268
Medical science and pharmacology, 112-14
Medieval technology, 193
Melanchton, P. (*Physics*), 261, 275, 285, 287 *n*, 289
Meng Shên, 120
Merton, R., 289
Mesolithic, 48
Mesues III, 165
Metraux, A., 398
de Meun, J. (*Romance of the Rose*), 233
Metalworkers, 70
Michel, A., 298 *n*
Michelson, 384
Micoquian, 53
Middle Ages, civilization of, 172
    clocks in, 184
    division of labor widespread in, 215
    dyeing in, 184
    hand tools in, 172, 173
    hydraulic undertaking in, 217
    inventive spirit of, 173
    lathes in, 181, 182
    regulations in, 217
    technical prescriptions in, 200
    technical progress in, 205
    transport in, 186-87
    travel in, 203
    vogue for machines began in, 180
    water mill, 175
Middle Paleolithic, 44, 45, 54
Miguel, Bishop, of Tarozona, 153
Milan Cathedral, 209
Millas-Vallicrosa, J., 128
Miller, D., 384 *n*
Milliet of Chales, Father, 298, 303, 317
Mills, attempts to boycott, 216
Milton, J., 265, 272
Minkowski, 384
Ming-i-pieh-lu, 114
Miolithic, 57
Monastery of San Cugat, 173 *n*
Mond, R. (*The Cemeteries of Armant*), 73
Monod, V. (*Dieu dans l'Univers*), 306 *n*
de Montecorvino, G., 195
Moore, G., 374, 376
Moore, W., 331
Morazé, C. (*The Nineteenth Century*), xi *n*
Morgan, 358
Morley, 384
Morse code, 357
Mose, translator, 165
Moslems' use of mangonels, 179
Moustierian. See Middle Paleolithic
Mousterian men, 44
Moxibustion, Chinese method of treatment, 113
Mozarabs, Spanish Christians, 138
Muhammad bed Mūsā al-Juarizmi, 133, 137, 143, 145, 148, 149
Mühlmann, W., 403, 408
Mumford, L., 225
Muntner, S., 132

Murdock, G., 399
Munich Congress, 327
Musée de l'Armée, Paris, 179
Myers, O. H. (*The Cemeteries of Armant*), 73

Nakshatras, 91, 92, 93, 94, 95
Nallino, A., 133
de Nangis, G., 190
Nan-kang Yüeh, 117-18
Nath Seal, B., 81
"Navagrāha," nine planets, 117
National Academy of Sciences, 412
Natural sciences, 315, 412
Navigation by stars, 190-91
Needham, J. (*Heavenly Clockwork*), 123 *n*, 127, 194 *n*
Needling and drilling, 55
Neolithic farmers, and animals, 63, 64
    fermentation used by, 65
    metallurgy, 66-67
    mines, 72
    pottery, produced by, 65, 66
    selective breeding by, 64
    use of cereals by, 64
Neolithic Revolution, 47, 57, 58
Neoplatonism, 246
Neoplatonists, 246
Nestorians, 131
Neugebauer, 75
Neurath, O., 367
Neurophysiology, 349, 352
Newton, I., xxviii
Newton's theory of motion of particles, 392
Nicholas of Cusa, 255
van Nieuwenhuijze, C., 331, 333
des Noettes, L., 187 *n*
Norman, R., 276, 281, 282
Norman, W., 269
North European Maglemosean, 47
Northrop, F. (*The Meeting of East and West*), 380
Numerals, use of, 75
Nushirwan, Emperor, 131

Oakley, K., 399
de l'Obel, 260, 261, 315
Ockham, 254
Odenwald, 199
Oecolampadius, 276
Ogburn, W., 338
Olivier, J., 211
Olorgesailie, 38
Olynthus, 66
Ommayads, 132
Order of Jesuati, 312
Ores, first to be smelted, 68
    where found, 70
Oresme, N., 270, 307
Origanus, 285
Origen, 235
Origins, return to, 246-48
Orff, K., 417
Orvieto, 183
Osmova, N., 338 *n*
Otto I, Emperor, 142
Ovid, 224
de Oviedo, A., 163

Paleolithic society, 51-52
Palissy, B., 261, 263, 264, 268, 280, 281, 282, 307, 308, 314
Palmieri, M. (*Della Vita Civile*), 245

Pamikkar, K. M. (*The Twentieth Century*), xi n
Paper, in China, 194
  in Samarkand, 194
Paracelsus, P., xxii, 278, 305
Pareti, L. (*Classical Civilizations and the Orient*), xi n
Paris Académie des Sciences, 309
Paris Academy, xiii
Parsons, W., xxii
Pascal, B., 307, 312
Patristicism, 252
Patrocles, 102
Paul, St., 265
Paul the Persian, 131
Pavlov, I., 373
Peano, 370
Pearson, K. (*The Grammar of Science*), 367 n, 399
Pedro of Aragon, 190
Pedro the Venerable, 153
Peirce, C., 363, 365
Peiresc, 298
Pelseneer, J., 292, 294, 309, 311
Pena, P., 261
"Pên-tsao," Chinese pharmacology, 113
Pereira, A., 309
Pericles, 79
Perigordian culture, 54
Perspective, discovery of, 248-50
Peruzzi, firm of, 211
Petech, L. (*Classical Civilizations and the Orient*), xi n
Petrarch, F., 260
Petty, W., 274, 282
Philippe III, 204
Philoponus of Alexandria, 190
Physical discontinuities, 358
Physical science, philosophy of, in the twentieth century, 362-93
Physics, 213
Pico della Mirandola (*De Ente et Uno*), 241, 246, 247
Pien Kang, 116
de Pietro, L., 209
Pi Shêng, 120, 194
Pittard, E., 406
Plancius, P., 281
Planck, M., 350, 368
la Place, 391
Plato, 97, 100, 249, 260, 306
Plato of Tivoli, 150
Plato Tiburtinus, 156
Platonism, 252
Platonists, 249
Platter, F., 261
Pliny, G. (*Naturalis Historia*), 129, 264
P'o-chang-fa, 111
Polo, Marco, 195
Ponsioen, J., 331, 333
de la Porrée, G., 224, 227, 228
Porphyry, 131, 164
Porphyrogenitus, 136
Porretani, 228, 231, 232
Post-Glacial period, 57
Pottery, discovery of, 49
Prajapati, Master-of-things-born, 95
Precession, 111
Price, D., 123 n
Printing, 194
  in Central Asia, 194
  in Egypt, 194
  in Japan, 194
Priscian, 227
Protagoras (*On the Gods*), 79
Protector Richard, 274
Protestantism, 292, 293, 300, 301, 304, 306
Ptolemy, 94, 227, 264
Pu-k'ung, 117
Puritans, in science, 277-82
Pythag rean ratios, 72
Pythagoras, 104, 352, 353
Pythagoreans, 254

Qimhi family, 158
Qimhi, J., 158
Quantum mechanics, 390, 393
Quintilian, M., 227
Qusta ben Luqa, 133

Rabelais, 297
Racemundo, Bishop, 138
Radcliffe-Brown, A. (*The Andaman Islanders*), quoted, 398, 399, 402, 403
Radioactivity, discovery of, 349
Raimondi, C., 243
Raimundo, Don, 154
de la Ramée, P., 265
Ramus, P., 265
Ray, J., 315
Ray, P. (*History of Hindu Chemistry*), 81 n, 83
Recorde, R., 263, 281
Redi, 316
Reformation, 275, 308
Reformers, 283
Reidwan of Damascus, 181
Religion, function of, 250
Religious beliefs and attitudes on development of science, 291, 293, 294
Renan, E., 135
Renaissance of antiquity, 223
Renaissance of Aristotelianism, 254
Renaissance Humanism, 240, 241, 250, 254, 255
Rheticus, 285
Ricci, 314
Richards, A., 407
Richeome, Father, 298
  quoted, 304
Richer, monk, 142
Ridley, M., 280, 285
Riemann, 369
Rigveda, 80, 89
Rijksmuseum, Amsterdam, 179
Rinascimento, the, xiv
Rivet, A., 288, 398
Robert of Anjou, 164
Robert the Englishman, 182
Roberval, 307, 312
de Robrouk, G., 195
La Rochelle, seal of, 188
Roger of Hereford, 158
Roman Catholicism, 259
Roman College, 302
Roman Inquisition, 302
Romans, irrigation system of, 217
Romein, J. M. (*The Twentieth Century*), xi n
Römer, 314
Rondelet, G., 261, 315
Rose, V., 154
Ross, A., 270, 278